Technology and
Market Structur

Technology and Market Structure

A Study of the Aircraft Industry

Almarin Phillips

University of Pennsylvania

Heath Lexington Books
D. C. Heath and Company
Lexington, Massachusetts

To C. S. P.,
who just was not here
the last time.

Table of Contents

List of Figures

List of Tables

Preface

For nearly twenty years, I have been interested in theoretical and empirical work dealing with relationships between technological change and market structures. About five years ago, the hypothesis advanced in this book began to shape my thinking. Exactly how the hypothesis developed is far from clear, but I am certain that early discussions at The RAND Corporation with George R. Hall, Richard R. Nelson, and James R. Schlesinger were instrumental to the process.

The present book has posed some unusual problems. As indicated in the text, Richard B. Heflebower convinced me that detailed case studies were necessary to distinguish my arguments from those of John Kenneth Galbraith and Joseph Schumpeter. For this purpose, however, a study dealing primarily with economic aspects of markets was inadequate; considerable knowledge of aircraft and of the history of aviation technology was required. I suspect that the few qualified aviation historians who may wander through these pages will be dissatisfied with my efforts at self-education in their field. At the same time, I am assured that economists will find some of the historical detail tedious. A balance had to be struck, but none may agree with the one selected.

The work also required excursions into the area of statistical models and quite extensive use of regression analysis. These sections, I know, will cause most of the aviation historians and my econometrician friends considerable displeasure. The former are likely to be repelled by seemingly complex procedures and equations; the latter, by the crudeness of the same procedures. Again, a balance had to be struck.

The theory itself gave problems. It is cast within a general class of dynamic response models such as the one I recently described in "Structure, Conduct and Performance—And Performance, Conduct and Structure?" in *Industrial Organization and Economic Development: Essays in Honor of Edward S. Mason* (1970). That is, elements in the theory suggest that market structures and the behavior of firms are determined in part by adaptive response to the performance of firms and the opportunities afforded by their environments. No effort has been made here to formalize the theory beyond verbal description and flow chart illustrations. It could be set forth in a system of equations, but I am not satisfied that enough is known about some parts of the system to say much about their forms. If the descriptions offered here are not so clear as some theorists might wish, it is precisely because I know too little about the system to be more specific.

Along this difficult way, I received a great deal of help which I wish now to acknowledge. Robert Perry of RAND, E. W. Robischon of the National Air and Space Museum, Eugene M. Emme of the National Aeronautics and Space Administration, Aaron J. Gellman, and Peter M. Bowers all contributed to my knowledge of aviation history and technology. The staffs of many libraries, particularly the Mathematical and Engineering Sciences Library of U.C.L.A., the Pacific Aerospace Library of the Aerospace Industries Association of America, the RAND library, and the library of the

National Air and Space Museum of the Smithsonian Institution, were most gracious.

David Sawers very kindly permitted me to use data he and R. A. Miller had assembled on aircraft operating costs prior to their own publication. Burton H. Klein has, over a period of years, persuaded me of errors in many of my approaches toward a more general theory of markets and technological change. He probably will not be satisfied with what appears here, but I think it would have been much worse had I not had occasions to talk things over with him. Oliver E. Williamson provided a number of useful comments on a late draft of the book. Through the long period of its preparation, George R. Hall generously participated in reading and rereading, arguing and rearguing, the whole work. Early drafts were skillfully typed by Angie Martins; later ones, by Florence Barrow.

Finally, I wish to acknowledge with deep thanks the research support for this effort provided by the Ford Foundation and The RAND Corporation.

Almarin Phillips

**Technology and
Market Structure**

1

Technology and Market Structure: An Overview

Introduction

This book examines relationships between changes in industrial technology and changes in market structures. For this purpose, the aircraft industry and the market for commercial transport aircraft are used to form a partial test of a fairly general and novel hypothesis.

By way of summary background, the commercial air transportation industry experienced its initial period of rapid growth in the United States after the passage of the Kelly Act of 1925 and the Air Commerce Act of 1926.[1] The Air Commerce Act provided, among other things, for the certification of aircraft types in order to promote greater safety. The first Approved Type Certificate (ATC) given under the Act was issued in March 1927, for the Buhl Airster C-3A, a three-place, open cockpit biplane. By the end of 1931, over 450 ATCs had been issued to 79 differently named aircraft manufacturers.[2] Of these, 104 aircraft types, produced by 32 differently named manufacturers, were landplanes with four or more seats. These aircraft were generally intended by their manufacturers for use as commercial transports.

Few of these planes were purchased in adequate quantities to permit their manufacturers to remain in business. Douglas, Boeing, Stinson, Consolidated, Lockheed, Curtiss, Fokker, and Ford—familiar names in the history of commercial aircraft manufacture—are among those receiving ATCs in this early period. So too are less familiar names such as Buhl, Alexander, American, Kreutzer, Hamilton, Bach, Ogden, Emsco, and Cunningham-Hall. These companies, along with many others, failed to produce an economically successful commercial transport.

By the end of 1932, there were 23 different types of planes representing nine different manufacturers in use by the principal domestic air carriers in the United States. During 1933, only five manufacturers supplied new aircraft to these carriers. By 1965, United States domestic trunk carriers were using 18 different aircraft types. These were produced, however, by only four American and three foreign manufacturers. Moreover, only two domestic manufacturers—Boeing and Douglas—supplied new aircraft to the trunk carriers in that year and, as subsequent events were to show, Douglas' position in the industry was extremely tenuous at that point. Thus, in a period of about 40 years the structure of the market for commercial aircraft in the United States changed greatly. By 1965 it was highly concentrated and, indeed, a strong probability existed that only one domestic firm would remain.

[1] A list of entering airline companies, arranged by year from 1914 to 1938, is provided in Appendix A.

[2] The counts are from the ATC listings in the *Air Commerce Bulletin* (1930–1932). The count of manufacturers is unadjusted for interlocking ownerships and for changes in names of companies.

Paralleling the changes in industry structure, very significant changes in technology occurred. The typical new transport aircraft of the late 1920s had gross take-off weights of less than 10,000 pounds, effective cruise ranges of less than 500 miles, cruising speeds of about 100 miles per hour, and seating capacities for perhaps 10 passengers.[3] Many of these planes had only one engine; even the trimotors had full take-off horsepower of 1350 or less. Fuselage construction was ordinarily of welded steel tubing with a fabric or currugated aluminum covering. Some wings were of a cantilever design with aluminum alloy spars and ribs, but maple spars and ribs with fabric covering were still common. Wings were externally braced and engines were mounted in the nose of the fuselage and on the systems of supporting wing struts.

The typical new transport aircraft of 1965 bore little resemblance to the earlier planes. The 1965 versions often had gross take-off weights in excess of 250,000 pounds, cruise ranges of over 4000 miles, economical cruising speeds of as much as 550 miles per hour and seating capacities, in mixed class configurations, for 130 to 150 passengers. All of these planes were multiple-engined, with total power ranging up to 68,000 thrust pounds. Fuselages and wings were of light metal alloys, with stressed skin monocoque and cantilever designs. The costs of operating the 1965 transports, corrected for price level changes, were a small fraction of the operating costs of their counterpart aircraft of 35 years earlier.

The historical pattern of increasing (or high) market concentration and (by some measure) rapid technological change is not unique to commercial aircraft manufacture in the United States. It has characterized the same industry in other countries. It extends to some degree to military and private aircraft types and to the manufacture of space vehicles. Beyond the aerospace group of industries, high market concentration and relatively rapid technical progress are common also in markets of the electrical equipment and communications, chemicals, motor vehicle, machinery, and instruments industries. And these same few industries account for a high percentage of total industrial research and development expenditures.

Facts—or casual observations—of the sort given above have been the foundation for a rather popularly accepted thesis that large firms operating in concentrated markets are responsible for a not insignificant share of the progress in industrial technology.[4] And for the record, I had minor involvement in the propagation of this thesis. In 1956, I found empirical evidence that "industries in which production is concentrated in a few firms and in which firms are relatively large tend to show greater evidence of technical change than do industries in which either or both of these conditions do not

---

[3] The principal characteristics of transport aircraft available for use by U.S. trunk carriers from 1926 through 1965 are given in Tables B-1 and B-2.

[4] The most widely known versions of this thesis are in J. K. Galbraith, *American Capitalism* (1952), J. A. Schumpeter, *Capitalism, Socialism and Democracy* (1947) and H. Villard, "Competition, Oligopoly and Research," *Journal of Political Economy* (December 1958).

exist."[5] The study had been suggested by the arguments of Galbraith and Schumpeter, which assign a clear causative role to the research and development activities of large firms in the creation of new technologies.

The evidence seemed persuasive at the time. It would have suggested that an important element in explaining the technological progressiveness in commercial aircraft manufacture was the growth of firms and increase in concentration which transpired after 1928. Yet, with no plausible economic explanation, I observed in the concluding sections of the 1956 paper that the statistically significant association between scale and concentration on the one hand, and measures of technological change on the other, could be misleading with respect to causation. The "association could be because there were characteristics of concentration and scale which foster technological development . . . or it could be due to technical changes having effects on concentration and scale."

The nearly neglected alternative explanation of the results found in 1956 is the one I now emphasize. It is not denied that firms in some market environments—including some large firms in some highly concentrated industries—make great contributions to technology and, occasionally, even to basic science. Nonetheless, I feel now that an important influence on market structures and on the research and development programs and innovative behavior of firms stems from the presence or absence of related technological and scientific changes which occur for reasons generally exogenous to market phenomena and the goals of particular firms. The argument to be presented is that a basic element causing the structural changes in the commercial aircraft industry was a scientific and technological environment which was itself changing—and changing for reasons largely unrelated to the goals of firms manufacturing commercial aircraft. And I suspect that the same is true of other industries during the periods when their products and production processes are undergoing fundamental change.

The alternative view has been presented in abbreviated form. It was argued that:

A progressing science which is related to the products and processes of particular industries operates on markets in ways such that some firms tend to become larger, more profitable, and more technologically progressive while others experience increasing difficulties in remaining viable. The latter tend either to remain small, in 'corners' of the market protected by various forms of product differentiation, or to disappear through mergers and failures. These results are not because 'the modern industry of a few large firms' is 'an almost perfect instrument for inducing technical change.' The results are instead because continuity in technical change made possible by a changing scientific environment is an almost perfect instrument for inducing a modern industry of a few large firms which, in turn, contribute to technology.[6]

[5] A. Phillips, "Concentration, Scale and Technological Change in Selected Manufacturing Industries 1899–1939," *Journal of Industrial Economics* (June 1956).

[6] A. Phillips, "Patents, Potential Competition, and Technical Progress," *American Economic Review* (May 1966), p. 304.

Richard Heflebower saw the alternative as "a basic challenge to the Schumpeterian doctrine of the competitive effect of large firms' leadership in 'creative destruction'. . . ." However, Heflebower observed as well that the crude empirical test presented was unpersuasive: the "finding could equally well support what Schumpeter asserted; namely, that large firm size and concentration encourage technological change." Empirical tests, to be persuasive, would require, Heflebower maintained, "the evaluation and dating of breakthroughs . . . for individual situations." [7]

The remainder of the present chapter will be used to clarify my more recent argument and to spell out its relations to the positions of Schumpeter and Galbraith. The rest of the work adopts the approach Heflebower suggested for one industry, with empirical testing, dating and evaluations of technological breakthroughs.

II. The Theories of Schumpeter and Galbraith

Few of the studies of technology and market structures carried on by economists in recent years have paid explicit attention to the effects of science and technology on economic processes.[8] The emphasis rather has been on the influence of economic processes and economic variables on science and technology. Understandably, that is, economists have sought to explain the world in terms of economic variables.

Schumpeter, above all, stressed the historical importance of the emergence of capitalism—viewed generally—on scientific developments. In the sweep of modern history, the sociological and political counterparts of Western European capitalism were, according to Schumpeter, essential to the creation of an intellectual environment conducive to scientific discovery and progress. But the early Schumpeter did not use this broad view of history to argue that it was the structure and performance of markets which governed technology in the microcosmic aspects of the capitalist process. Quite the reverse is true.

The Theory of Economic Development and the closely related work, *Business Cycles*, view particular developments and directions of science and technology as largely independent of particular markets in a capitalist society. *The Theory*, without attempting historical or empirical tests, pays little attention to either the scientific source of inventions or the motivation of the inventor. Whatever the source and motivation, it is implicitly assumed that a discontinuous stream of more or less significant inventions occurs over time. These afford Schumpeter's entrepreneur the opportunity to attempt innovations. The entrepreneur

---

[7] R. Heflebower, "Comment," *American Economic Review* (May 1966), p. 317.

[8] Some exceptions are R. R. Nelson, M. J. Peck and E. D. Kalachek, *Technology, Economic Growth and Public Policy* (1967), pp. 34–43; W. S. Comanor, "Market Structure, Product Differentiation, and Industrial Research," *Quarterly Journal of Economics* (November 1967); F. M. Scherer, "Firm Size, Market Structure, Opportunity and the Output of Potential Inventions," *American Economic Review* (December 1965).

was himself motivated only in part by the possibility of purely economic rewards. He was the atypical capitalist who, instead of attempting to protect markets from the erosion of economic rewards which is usually associated with change, wished to introduce change to satisfy his own peculiar goals.

From the stream of invention—ostensibly made for reasons independent of particular markets—and from entrepreneurs dipping into this stream for innovations, Schumpeter fashioned his theory of economic development. The aggregative aspects of the theory consist of generalizations drawn from the impact of a new technology on a particular market. Utilizing the initial assumptions of a static, circular flow equilibrium for aggregate economic activity and the conditions of long-run competitive equilibrium for the individual product markets, Schumpeter followed with an analysis of the disequilibrating effects of innovation and of the subsequent reequilibrating effects of the market forces inherent in his system. The successful innovator, in brief, created a monopoly in a particular market, only to have that monopoly successively whittled away by the entry of swarming, secondary innovators. The swarming tended to reproduce the initial conditions of competitive equilibrium in particular markets. At the same time, technical and economic interrelations among markets led to cyclical investment behavior and higher levels of real income. The latter, of course, were the principal variables of Schumpeter's interest, though not the ones of greatest relevance here.

The point to be emphasized about *The Theory* is the direction of causation. The milieu of the capitalist process did, indeed, foster science and technology. The latter gave rise to invention, a necessary ingredient for innovation. Given invention, the spirit of the entrepreneur provided a sufficient condition for innovation. The innovation then directly influenced the structure of particular markets and, through secondary innovations, indirectly influenced other markets. With some change in terminology appropriate for this book, the system of *The Theory* is shown in Figure 1-1. The dashed feedback loop from the profits and output achievements of the firms to market structure represents the swarming of secondary innovators and the demise of firms utilizing the old technology. Market structure, that is, is affected by the entry of new firms and the failure of old ones as the process of technological change occurs.

At this stage in his career, the argument that market structure determines the research, development, and innovative behavior of firms and their contributions to technology and science was neglected by Schumpeter. Two or three decades later, the Schumpeter of *Capitalism, Socialism and Democracy* offered a different view, perhaps because of the different historical context in which the latter was written. In the 1930s, Schumpeter foresaw the demise of entrepreneurial capitalism. Invention remained an important part of his system, but the role of an inventor who is independent of market processes was cut from the plot. Enterprises remain—especially giant industrial units—but the individual entrepreneur is ousted. Invention and, since the topic is not treated separately, presumably the necessary increments to science that underlie the inventions, are in this later view seen to be routinized by managers and trained specialists in ways that satisfy the bureaucratically set goals of large firms.

Market structure continues to be determined by technological change. Technological success and market success are generally identical, however, and they result in increased market concentration as small and medium sized firms are excluded from markets by their larger, more successful rivals. Price competition is generally supplanted by technological, innovative competition and, once concentrated, market structures are threatened only through long-run forces of creative destruction. For reasons not fully explained by Schumpeter, any tendency for entry by new firms utilizing existing technologies would not be strong enough to cause the general deconcentration of markets.

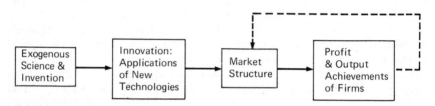

Figure 1-1 Relations between Science, Technology, and Market Structure in Schumpeter's *Theory of Economic Development.*

The market structure-technological change system in *Capitalism, Socialism and Democracy* is a short, closed-loop scheme, as shown in Figure 1-2. Successful technical change leads to—or is identical with—market success and increased market concentration. The rewards to the managerial groups that are associated with market success give rise to additional research, development, and scientific effort. These, in turn, lead to further market success and to higher rewards. Science and technology, it seems, become the handmaidens of managers and applied technicians until the fruits of the process result in the full elimination of the entrepreneurial class. Eventually, Schumpeter felt, scientific socialism would emerge.

The Galbraith version of relations between technical change and markets opened the system again, but with a direction of causation just the opposite of that presented by Schumpeter in *The Theory of Economic Development.* Differences and changes in market structure are acknowledged, but they are not explained by differences and changes in the technologies related to the markets. Market structures are simply assumed. Aspects of science and technology other than those developed by or for market-oriented firms or market-oriented purposes are not considered as important in the explanation of market performance. That is, there is no discussion of developments in science and technology which are exogenous to the market process.

In the Galbraith system, oligopolistic firms—ostensibly viewed as a homo-

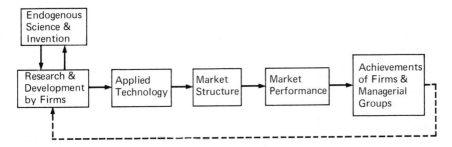

Figure 1-2 Relations between Science, Technology, and Market Structure in Schumpeter's *Capitalism, Socialism and Democracy.*

geneous subset—are able to carry on research, development, and innovative activities because of the financial achievements deriving from their protected market positions. The stimulus that accounts for their use of resources in technological activities rather than for other purposes is not detailed, but it seems to originate from some characteristics of market-share and technical rivalry which Galbraith feels are likely to prevail among oligopolistic firms.

Firms in more atomistically structured markets, in contrast, are just consumers of technical changes created by oligopolistic firms from whom purchases are made and/or created by government and quasigovernment research and development agencies. The latter activities are seen as public efforts to overcome the shortcomings in the performance of atomistic markets and, in this sense, are themselves indirectly market determined. In both the oligopolistic and atomistic cases, the chain of causation shown in Figure 1-3 runs from market structure to firm behavior and, from this, to changes in applied technology, market performance and the achievements of firms and their managers. In neither the atomistic nor the oligopolistic case is the entry of new firms or the failure of old ones seen as a source of change in market structure.

Inadequacies of the Schumpeterian and Galbraithian Theories

If the later Schumpeterian or the Galbraithian theory were correct, large firms in concentrated markets would generally display more technological progressiveness than do others. More accurately, if either theory is correct, differences in measures of technical progressiveness between firms such as these and other firms should be more than proportional to the differences in the sizes of the firms.

Edwin Mansfield has demonstrated quite conclusively that there is little empirical support for such broad generalizations. Summarizing the results of

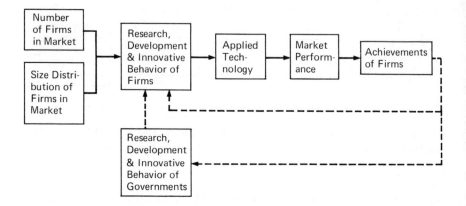

Figure 1-3 Relations between Technology and Market Structure in Galbraith's *American Capitalism.*

recent research—much of which comes from his own contributions—Mansfield finds that: [9]

(1) there is usually no tendency for the ratio of R and D expenditures to sales to be higher among the giants than among their somewhat smaller competitors" in a given industry. Nonetheless, "firm size often must exceed a certain minimum for R and D to be profitable.

(2) in most industries, the limited data that are available do not seem to indicate that only the largest firms can support effective R and D programs; there is generally no indication that the largest programs have any marked advantage over somewhat smaller ones.

(3) in most industries for which we have information . . . when the size of R and D expenditures is held constant, increases in size of firms are associated with decreases in inventive output.

(4) if [the types of innovations] require very large amounts of capital, it appears that the substitution of fewer large firms for more smaller ones may lead to more rapid introduction [of new processes and products]; if they require small amounts of capital, this may not be the case.

(5) the very small amount of evidence . . . bearing on [the] question seems to suggest that greater concentration in an industry may be associated with a slower rate of diffusion.

In sum, Mansfield holds that, "Contrary to the allegations of Galbraith, Schumpeter and others, there is little evidence that industrial giants are needed in all or even most industries to insure rapid technological change and rapid utilization of new techniques."

[9] E. Mansfield, *The Economics of Technological Change* (1968), pp. 215–217.

In a sense, detailed statistical studies are unnecessary to indicate the inadequacies of the Schumpeterian and Galbraithian hypotheses. Viewing each as even the broadest of generalities, there are simply too many instances in which the gross facts of technological change and of market operations are not in accord with the theories.

Galbraith is, of course, correct that industries engaging in substantial amounts of research and development and characterized by a seemingly high rate of technological progress tend to be oligopolistic. One need only cite the relevant data for the aerospace, computer machinery, chemical products, electrical machinery or ethical pharmaceutical industries to demonstrate that research and development is heavily concentrated in oligopolistically structured industries and that these industries, by any quantifiable standards, have been relatively innovative. Galbraith is also correct that less concentrated industries such as bituminous coal and agriculture, which have been technologically progressive in the sense of having high rates of increase in output per unit of factor input, have utilized the results of research and development carried out under government auspices and have used as inputs articles that were themselves product innovations coming from oligopolistically structured industries.

As Markham has noted, however, there are on the other hand some "spectacular examples of highly concentrated industries . . . that rank low in research and development" activities and whose record of technological change is less impressive.[10] Beyond tobacco products and steel, which he mentions, there are industries such as distilled liquors, shipbuilding, meat packing, glass containers, plate glass, newspapers, lead and copper which, although highly concentrated on a national or regional basis, would not likely be cited by anyone seeking to defend the Galbraith view. Oligopoly, it is clear from this as well as from the works reviewed by Mansfield, is not uniquely related to and ought not be considered a *cause* of rapid technological change.

The neglect of the question of *causation* appears to me to be basic in the failure of economics to erect satisfactory generalizations concerning market structure and technological change. The bulk of the evidence of empirical studies is, indeed, that Galbraith and Schumpeter were wrong, but none of these studies has suggested an alternative explanation at nearly the same level of generality. And, more importantly, the bulk of these studies have been carried out in ways which explicitly or implicitly treat technological change as endogenous to an economically motivated system describing the operation of markets. That is, failure to consider any effects from a generally exogenous technology or science on market processes marks most of the empirical studies as well as the Galbraithian and the later of the Schumpeterian generalizations.

That there are such exogenous effects seems reasonably clear. They derive largely from firms carrying on additional development after seminal research done elsewhere. The earlier theory of Schumpeter, it was noted, gave a promi-

[10] J. W. Markham, "Market Structure, Business Conduct and Innovation," *American Economic Review* (May 1965), p. 327.

nent role to such exogenous events. But beyond mere assumptions made for theoretical convenience, there are histories [11] and statistical studies [12] indicating the existence of the effects. For every case of freon, LP records, nylon, tetraethyl lead and the transistor, the origins of which trace quite directly to the commercial interest of firms, there are other innovations such as the fluorescent lamp, television, wireless telephony, streptomycin, penicillin, catalytic cracking, Cinerama, and synthetic light polarization, whose origins trace at least as directly to individuals.

On a more general level, there are obvious research and development activities carried on by nonprofit organizations and active scientific disciplines closely related to the technologies of the aerospace, computer, chemical products, electrical machinery, and pharmaceutical industries. It is more difficult to find analogous activities in the cases of distilled liquors, shipbuilding, meat packing, glass containers, plate glass, and other, less technically progressive industries. It could be true that profit motivated and nonprofit research and development spring from common causes. It could also be argued, in the sense of the scheme given in Figure 1–2, that what are ostensibly scientific activities exogenous to market processes are in fact a subloop of these processes. The weight of the evidence remains, however, to indicate the continued existence of some substantial amount of research the potential commercial purposes of which are so vague that market considerations do not help to explain them.

To insist on the existence of science and invention exogenous to market processes and to suggest that such science and invention may affect market processes is not at all equivalent to a reversion to the Schumpeter scheme of Figure 1-1. In it, no role is ascribed to the research and development activities of existing firms. Given the records of firms in such industries as computer machinery, chemicals, and ethical pharmaceuticals, it seems plausible that both the related science and the structures of markets may be affected by the R and D activities of firms. And it is possible that some combination of effects from exogenous science and the R and D activities of existing firms influence the ability of new firms to enter markets. What observed reality appears to require is a synthesis of the schemes represented by Figures 1-1, 1-2, and 1-3. The Schumpeterian and Galbraithian views of relations between market structure and technological change are not so much wrong and inconsistent as they are, each viewed alone, incomplete.

An Overview of an Eclectic System

A more complete view of the relationships between market structure and technological change incorporates features from each of the Schumpeterian

[11] Most notably, J. Jewkes, D. Sawers and R. Stillerman, *The Sources of Invention* (1958),
[12] In addition to my own *Patents, Potential Competition and Technical Progress*, see especially F. M. Scherer, "Firm Size, Market Structure, Opportunity and the Output of Potential Inventions," *American Economic Review* (December 1965).

and Galbraithian hypotheses. From *The Theory of Economic Development* comes a role for science and technological advances carried on for reasons quite unrelated to the market goals or achievements of existing firms and to the performance of existing markets.[13] In the United States, this exogenous science and progress in technology is in part the result of the research of individuals. But it includes also research results from the universities and colleges, government agencies, some nonprofit, nongovernment research institutions and, while probably not independent of these, from basic research carried out by firms whose other, more applied research and development activities are an integral part of the market process.[14]

A great deal of this exogenous science and technical development is of a sort that has no visible use for firms over any foreseeable period of time. The titles of dissertations submitted by doctoral candidates are good evidence of this fact. So too are the grumblings of congressmen about research titles and publications of government agencies. It is not universally true, however, that all exogenous research is unrelated to firms' activities. Some of the scientific and technical developments carried on for reasons independent of the market and of the goals of firms create visible opportunities for firms to produce new products or to use new production methods.

Figure 1-4, which portrays the eclectic system, shows a link from an element depicting an exogenous science and technological progress to the research and development activities of firms. Where a recognized scientific discipline is related to the technologies and products of existing firms—related in the sense that those managing the firm perceive of potential opportunities arising from the findings of the exogenous science—a complementary research and dedevelopment (R and D) activity in the firms is likely. The R and D consists of two functions that may be performed more or less well. One is a search of the progress in the exogenous science.[15] The other is the development of some aspects of this progress into forms that are anticipated to contribute to the profit, sales, growth, or security goals of the firm and its managers.

[13] As used here, science means not a static body of knowledge but rather an ongoing inquiry, the result of which is more or less constant change in bodies of knowledge.

[14] There may be semantic difficulties with respect to the latter. Burton H. Klein, surely an experienced participant as well as an astute student of research activities, has suggested in conversations that the term exploratory research be used to designate investigations carried on by firms when the research, as carried out, has no specific *ex ante* economic goal. The firm, Klein argues, nonetheless supports only the general types of research it feels will contribute to its success over a period of time. I have included the possibility of something akin to pure research in firms because I feel there is sometimes an organizational need for firms to allow scientific personnel to engage in such research as a necessary concomitant of their employment. I do not disagree with Klein that this research tends to concentrate in areas relating to the technologies of the industry—obviously most scientific personnel will have training and research interests so related. Neither do I dispute that in particular instances great rewards accrue to firms from these activities.

[15] Indeed, the extent of subscriptions to scientific publications and the frequency of attendance at the meetings of scientific organizations might be used as crude indications of the relatedness of science to particular firms.

The economic reasons for hypothesizing this relationship and for its general functional form are rather conventional. As is developed below, exogenous scientific or technological activities that have been or promise to be sources of new products and production technologies yield an environment such that failure by a single firm to engage in the R and D function means that it is increasing one type of risk. Other firms which do so engage may successfully develop a new product or process that will ultimately lower the achievements of firms which have not undertaken R and D. But, it is to be emphasized, re-

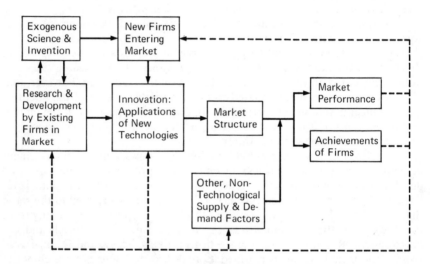

Figure 1-4   Eclectic System of Relations between Market Structure, Market Performance, and Technological Change.

ductions in this risk through R and D spending may at some point increase other types of risk more than commensurately. There is undoubtedly something analogous to diminishing returns in at least the search function of R and D. Beyond some point, the increasing costs of that activity will increase rather than decrease the risks of financial or organizational failure. And, where there is no exogenous science reasonably related to the activities of a firm, this relation may obtain for all levels of scientific R and D activity.

In this framework, the R and D activity of the firm is in one respect a risk-reducing activity, where an optimal balance must be sought between risks of two sorts. Given the progress in exogenous science, there is the risk that the firm will fail to achieve goals adequately because other firms will be first to innovate successfully. This risk is reduced by increasing the R and D activity. On the other hand, R and D is resource-using and, again given the progress in exogenous science, the higher the levels of R and D the more likely it is that, in the conventional sense, the *ex post* results will show incremental costs to have exceeded incremental returns. This, too, is in the direction of failure.

Figure 1-4 also shows a feedback link from the research and development activities of firms back to the exogenous science and technology. This is to account for the additions to knowledge accounted for by firms. It is quite different in nature, however, from the connections shown in Figure 1-2 to depict the theory contained in *Capitalism, Socialism and Democracy*. In the latter, exogenous technology plays no explicit role. Here, R and D tends to exist only in firms which have products or processes for which there is related, exogenous scientific and technical development. While firms are seen as contributing back to exogenous and related science and technology, the latter are the *sine qua non* of market-related R and D in the first instance, and the feedback is something of a serendipitous spillover.

Put alternatively, there are many scientific and technical research areas for which one can find little or no corresponding R and D firms. This is the case where there are no perceived relationships between the exogenous science and the achievement of goals of firms. Not obvious, however, are R and D efforts by firms for which there is no corresponding science or other forms of exogenous technological developments.

The creative destruction of *Capitalism, Socialism and Democracy* is not denied. Developments in exogenous science which existing firms have failed to utilize may, as shown in Figure 1-4, lead to perceptions by new firms that goals may be accomplished through innovation.[16] Presumably, some standard hypotheses relating to barriers to entry help to explain the strength of these tendencies. Thus, economies of scale, customer allegiances to the existing products and firms, advertising advantages and other possible absolute cost advantages for established firms are usually considered to establish a limit price.[17] So long as existing firms do not charge above this price, entry is forestalled.

In the context of the economics of technological change, the same factors give rise to a concept of a limit rate of technical progress. Some combinations of price *and* R and D and innovative behavior by existing firms—given scale economies, customer allegiances, cost advantages, and so on—define limits to entry by new firms. The lower the prices of established firms and the more advantage they take of innovations made possible by exogenous scientific and technical developments, the less likely it is that others will enter. With respect to technical developments, the exclusion of newcomers arises when, in the words of Judge Hand in the *Alcoa* case, established firms "progressively . . . embrace each new opportunity."

Other matters are involved, however. As Mansfield has shown, the efficient

[16] Not necessarily newly formed firms. New, in this context, means only entry into markets by firms hitherto not in those markets.

[17] For additional explanation, see Joe S. Bain, *Barriers to Entry* (1956) and Franco Modigliani, "New Developments on the Oligopoly Front," *Journal of Political Economy* (June 1958).

use of particular innovations may be denied to firms below certain sizes.[18] In addition, particular innovations may necessitate capital outlays which make them unavailable to smaller firms—and to new firms as well. Patents held by established firms impede entry; those held by new firms, to foster it.

Unfortunately, no clear and general hypothesis exists concerning the determinants of the behavior of established firms in continuing to explore and to mine the economically feasible resource created by exogenous science. The firm, once successful, has the ability but not necessarily the motivation to continue to be scientifically progressive. The tenacity with which some firms cling to old products and processes is nothing short of amazing.[19] Yet other cases can be cited—Bell Telephone Labs, perhaps—where motivation is not readily apparent and technical progress seems to continue, almost as an objective in its own right.

With these caveats about the limited knowledge of the process, it is still the underlying argument of creative destruction which explains the links from exogenous science and technology, through either R and D by existing firms or by new entrants, to innovation and to market structure. The entering, innovating firms, Schumpeter argued, displace the existing firms. But in the same fashion, existing firms that succeed in maintaining R and D activities that enable them to adapt effectively to their scientific environments and which are motivated so to adapt tend to displace those with ineffective R and D or low motivations. Given the inherent uncertainties in technological change and the difficulties of rationally fashioning an effective research and development program, some will succeed better than others. If the resulting innovations are products with relative demands that depend on the timing and nature of the technological change, market structures will be directly affected. Some firms will tend to lose sales and market shares; some, to gain. Some firms will experience relatively high costs and low profits; others, lower costs and higher profits.

It is, of course, the resulting dimensions of prices, costs, product differences, and product innovation which define market performance. And from both of these, influences spread back to business behavior and market structure, partially but not fully closing the system of relationships. Schumpeter, in *The Theory of Economic Development*, posited that these feedback effects would tend to reproduce a competitive structure. But Schumpeter was dealing with a once-and-for all sort of innovation. Or, at least, he paid no attention to the possibility of a series of innovations affecting a particular market with inadequate time between innovations for the competitive structure to become reestablished or to the possible existence of other entry barriers. Neither did Schumpeter, at this stage, recognize the possibility of firms responsively adapt-

[18] Edwin Mansfield, "Size of Firm, Market Structure and Innovation," *Journal of Political Economy* (December, 1963).

[19] An excellent illustration is the entrance by General Motors in the early 1930s into the manufacture of locomotives. Steam locomotive manufacturers showed not just disinterest, but actual disdain for diesel locomotive development. In subsequent chapters the same sort of behavior appears for numerous manufacturers of aircraft.

ing to a changing technology through an R and D activity. It is this responsive adaptation of firms in an environment in which related science creates more or less continuous opportunities for innovation which, with other more or less effective entry barriers, explains the correlation between market concentration and technological change.

The interrelations of the principal parts of the system shown in Figure 1-4 can be described generally. They consist of the links running from exogenous science, through either entering firms or existing firms, to innovation, market structure, market performance and achievements of firms, and then back to R and D and innovation. Save for the outside science, which may itself receive spillover contributions from the market-oriented R & D, and save for numerous (and important) nontechnological factors which may affect behavior, structure and performance, the system is closed. Arbitrarily beginning the description with the R and D component, the hypothesis is that this activity, based on its search of exogenous science, may afford opportunities for further development and innovation. Innovations, as they occur, tend to alter market structure, with the successfully innovating firms increasing their market shares, profits and other relevant measures of achievement. The successful achievement is at once the visible result of innovation and the source of slack internal to the successful firm.[20] The slack conditions permit—but do not require—additional R and D which may in turn lead to further innovation and further market success by the already successful firm.

The firms adversely affected by the innovation have fewer rather than more internal resources. While the need for additional R and D may be recognized —especially by those in that activity in these firms—as the means to market success and the eventual reestablishing of slack conditions, others in the firm may resist the redistributional aspects of such a behavioral shift. Further, because the R and D may in any event be undertaken in something of a crisis environment in the firm, because of the uncertainty necessarily attaching to attempts to pull new innovations from searches of the related science, and because of other, non-technical barriers to the use of the new technology, success will not be automatic. Failure, with consequent market concentrating effects, is the result for at least some of the firms.[21]

A More Detailed View of the Individual Firm in the Eclectic System

As noted above, a clear theory of the behavior of individual firms over time in this system is difficult to fashion. Viewing a single firm at a point in time the

[20] See Simon and March, *Organizations* (1958) and Cyert and March, *A Behavioral Theory of the Firm* (1963) for extended discussion of the concept of slack. For our purposes, it denotes a condition in which particular activities in a firm may be increased without decreasing the rewards to others in the organization.

[21] In this context, failure means exit of a firm from the group comprising the supply side of the market. The firm may disappear through bankruptcy, but it may also disappear through merger or withdrawal into a geographic and product market in which it no longer is in rivalry with the successfully innovating firms.

effects of the exogenous science on the planning of development and innovation can be indicated, however. In Figure 1-5, expected net revenue of the firm is plotted on the vertical axis; the time selected for innovation is plotted on the horizontal axis. The figure is based on evaluations by the firm at $t = 0$ of the effects on net revenue if it attempts to innovate at $t = 1$, $t = 2$, and so on.

Curve A depicts the partial effects on changes in expected net revenue from developing and introducing, say, a new product. In order to incorporate the possible revenue effects of being the first to innovate successfully, this curve

Changes in Expected
Net Revenue from
Innovation at t

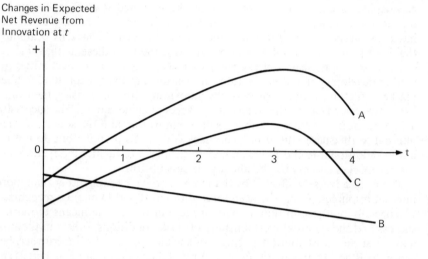

Figure 1-5 *Ex ante* View of Effects on Net Revenue from Innovation at Future Points in Time.

is discounted at each point in time by $(1 - P_t)$, where P_t is the probability assigned by the firm to the chance that by time t another firm will have already made the successful innovation. Curve A is taken to be negative in the immediately future period, with positive contributions to net revenue in a period beyond this. The negative portion reflects high costs of development and, perhaps, large revenue losses from sales of existing products when early innovation is planned.

The longer the firm waits, the more may be gained from advances in science and from development work done outside the firm. These advances are paid for by others and, if they occur, will tend to reduce the development costs of the firm for the innovation in question. If there is scientific and development work going on elsewhere which appears related to the conceived innovation,

P_t should tend to rise with time and, hence $(1 - P_t)$ tends to fall. The expected value of innovation at times further into the future grows at a decreasing rate and may eventually decline because of the effects of discounting by $(1 - P_t)$.

Curve A is defined to include only the net revenue effects of being first to innovate successfully, discounted at each point in time by the probability that the circumstance of being first in fact obtains. Curve B contains the probability discounted effects on changes in net revenue if the firm is not the first to innovate successfully. The curve is based on the assumptions that sales (and profit) losses will occur to the firm if another leads it in successfully innovation and that, *ex visu* $t = 0$, the probability of this occurring, P_t, rises with time. It is because of the latter relation that curve B is shown to fall as t increases.

Adding curves A and B yields C, the total changes in expected net revenue of the firm attributable to innovation, as the date it selects for innovation is considered into the future. Curve C reaches a peak in this case at $t = 3$. That is, given only the factors considered here, planning for introduction of the innovation at that point in time is the optimal choice.

Figure 1-5 permits a few observations concerning the individual firm and its expenditures on R and D. First the notion of the relatedness of an exogenous science or technology to firms' activities can be understood through consideration of curve A. The essential idea is that the exogenous accretions to knowledge may—or may not—provide a stimulus to development expenditures by firms. A necessary condition for the stimulus to exist is that the discounted total net gains from innovation must at some point in time be positive. That is, there must be some points within the planning horizon of the firm where curve C crosses the horizontal axis.

In the sense used here, the outside science or technology is the more related the higher is the undiscounted A curve. The science is related in the economic sense that, ignoring the behavior of other firms, it creates opportunities for investment in development programs which promise positive returns. The C curve and, hence, innovative behavior depend on this relatedness, but they depend on other things as well.

Second, the easier it is for others to follow and, through following, to share in the gains from innovation, the lower will the discounted A and C curves tend to be. Other things equal, ease in following by other firms means that the developing firm will find it difficult to appropriate the rewards from innovation. It thus tends to discourage development expenditures by individual firms. Or, to put it differently, ease in following could go so far that it encourages firms to postpone development and innovation to the time that exogenous science or technology has advanced so that only small development expenses for single firms are involved.

Third, the A curve tends to peak and the B curve tends to fall more rapidly the higher is the P_t value. It follows, again with other things equal, and ignoring possible adverse effects on the rate of development spending, that the absence of collusive agreements governing the timing of innovation and the absence of entry barriers each tend to encourage more rapid innovation. Both the entry barriers and collusive agreements concerning innovation tend to reduce P_t. It is true, nonetheless, that without the barriers or agreements the P_t values may appear so high that the C curve is everywhere negative as viewed by many—perhaps even all—individual firms. For these firms no development expenditures aimed at being the first to innovate successfully can be justified. One can see, however, that these circumstances are likely to cause some firms to attempt to erect entry and following barriers and to reach tacit or overt agreements concerning the timing of their own innovations if science is so related that the undiscounted A curve is strongly positive.

The approach underlying Figure 1-5 has one fundamental deficiency even as static analysis. The C curve may be fairly well defined in the uninteresting case when there is no closely related science or technology. In this instance C is near or in the negative region throughout. Where such is not the case, the presence of closely related science and technology means that there is great uncertainty with respect to potential contributions therefrom. The firm can make only crude estimates of what its own development costs would be in order to achieve a particular innovation by any point in the future. Or, given its rate of development expenditure, the firm can make only crude estimates of the time when it will be able to introduce an innovation. Since this applies to all firms and since knowledge by one firm of the development progress of others is incomplete, the P_t variable is also uncertain.

The addition of these uncertainty elements means that the C curve can be regarded as no more than the mean expected (or, perhaps better, the best guess) value, with a probability distribution (or, perhaps better, an undefined range) of values about it. This means that the firm, no matter how clever and diligent its management, can make errors. It can err by planning for early innovation only to find that the development costs and development time are greater than expected. It can err by postponing the planned innovation date in order to reduce technological uncertainties and then find that an existing firm succeeds before it. It can err by misjudging the degree of adherence to collusive agreements or the effectiveness of entry barriers. Any of these sorts of errors can threaten the firm's viability, just as their avoidance can produce great success.

There is another even more fundamental deficiency in the approach of Figure 1-5. The eclectic system is above all, a dynamic one. Static views of the firm fail to reflect its behavior in this dynamic environment. The firm does not, of course, make at $t = 0$ a decision with respect to development which is independent of prior events or which cannot subsequently be modified. Indeed, R and D in the firm is a series of time interdependent, sequential decisions. What was decided and done yesterday affect today's views of the C curve and the variance about the C curve.

It is in this dynamic context that using Burton Klein's terminology, exploratory research by the firm, is necessary. Where there is a closely related science or other exogenous technological changes, a part of the R and D activity of some firms is just probing into the science and technology to see what is new, to experiment, and to make rough estimates of the technical feasibility and the costs of developing particular products or processes. Decisions to undertake development rest on the knowledge produced in the exogenous activity and, within firms, a conception of how that knowledge may be used to the advantage of the firm. Exploratory research, that is, helps to define and to reduce the variance in the A and C curves over time. The $t = 0$ convention used in Figure 1-5 views development and innovation at just that point in time when a decision to develop is under consideration.

There is yet another dynamic aspect of firm behavior which requires explanation. Initial success, it is apparent, makes possible additional R and D, further innovation and further success. But success need not be continuously reinforcing for a variety of reasons. If, for example, success leads to more R and D, that activity could turn to types of research which are rewarding to the researchers but unproductive from the view of goals of the entire firm. Or, again, success emanating from R and D in one narrow area of technology and one type of product or process may lead to continued efforts in the same areas when the exogenous science is, in fact, offering higher potential gains in others. Not to be ignored is the possibility that the firm may use up the slack coming from innovative success in the enjoyment of the quiet life.[22] Unhappily, behavioral theory is currently inadequate to generalize about the circumstances which lead to these alternative forms of behavior. Nonetheless, they clearly affect the nature of the feedbacks shown in Figure 1-4 from market performance and achievements in firms to R and D, innovation and, ultimately, market structure.

The Effects on Market Structure

Even given the difficulties of finding behavioral generalizations concerning individual firms, it is possible to be somewhat more specific with respect to the probable nature of the concentration effects in different technological contexts. At one extreme—illustrated by the implicit assumptions in *The Theory* that led Schumpeter to conclude that a competitive equilibrium tends to re-emerge after an innovation—there is no continuing exogenous science so related to the products and processes of firms that purposive development by existing firms is economically rewarding. Here, to be sure, technological change does not tend to cause concentration. To the contrary, the competitive equilibrium emerges because of the absence of further technological change and the absence of other impediments to competitive structure and behavior. Concentration, of course, may exist in such a technically stagnant market, with its base in such familiar things as resource preemption, economies of scale or monopolistic behavior among the firms.

At a step removed from this, the exogenous science and technical develop-

22 Cf. J. R. Hicks, "The Theory of Monopoly," *Econometrica* (1935).

ment may create opportunities for only small product changes and essentially evolutionary and small changes in production functions. What is meant is that, from the firm's point of view, the possible changes in technology are not such that failure immediately to incorporate them in products or processes significantly disadvantages it in terms of either consumer demand or costs. Referring again to Figure 1-5, the A curve is only slightly positive anywhere and the B curve is very close to zero throughout. The concentration effect in these circumstances would be weak. There is no perceived exogenous science offering opportunities for substantial gains or creating risks of substantial losses.

In general, it seems reasonable to conclude that the concentration effects of given innovations will be the stronger as the A curve and B curve are further removed from zero. The gains to the successful firms are large and cause somewhat commensurate losses to the unsuccessful ones. Since the A curve depends in part on the relatedness of the exogenous science, it does appear that, at least for single innovations, the concentration effect tends to be more pronounced when the science is closely related.

Whether the concentration remains and whether the few large firms involved in the high concentration remain in relatively the same market positions depend on a number of factors. If progress in a closely related exogenous science continues and if neither collusive agreements among existing firms nor barriers to entry arise, a turnover in the market positions of the larger firms and occasional entry by new firms seems probable. The leading firms are unlikely to experience the same fortunes in the relative successes of their developments and innovations over time. On the other hand, the market power stemming from their positions in a concentrated market could be used to effect collusive behavior and barriers to entry. Should this occur, the structure will retain both high concentration and stable relative positions for the firms.

In addition to the relatedness of science as defined above, there are statistical as well as theoretical reasons to believe that the concentration tendency will be stronger where the innovative opportunities require large resources and entail significant changes in the *modus operandi* of the firms.[23] As noted above, large resource needs may preclude smaller firms or firms without existing slack from attempting to innovate; large changes in the nature of products and processes may deter some firms from perceiving opportunities and attempting innovation even though they have financial capability.[24]

Finally, it should be noted that, whatever the structure of the market, the tendency to concentration depends on the existence of an exogenous science and technical developments which create innovative opportunities. If the

[23] E. Mansfield, in "Size of Firm, Market Structure and Innovation," *Journal of Political Economy* (December 1963), found that innovations requiring relatively large minimum capital outlays tend to occur relatively more frequently in larger firms than do innovations requiring more moderate outlays.

[24] S. C. Gilfillan, *The Sociology of Invention* (1935), notes the behavioral resistance of firms —especially small proprietorships—to large changes in methods or products.

progress in the science slows or moves in directions which lead to fewer innovative opportunities, technical progress in the market and the concentration tendency resulting therefrom are concomitantly slowed.

The Organization of the Study

The fact that empirical studies have generally failed to find relations between technological change and market structure of the sort hypothesized by Galbraith and Schumpeter is hardly relevant to the hypothesis I am advancing. With the causal nexus suggested by my hypothesis, highly concentrated industries may exist with no observable tendency for rapid technological change. Industries of low concentration may be observed at times when they are experiencing rapid technological change. It is expected, however, that extensive R and D programs and high rates of product or process innovations occur within industries over a period of time only where there is related but exogenous scientific progress. This progress, I argue, makes R and D necessary for firms to survive and, because of the virtual inevitability of management errors in this milieu, tends to cause increases in concentration and changes in the relative positions of firms over time.

R and D is, in fact, concentrated in a fairly small number of industries. Thus, examples of the extremes of the hypothesized relationships should be found in these few industries. And the manufacture of aircraft is one of these. I will show in this volume that the technology embodied in aircraft used by commercial airlines has come in large measure from research and development undertaken by or on behalf of governmental agencies. As is detailed in Chapter 7, the basic R and D was carried on principally for purposes which were at best only remotely concerned with the production of new types of commercial aircraft. After 1930, manufacturers of commercial planes appear to have adopted, developed, and applied the results of these scientific and technological advances, with an ensuing stream of faster, larger, and more economical commercial aircraft. With the new technology came tendencies for the aircraft manufacturing industry to become more concentrated and, from time to time, for large changes to occur in the market positions of particular firms. The task of the book is to trace, insofar as possible, the relations between the underlying scientific technological developments, their adaptation to commercial aircraft and the resulting changes in the structure of the commercial aircraft manufacturing market.

The analysis is done in considerable detail. Chapter 2 describes changes in the size and composition of the fleets of United States trunk carriers from 1932 to 1965 and, from these, develops measures of market concentration. Changes in the number and relative shares of manufacturers of aircraft for this carrier market are derived.

The third chapter is a statistical study of relations between the technical characteristics of the aircraft and their operating costs. The procedures permit estimates of operating costs of all aircraft developed for use as commercial transports, including those which were not used as well as those which were.

Chapter 4 incorporates some aggregative measures of technological change —primarily aircraft operating cost and performance data—into a statistical model of the market for commercial aircraft. This model covers the period from 1932 to 1965 and offers explanations of changes in passenger mile demand and changes in the seat miles supplied by the airlines. Certain aspects of technological change, it appears, have significant effects on these but so do such routine economic variables as price, income, and rates of return. It is not true, however, that these economic variables explain a large percentage of the variance in the overall demand for new aircraft. The large degree of unexplained variance in the latter, I argue, is consistent with the notion that the timing of the introduction of new and significantly different types of planes —with which overall demand for new aircraft is related—depends on non-economic and essentially exogenous developments in science.

Chapters 5 and 6 are considerably more detailed. They use the results of the previous chapters to ascertain the factors affecting the choices of individual aircraft used by particular trunk carriers. The market failures—planes which were not adopted for use—are compared with their successful contemporaries. An investigation of the relative shares of the aircraft which were used is presented. A formal statistical study is made which indicates for the years 1947–1965 the importance of the operating costs of new planes relative to those being replaced and of the relative operating costs of alternative new aircraft in carrier equipment choices. The estimated effects of costs and of other technical factors in equipment choices are then used to generate estimated demands for particular planes for these years. These estimates are converted to market shares for particular aircraft and particular manufacturers and compared with the actual shares derived in Chapter 2. From this emerges a picture of the role of technological change in the shaping of the structure of the manufacturing industry.

This leaves for investigation the sources of the technological changes and, in particular, the influence of exogenous science and technology on developments and innovations in commercial aircraft. This is done in Chapter 7, in which the activities of the National Advisory Committee on Aeronautics, of various Army and Navy research institutions and of sponsored research in commercial firms are described. A number of military aircraft developments which appear to be direct antecedents to commercial developments are noted. It is argued that it is because of these preceding and relatively continuous background developments that the technology of commercial aircraft changed as it did. In attempting to bring about these changes, some manufacturers, it is contended, succeeded; some failed. Market structure changed and tended to become more concentrated.

Chapter 8 is a summary of the theory and of the supporting empirical facts found in the market for commercial aircraft. The results of a few related studies covering other industries are reviewed in the light of the findings here.

2

The Structure of the Market for Commercial Aircraft: 1932–1965

Introduction

This chapter traces the composition and concentration of the fleets of aircraft operated by the domestic trunk airlines of the United States during the period 1932–1965. From the data on these fleets, estimates are made of the structure of the market for commercial aircraft through the same period. Subsequent chapters relate the changes in market structure to changes in technology.

Definition of the Market

The aircraft market under consideration is considerably more narrow than that of the entire aerospace or aircraft industry. The market is limited to those firms developing and manufacturing aircraft intended for use by the domestic trunk lines. Indeed, in the resulting count of market shares of the aircraft manufacturers, only the sales to the domestic trunk carriers are included even though some of the same planes were purchased by other United States carriers, by foreign carriers, by the armed forces, and by companies and individuals for private use.

This restricted view of the market is imposed by data limitations and is not, of course, ideal. On the other hand, estimating the market structure of the commercial aircraft manufacturing industry from data on the fleets of the trunk carriers has some offsetting advantages. In particular, this method of estimation assures the exclusion of most of the aircraft types which are not close substitutes for commercial transports. Since a DC-3 and, say, a Piper Cub are not good substitutes—whether viewed in terms of transport buyers' cross-demand or aircraft sellers' cross-supply functions—such exclusions have clear theoretical justification.

All of the exclusions of aircraft caused by defining the market with reference to the trunk line demand for aircraft are not so clear-cut as the DC-3 and Piper Cub example, however. Moreover, additional adjustments of the data on the aircraft in even the trunk line fleets were necessary. Flying boats and amphibians are not included in the market on the grounds that they are not close substitutes for landtype planes. It is true, nevertheless, that a few amphibians and flying boats were used by the domestic trunk lines in the early years covered by the study. For this period it might be argued that these planes were close substitutes. The fact that they were most commonly used by international carriers, by domestic carriers operating coastal routes or routes around the Great Lakes suggests that this was not the case even then. Since World War II, landtype planes have been used almost universally by the international as well as by the principal domestic airlines. Flying boats have disappeared from airline use and amphibian operations have been restricted to those few route situations for which they are peculiarly appropriate.

Freight aircraft such as the Curtiss C-46 were also subtracted from the carrier fleets before the market structure estimates were made. In some cases, however, it was not possible to separate freight and passenger versions of the same model. For example, data on the number of DC-6As—cargo planes—and DC-6Bs—passenger planes—are consolidated for some years. Because of this, the total number, including the freight planes, was used for all years. Since the domestic trunk lines are primarily passenger carriers, the inclusion of an unidentifiable number of cargo planes is unlikely to be substantial enough to affect the overall results.

The market is also restricted to that for new aircraft, since aircraft manufacturers neither engage in nor control the sales of used transports. This restriction required the elimination, prior to estimating sales of aircraft manufacturers, of aircraft which were bought by the trunk line carriers from the used aircraft market. Actually, viewing the trunk line fleet in its entirety—that is, with a cancelling of interline aircraft transfers among the trunk carriers—few used planes had to be subtracted save for the years immediately after World War II. From 1943 to 1946, large numbers of used transport aircraft were sold to the lines by the government but additions to the overall fleet in other years are mostly of new planes.

The consideration of used aircraft also indicated that failure to consider directly the demand for planes by nontrunk carriers in the United States is of very minor importance. There were, of course, only few nontrunk, scheduled carriers from 1932 until after World War II. The omission of their demand would be of minor significance in any case. But, regardless of their number, the fact is that they almost exclusively operated used planes acquired second or thirdhand from the trunk carriers. The small lines which survived into the mid-1930s flew, at best, used trimotors sold by the larger carriers when they made acquisitions of the Boeing 247, and of the Douglas DC-2 and DC-3. Indeed, most of the smaller trunk carriers also had fleets composed of secondhand planes. After World War II, the nonscheduled carriers most commonly flew used DC-3s, DC-4s, and DC-6s. The growing feeder and local service carriers operated used DC-3s and, later, used Martin 202s and 404s and used Convair 240s, 340s, and 440s. Until the appearance of the Fokker-Fairchild F-27 and, after 1964, of the Boeing 727, Boeing 737, Douglas DC-9, and the BAC-111, the nontrunk carriers were really not part of the market for new transport carriers.

The Fleets of the Domestic Trunk Airlines

Ascertaining the composition of airline fleets before 1938 was difficult. Separations between the trunk and other domestic air carriers are not made in published data of anything as detailed as aircraft ownership by individual carriers prior to 1938. There are, in fact, no regularly published and reliable data on the composition of any aggregative airline fleet prior to 1938 and the passage of the Civil Aeronautics Act. As a consequence, it was necessary to trace airline histories and to develop as completely as possible a set of airlines that operated from 1932 through 1937 routes similar to those that by 1938 were the defined trunk line system. It was not possible to find data on the fleet composition of all such lines, however.

Table 2-1 indicates the airlines for which reasonably accurate details on fleet composition could be found for every year from 1932 to 1937. Scheduled air carriers listed by the Commerce Department's *Air Commerce Bulletin* as entering service between 1929 to 1938 are shown in Table A-1. The same table gives less reliable information on lines entering service in years prior to 1929. It is obvious from this more complete listing that the aircraft of many carriers are omitted for the 1932–1937 years. Table 2-2 shows, however, that only small numbers of these survived through those years and that the omitted carriers in each year are the relatively small ones. In 1932 for example, the 17 carriers whose fleets could be defined had 374 transport aircraft with seating capacity for four or more passengers. The remaining 82 planes reported as the full aircraft census were smaller planes, amphibians, or flying boats owned by the same lines or unidentifiable other types owned by the 12 other carriers operating that year whose fleets could not be counted.

Table 2-3 gives the trunk line carriers included in each year, 1938–1965. Airline names given in the table are those of the most recent years. Marquette Airlines which was an officially designated carrier from 1938 to 1941 is excluded. Marquette owned three Stinson Trimotor aircraft in 1938 but apparently provided regularly scheduled passenger service for only a short period in that year. What was then Transcontinental and Western Air, Inc., later operated Marquette's routes and absorbed the airline in December 1941. Also excluded—though included in some publications as domestic trunk lines in 1938—are Mayflower Airlines, Airline Feeder System, and Wilmington-Catalina Airways. The latter were more properly local service airways and, in any event, would not have been buyers of the relevant types of new aircraft.

The detailed data on the composition of the fleets of the carriers are given in tables of Appendixes C, D, and E. Tables 2-4 and 2-8 aggregate this information to the entire trunk line fleet and convert it to yield estimates of the shares of particular aircraft types and manufacturers in the aircraft acquisitions of these lines.

Table 2-4 consolidates the detailed information into the relative shares of the fleet accounted for by the four aircraft types with the largest usage at the end of each year. The table does not identify the particular aircraft or their manufacturer. These, of course, change through time. Neither is the table in conventional concentration ratio form. The percentages are not of total yearly outputs or sales—flow concepts—but rather of total aircraft in the fleets—a stock concept. On this basis, the dominance of the largest single type ranges from a low of 14.9 percent (the Boeing 727 in 1965) to a high

Table 2-1

Scheduled Air Carriers for which Fleet Composition Data Are Available, 1932–1937

Carrier	Years of Operation in Period 1932–1937
American Airlines	1932–1937
Boston-Maine Airways [a]	1937
Bowen Air Lines [b]	1932–1935
Braniff Airways	1932–1937
Central Airlines [c]	1934–1935
Chicago and Southern Air Lines [d]	1934–1937
Columbia Airlines	1935
Continental Air Lines [e]	1937
Delta Air Lines	1934–1937
Eastern Air Lines	1932–1937
Hanford's Tri-States Airlines [f]	1932–1937
Long and Harmon [g]	1933–1934
Ludington Airlines [h]	1932
National Airlines	1934–1937
National Airways, Inc. [i]	1933–1936
National Parks Airways [j]	1932–1936
Northwest Airways	1932–1937
Pacific Seaboard Air Lines [k]	1933
Pennsylvania Airlines [l]	1932–1935
Pennsylvania-Central Airlines	1936–1937
Rapid Air Transport [m]	1932–1933
Trans-american Airlines Corp. [n]	1932
Transcontinental and Western Airlines	1932–1937
United Airlines	1932–1937
United States Airways	1932–1933
Varney Air Transport [o]	1932–1936
Wedell-Williams Air Service [p]	1933, 1935
Western Air Express	1932–1937
Wyoming Air Service [q]	1932–1937

[a] National Airways, Inc. from 1932 to 1936; Northeast Airlines after 1938.

[b] Absorbed by Braniff in 1935.

[c] Merged with Pennsylvania Airlines to become Pennsylvania-Central Airlines in 1936. Name changed to Capital Airlines in 1948.

[d] Pacific Seaboard Air Lines to 1934. Absorbed by Delta Air Lines in 1953.

[e] Varney Air Transport (or Varney Speed Lines or Varney Air Service) from 1932 to 1937.

[f] Name changed to Mid-Continent Airlines in 1938. Absorbed by Braniff in 1952.

[g] Merged with Braniff in 1935.

[h] Absorbed by Eastern Air Transport in 1933.

[i] See note a.

[j] Also known as Alfred Frank Air Line. Merged with Western in 1937.

[k] See note d.

[l] See note c.

[m] Operated Kansas City–Omaha route, 1932–1933.

[n] Corporate existence terminated in 1932 after control was assumed by the Aviation Corporation.

[o] See note e.

[p] Discontinuous service, 1933, 1935. Merged with Eastern in 1937.

[q] Name changed to Inland Air Lines in 1938. Absorbed by Western Air Lines in 1952.

Table 2-2

Carriers for which Fleet Composition Data Are Available Relative to All Scheduled Carriers, 1932–1937

	Number of Scheduled Carriers Operating in Year	Total Number of Aircraft in Use End of Year	Number of Carriers for Which Fleet Data Are Available	Total Number of Aircraft in Detailed Fleet Data [a]
1932	29	456	17	374
1933	24	418	19	336
1934	22	423	19	334
1935	23	363	20	321
1936	21	280	16	257
1937	17	291	15	235

[a] Landtype aircraft with seating for four or more passengers.

Sources: Handbook of Airline Statistics (1965); *Aero Digest* (July, October, November, 1932; June, 1934; October 1937); *Moody's Manual* (1933, 1934, 1935); *Aircraft Yearbook* (1933); W. R. Matthews, "Curtiss Condor II," *American Aviation Historical Society Journal* (Spring, 1967); V. D. Sealy, "Boeing's Pacesetting 247," *American Aviation Historical Society Journal* (Winter, 1964).

of 94.2 percent (the DC-3 in 1945). The percentage accounted for by the four types in greatest use ranges from 45.2 percent (1964) to 100 percent (1942 through 1945). In general, the concentration of fleet ownership by type of aircraft rises from 1932 to 1945 and falls thereafter.

Table 2-5 shows shares of fleet ownership in terms of the manufacturers of the aircraft. These shares show some rather pronounced shifts as the aircraft of one manufacturer displace those of others. The changes from 1932 to 1933 are mainly those arising from the introduction of the Boeing 247 and Curtiss Condor II and their replacing Ford, Stinson, and Fokker aircraft. From 1934 to 1946, the DC-2, and DC-3 dominate the figures, with Douglas having manufactured 95.4 percent of the aircraft in trunk line fleets in 1946. After this, Lockheed's "Constellation" series and the Martin and Convair 202s, 404s, 240s, and 440s effect the main changes through 1958. In 1959, the Lockheed 188 Electra was added, followed by the Boeing and Douglas jet aircraft.

Discerning changes in shares of sales of new planes from Tables 2-4 and 2-5 is difficult. Tables 2-6 and 2-7 give concentration in terms of additions of new aircraft to the fleets between December 31 of one year and December 31 of the next. The underlying data come from the tables of Appendix C rather than from the detailed data on the fleets of each line given in the tables of Appendix D. Thus, the additions in the number of a particular aircraft in the fleets is the number brought into the fleets from purchases less the reductions from sales, other retirements of aircraft from passenger operations and accidents. Interairline transfers among the trunk carriers cancel out.

Table 2-3

Domestic Trunk Lines, 1938–1965

Carrier	Years of Trunk Line Operation [a]
Big Four	
American Airlines	1938–
Eastern Air Lines	1938–
Trans-World Airlines	1938–
United Air Lines	1938–
Other Domestic Trunk Lines	
Braniff Airways	1938–
Capital Airlines [b]	1938–1960
Chicago and Southern Air Lines [c]	1938–1952
Colonial Airlines [d]	1939–1955
Continental Air Lines	1938–
Delta Air Lines	1938–
Inland Air Lines [e]	1938–1951
Mid-Continent Airlines [f]	1938–1951
National Airlines	1938–
Northeast Airlines [g]	1938–
Northwest Airlines	1938–
Western Air Lines	1938–

[a] Years from 1938 to last full year of operation.

[b] Absorbed by United Air Lines, June 1, 1961.

[c] Absorbed by Delta Air Lines, May 1, 1953.

[d] Absorbed by Eastern Air Lines, June 1, 1956.

[e] Absorbed by Western Air Lines, April 10, 1952.

[f] Absorbed by Braniff Airways, August 16, 1952.

[g] Operated as Boston and Maine Airways, Inc., 1936 to 1938.

These unadjusted additions approximate sales by manufacturers to the domestic trunk carriers only when few used aircraft of the same types are being brought into the fleets and when reductions of the same types from sales, retirements, and accidents are small. As noted above, the only period when used aircraft came into these fleets in appreciable numbers was between 1943 and 1946 when aircraft were released by the military and converted to passenger use. These years are omitted from Tables 2-6 and 2-7. In all other years, additions of aircraft not in current production are also excluded, as shown in notes to Table 2-6. These planes necessarily came from the second-hand market. This adjustment, it is believed, eliminates virtually all purchases

Table 2-4

Concentration of Fleets in Four Aircraft Types with Largest Usage, 1932–1965

Year (Dec. 31)	Total Aircraft in Fleets	Concentration (percent)				Number of Types in Use
		Largest One Type	Largest Two Types	Largest Three Types	Largest Four Types	
1932	374	16.8	32.1	40.6	48.1	23
1933	336	16.1	29.1	38.9	47.8	22
1934	334	17.1	31.1	42.2	51.2	22
1935	321	17.7	35.4	46.6	56.2	16
1936	257	21.4	42.4	58.4	69.6	14
1937	235	32.3	53.6	74.0	89.8	9
1938	231	42.0	61.9	78.8	93.1	7
1939	261	52.5	69.3	84.3	97.3	7
1940	338	68.6	77.8	86.7	93.8	8
1941	342	78.1	86.3	90.9	94.7	6
1942	164	93.9	100.0	—	—	2
1943	191	91.1	98.4	99.5	100.0	4
1944	271	93.4	99.3	99.7	100.0	4
1945	397	94.2	98.7	100.0	—	3
1946	634	69.9	95.4	97.3	99.2	5
1947	723	58.1	81.5	92.3	96.4	7
1948	762	48.3	67.3	80.8	89.9	8
1949	782	40.4	60.9	74.2	86.6	9
1950	792	36.5	54.9	68.7	81.7	9
1951	821	34.7	51.6	68.3	80.8	10
1952	914	26.9	44.5	58.1	69.1	11
1953	950	18.9	36.2	49.2	60.2	12
1954	964	19.2	32.2	44.2	55.5	12
1955	1010	18.8	31.5	43.2	53.9	13
1956	1098	19.9	32.3	43.1	52.9	13
1957	1211	22.0	36.0	49.1	58.0	14
1958	1244	21.7	38.9	51.7	60.0	15
1959	1258	21.4	36.4	47.3	55.1	16
1960	1226	21.0	35.6	44.8	53.5	17
1961	1196	18.6	33.0	43.2	51.9	17
1962	1124	17.1	31.7	42.1	50.7	18
1963	1064	16.9	29.9	40.9	50.2	17
1964	1105	15.5	26.1	35.7	45.2	17
1965	1122	14.9	28.0	39.1	49.7	18

of used aircraft from Tables 2-6 and 2-7. Nonetheless, sales of used aircraft do tend to offset current purchases of new planes in some classifications in some years. This is true, for example, in the cases of the Ford and Stinson Trimotors in the early years and of the Boeing 707s and DC-8s in later years. In these instances, older models were being replaced by newer ones and the additions figures underestimate manufacturer's sales to the lines.

As would be expected, concentration is higher in terms of additions of new types of aircraft than it is in terms of stocks of aircraft. In December of 1933, the largest single type of aircraft accounted for only 16.1 percent of the fleet;

Table 2-5

Concentration of Fleets by Manufacturers of Aircraft, 1932–1965
(percent)

Year (Dec. 31)	Douglas	Boeing	Lockheed	Consolidated [a]	Martin	Stinson	Fokker	Curtiss-Wright [b]	Ford	Foreign	All Others
1932	0.0	19.0	8.0	0.8	0.0	15.5	15.0	7.0	16.8	0.0	17.9
1933	0.3	29.7	11.6	2.1	0.0	11.9	8.9	10.1	13.1	0.0	12.3
1934	6.3	29.6	12.9	2.1	0.0	14.4	1.8	9.9	14.1	0.0	8.9
1935	17.7	28.6	18.1	1.9	0.0	15.0	0.3	6.8	8.1	0.0	3.6
1936	32.7	24.1	20.2	1.9	0.0	10.9	0.0	3.1	3.1	0.0	4.0
1937	53.6	20.4	21.7	0.0	0.0	4.3	0.0	0.0	0.0	0.0	0.0
1938	61.9	16.9	19.5	0.0	0.0	1.7	0.0	0.0	0.0	0.0	0.0
1939	69.3	14.9	14.9	0.0	0.0	0.8	0.0	0.0	0.0	0.0	0.0
1940	77.8	10.4	11.2	0.0	0.0	0.6	0.0	0.0	0.0	0.0	0.0
1941	81.9	9.6	8.5	0.0	0.0	0.0	0.0	0.0	0.0	0.0	0.0
1942	93.9	0.0	6.1	0.0	0.0	0.0	0.0	0.0	0.0	0.0	0.0
1943	91.1	0.5	7.3	0.0	0.0	0.0	0.0	0.0	0.0	0.0	1.0
1944	93.4	0.4	5.9	0.0	0.0	0.0	0.0	0.0	0.0	0.0	0.4
1945	94.2	1.3	4.5	0.0	0.0	0.0	0.0	0.0	0.0	0.0	0.0
1946	95.4	0.8	3.8	0.0	0.0	0.0	0.0	0.0	0.0	0.0	0.0
1947	92.3	0.7	5.8	0.0	0.0	0.0	0.0	0.0	0.0	0.0	0.0
1948	80.8	0.7	6.3	9.1	1.2	0.0	0.0	0.0	0.0	0.0	0.0
1949	74.1	1.9	8.4	12.4	3.1	0.0	0.0	0.0	0.0	0.0	0.0
1950	68.7	1.9	12.2	13.0	3.1	0.0	0.0	0.0	0.0	0.0	0.0
1951	68.3	1.9	13.6	12.4	4.2	0.0	0.0	0.0	0.0	0.0	0.0
1952	58.1	1.8	14.9	13.5	3.7	0.0	0.0	0.0	0.0	0.0	0.0
1953	50.8	1.7	15.6	20.1	11.8	0.0	0.0	0.0	0.0	0.0	0.0
1954	49.8	1.1	15.9	21.6	11.8	0.0	0.0	0.0	0.0	0.0	0.0
1955	49.0	1.0	17.8	20.5	11.6	0.0	0.0	0.0	0.0	0.8	0.0
1956	46.5	0.8	17.4	20.5	10.9	0.0	0.0	0.0	0.0	4.9	0.0
1957	46.7	0.7	18.4	20.5	9.8	0.0	0.0	0.0	0.0	4.9	0.0
1958	48.0	0.7	18.4	18.0	8.4	0.0	0.0	0.0	0.0	6.4	0.0
1959	43.8	4.5	24.5	14.0	6.8	0.0	0.0	0.0	0.0	6.5	0.0
1960	44.5	6.9	23.1	13.7	5.9	0.0	0.0	0.0	0.0	6.0	0.0
1961	41.2	11.8	23.2	13.6	3.0	0.0	0.0	0.0	0.0	7.2	0.0
1962	39.4	15.6	21.8	14.1	1.4	0.0	0.0	0.0	0.0	7.7	0.0
1963	38.1	18.0	22.6	14.2	0.0	0.0	0.0	0.0	0.0	7.2	0.0
1964	33.2	27.1	20.5	12.2	0.0	0.0	0.0	0.0	0.0	6.9	0.0
1965	26.8	36.2	17.6	11.7	0.0	0.0	0.0	0.0	0.0	7.7	0.0

[a] Convair after 1947.
[b] Includes Curtiss Aeroplane and Motor Co., Curtiss-Robertson and Travel Air.

Table 2-6

Concentration in Additions of New Aircraft to Overall Domestic Trunk Line Fleet, Four Types with Largest Additions, 1933–1941, 1947–1965.

Year	Apparent Additions of New Aircraft [a]	Concentration (percent)				Number of Types with Increases in Overall Fleet Use [b]
		Largest One Type	Largest Two Types	Largest Three Types	Largest Four Types	
1933	85	63.5	83.5	94.1	98.8	5
1934	67	29.3	56.0	70.7	84.0	7
1935	61	59.0	91.8	100.0	—	3
1936	42	69.0	92.9	100.0	—	3
1937	54	87.0	98.1	100.0	—	3
1938	24	87.5	100.0	—	—	2
1939	41	97.6	100.0	—	—	2
1940	112	84.8	95.5	100.0	—	3
1941	36	97.2	100.0	—	—	2
1947	105	74.3	91.4	100.0	—	3
1948	115	60.0	81.7	94.8	100.0	4
1949	58	48.3	81.0	98.3	100.0	4
1950	51	60.8	78.4	90.2	100.0	4
1951	63	44.4	73.0	88.9	96.8	5
1952	148	52.7	68.9	81.8	93.9	6
1953	127	58.3	74.8	87.4	93.7	6
1954	75	60.0	84.0	93.3	100.0	4
1955	55	43.6	72.7	87.3	96.4	5
1956	125	36.8	59.2	76.8	92.0	5
1957	179	39.1	65.9	80.0	92.7	6
1958	82	54.9	71.9	81.7	90.2	6
1959	166	57.8	88.0	98.8	99.4	5
1960	97	39.2	61.9	76.3	88.7	6
1961	125	26.4	45.6	64.8	78.4	6
1962	66	27.3	51.5	74.2	86.4	6
1963	23	60.9	78.3	87.0	95.7	5
1964	119	73.9	85.7	92.4	98.3	5
1965	135	58.5	72.6	82.2	91.1	6

[a] Omitted from positive year-to-year changes in the number of particular types shown in Table 4 are the following: 1933, 5 Bellanca "Pacemakers"; 1951, 6 Boeing 377s; 1954, 1 Lockheed L-18; 1955, 3 DC-3s and 6 Lockheed L-0/749s; 1956, 1 Lockheed L-18; 1960, 2 CV-240s; 1962, 3 Lockheed 1649s. These aircraft were not in current production in the years indicated.
[b] Based on the types shown in Table B-1.

the four largest, 47.8 percent. Twenty-two types were in the fleet. During 1933, however, Table 2-6 shows that 63.5 percent of all additions of new planes to the domestic fleet were aircraft of a single type and that 98.8 percent of all additions were from just four types. Only five new types were added to the fleet in that year. In all years except 1961, 80 percent or more of the additions of new planes involved less than five types of aircraft.

Viewed by manufacturers, as in Table 2-7, the concentration in additions to the fleet appears higher. Particular manufacturers at times had more than one aircraft type involved in the additions. This was the case, for example, for Douglas in the 1950s—when both DC-6Bs and DC-7s were being added—and for Boeing in the mid-1960s—when 707s, 720s, and 727s were being added. There are other instances as well. After 1934, no more than four domestic manufacturers are represented in the additions of new planes in

Table 2-7

Concentration in Additions of New Aircraft to Overall Domestic Trunk Line Fleet by Manufacturers of Aircraft, 1933–1941, 1947–1965.

	Concentration (percent)							No. of Domestic Manufacturers with Aircraft Included in Additions
Year	Douglas	Boeing	Lock-heed	Consoli-dated	Martin	Foreign	All Other	
1933	1.2	63.5	10.6	4.7	0.0	0.0	20.0 [a]	5
1934	29.9	4.5	16.4	0.0	0.0	0.0	49.2 [b]	7
1935	59.0	0.0	32.8	0.0	0.0	0.0	8.2 [c]	3
1936	69.0	0.0	31.0	0.0	0.0	0.0	0.0	2
1937	87.0	0.0	11.1	0.0	0.0	0.0	1.9 [d]	3
1938	87.5	0.0	12.5	0.0	0.0	0.0	0.0	2
1939	97.6	0.0	2.4	0.0	0.0	0.0	0.0	2
1940	84.8	4.5	10.7	0.0	0.0	0.0	0.0	3
1941	97.2	0.0	2.8	0.0	0.0	0.0	0.0	2
1947	74.3	0.0	17.1	0.0	8.6	0.0	0.0	3
1948	21.7	0.0	5.2	60.0	13.0	0.0	0.0	4
1949	1.7	17.2	32.8	48.3	0.0	0.0	0.0	4
1950	9.8	0.0	60.8	11.8	17.6	0.0	0.0	4
1951	47.6	0.0	23.8	0.0	28.6	0.0	0.0	3
1952	14.9	0.0	16.2	16.2	52.7	0.0	0.0	4
1953	29.1	0.0	9.4	58.3	3.1	0.0	0.0	4
1954	66.7	0.0	9.3	24.0	0.0	0.0	0.0	3
1955	38.2	0.0	43.6	3.6	0.0	14.5	0.0	3
1956	40.0	0.0	8.0	15.2	0.0	36.8	0.0	3
1957	65.9	0.0	18.4	12.8	0.0	2.8	0.0	3
1958	59.8	0.0	14.6	0.0	0.0	25.6	0.0	3
1959	10.8	30.1	57.8	0.0	0.0	1.2	0.0	3
1960	39.2	35.1	11.3	14.4	0.0	0.0	0.0	4
1961	9.6	45.6	12.0	19.2	0.0	13.6	0.0	4
1962	12.1	51.5	0.0	31.8	0.0	4.5	0.0	3
1963	8.7	69.6	0.0	21.7	0.0	0.0	0.0	3
1964	6.7	91.6	0.0	1.7	0.0	0.0	0.0	3
1965	12.6	78.5	0.0	0.0	0.0	8.9	0.0	2

[a] Curtiss-Wright.

[b] Stinson, with 21.0 percent; Vultee, with 14.9 percent; Curtis-Wright, with 9.0 percent; and Ford, with 4.5 percent.

[c] Stinson.

[d] Beechcraft.

Table 2-8
Numbers and Types of Aircraft with Reductions in Fleet Use, 1933–1965

		Four Types with Largest Reductions in Fleet Use							
Year	Gross Reductions	Type	Number	Type	Number	Type	Number	Type	Number
1933	128	B-40	24	Fairchild 71	20	Ford	19	Stinson Single Engine	15
1934	69	Fokker F-10	14	Fokker Single Engine	10	Pilgrim	10	Flamingo	9
1935	74	Ford	21	Hamilton	7	Stinson Trimotor	6	Condor II	6[a]
1936	106	B-40	26	Ford	18	L-Orion	15	Stinson Trimotor	15
1937	76	Stinson Trimotor	18	Vultee	10	Ford	8	Condor II	8
1938	28	B-247	9	L-Vega	5	Stinson Trimotor	5	DC-2	4[b]
1939	11	L-14	7	DC-2	2	Stinson Trimotor	2	—	—
1940	35	DC-2	13	L-10	10	B-247	9	L-12	3
1941	32	DC-2	18	L-10	8	L-14	2	B-247	2
1942	178	DC-3	113	B-247	28	L-10	16	DC-2	13
1943	—	—	—	—	—	—	—	—	—
1944	1	Beech 18	1	—	—	—	—	—	—
1945	2	Stinson Single Engine	1	B-247	1	—	—	—	—
1946	6	L-18	6	—	—	—	—	—	—
1947	23	DC-3	23	—	—	—	—	—	—
1948	76	DC-3	52	DC-4	24	—	—	—	—
1949	53	DC-3	52	L-18	1	—	—	—	—
1950	41	DC-3	27	DC-4	14	—	—	—	—
1951	40	M-202	21	CV-240	6	B-307	5	DC-3	4

Table 2-8 (continued)

Four Types with Largest Reductions in Fleet Use

Year	Gross Reductions	Type	Number	Type	Number	Type	Number	Type	Number
1952	55	DC-3	39	DC-4	13	CV-240	3	—	—
1953	89	DC-3	82	CV-240	6	DC-4	1	—	—
1954	62	DC-3	39	DC-4	14	B-377	5	L-0/749	3
1955	18	DC-4	9	L-18	3	CV-240	3	B-377	1 [c]
1956	38	DC-4	24	DC-3	10	M-404	2	B-377	1 [d]
1957	66	DC-4	37	DC-3	26	M-404	2	L-0/749	1
1958	49	CV-240	23	DC-3	10	DC-4	8	L-0/749	3 [e]
1959	152	DC-3	32	CV-240	26	DC-7	25	CV-340/440	22
1960	131	L-0/749	29	CV-340/440	24	DC-3	15	M-404	13
1961	155	M-404	36	DC-6	34	CV-240	20	DC-4	18
1962	141	DC-6	31	L-0/749	26	M-404	20	DC-3	19
1963	83	DC-7	26	M-404	16	DC-6	12	V-745 [f]	9
1964	78	DC-7	35	L-1049	11	CV-240	10	DC-6	9
1965	118	DC-7	59	DC-6	24	L-1649	17	L-1049	8

[a] Six Bellanca "Pacemakers" also.
[b] Four Lockheed L-10s also.
[c] One M-202 and one M-404 also.
[d] One CV-240s also.
[e] Three L-18s also.
[f] Nine CV-340/440s also.

any year. In 1965, Boeing and Douglas produced all of the five types of domestic aircraft added—the 707, 720, 727, DC-8, and DC-9. The last entered service very late in the year. Twelve BAC-111 were also added.

Table 2-8 shows the principal types of aircraft that were removed from service by the domestic trunk carriers in each of the years. These data, as are those in Tables 1-6 and 1-7, are based on data in Appendix C. They also cancel out intercarrier transfers of aircraft, but include losses due to crashes as well as reductions due to sales, retirements, and mandatory leases and sales to the government. The latter explain almost entirely the reductions in the fleet in 1942. They also affect the years 1950 and 1951, when commercial carriers supplied a number of four-engined aircraft—some of which were taken directly from production lines—to the Military Air Transport Service.[1]

The introductions of the Boeing 247, DC-2, Lockheed L-10, and DC-3 from 1933 through 1936 resulted in the eliminations from the fleets of the aircraft of numbers of other manufacturers. In addition to those shown in Table 2-8, Boeing B-80s, older Stinson Trimotors, Fokker "Super Universals," Fokker F-10s, and F-32s, "Travel Airs," Hamilton "Silver Streaks," and Fairchild "Pilgrim" 100s were taken from the fleets in 1933. In 1934, additional "Travel Airs," Boeing B-40s and B-80s, Stinsons, and Fokkers were removed from use; other reductions in the fleets involved the older Curtiss Condor Transport, Lockheed "Vegas" and "Orions," Curtiss-Robertson "Kingbirds," Bellanca "Pacemakers," "Flamingos," and Ryan "Broughams." By 1938, the culling of single-engined aircraft and of multi-engined aircraft of the wood and steel frame, and fabric covered construction was virtually completed. Because so large a share of all additions of aircraft from 1937 to 1947 were of Douglas manufacture, the bulk of fleet reductions in the post–World War II period were necessarily Douglas' as well. Indeed, in only four years between 1947 and 1965 did reductions in aircraft manufactured by companies other than Douglas appear as the largest single type with reduced use.

Attention turns now to the role of technological change in these shifts in demand and market structure. The next chapter begins this investigation by relating changes and differences in technology to changes and differences in aircraft operating costs.

---

[1] See "Airlines Largest Factor in Airlift Potential," *Aviation Week* (February 26, 1951), p. 86. In early 1951, the domestic trunk carriers had a total of 25 DC-4s, DC-6s, Boeing 377s, and Lockheed "Constellations" in use on the Pacific Airlift.

Relations between Operating Costs and Aircraft Technologies. 1932–1965

Introduction

A number of the characteristics of the aircraft used by the domestic trunk airlines are given in Appendix B. These offer information on differences in the technology "embodied" in particular aircraft at various points in time and on the changes in "embodied" technology over time. This chapter uses these characteristics to explain statistically the relations between the differences and changes in technology and the differences and changes in operating costs. From the view of orthodox economics, operating costs ought to be a principal avenue through which technological change affects the demand for particular planes. And these demands, of course, are prime determinants of the structure of the manufacturers' market.

A Sample of Aircraft Operating Costs

Direct aircraft operating costs are composed of flying operations expenses, direct maintenance of flight equipment, and depreciation of flight equipment. Flying operations expenses include expenses for pilots, copilots, and other flight personnel, aircraft rentals, fuel and oil, equipment insurance, and a variety of other less significant items. Direct flight equipment maintenance expenses include charges for labor and materials for airframe and engine maintenance, outside repairs, and other items. Depreciation is recorded for engines and airframes. Excluded from direct aircraft operating costs are the expenses of ground operations, ground and indirect maintenance, and depreciation of nonflying plant and equipment.

Miller and Sawers have collected data on direct operating expenses for various aircraft, expressed in cents per available seat mile, from the early 1930s through 1964.[1] To these were added comparable data reported for 1965 operations of jet and turboprop aircraft. Observations prior to 1938 are few. All observations are affected by accounting conventions, particularly depreciation practices, and by such unrecorded sources of variance as differences in flight stage lengths, intensity of aircraft utilization, and costs of input materials and labor.

A three-part sample was drawn from these data. The three parts were for piston-engined aircraft, turbojet and turbofan aircraft, and turboprop aircraft, with each part providing cross-section cost data for different planes in use in particular years as well as cost data for particular planes over time. The piston-engined aircraft sample has observations of direct operating

---

[1] R. E. Miller and D. Sawers, *The Technical Development of Modern Aviation* (1968), Chapter II and Appendix I.

Table 3-1

Cents per Seat Mile of Direct Aircraft Operating Expenses for a Sample of Piston
Engined Aircraft, 1932–1964.

	Aircraft	Year of Observation	Direct Operating Expenses	
			Including Depreciation	Excluding Depreciation
1	Ford Trimotor	1932	4.33	2.91
2	Ford Trimotor	1937	3.84 [a]	2.99 [a]
3	Lockheed Vega	1937	3.66 [a]	3.18 [a]
4	Boeing 80A	1932	4.71	3.29
5	Boeing 247	1937	3.08 [a]	2.42 [a]
6	Boeing 247	1938	3.08	2.49
7	Boeing 247	1939	2.98	2.49
8	Boeing 247	1940	2.50	2.49
9	Boeing 247	1941	3.05	2.71
10	Lockheed L-10	1939	2.58	2.17
11	DC-3	1937	1.85 [a]	1.39 [a]
12	DC-3	1939	2.13	1.73
13	DC-3	1941	1.80	1.48
14	DC-3	1948	1.87	1.73
15	DC-3	1954	2.32	2.16
16	Lockheed L-18	1941	3.09	2.50
17	Lockheed L-18	1942	3.02	2.37
18	Lockheed L-18	1950	2.58	2.54
19	Lockheed L-18	1953	2.65	2.63
20	Lockheed L-18	1956	3.43	3.16
21	Boeing 307	1948	2.34	1.66
22	Boeing 307	1949	2.38	1.61
23	Boeing 307	1950	1.80	1.61
24	DC-4	1948	1.85	1.29
25	DC-4	1950	1.67	1.38
26	DC-4	1952	1.48	1.36
27	DC-4	1955	1.52	1.51
28	DC-4	1959	2.16	2.15
29	Lockheed L-049	1948	2.10	1.57
30	Lockheed L-049	1951	1.96	1.54
31	Lockheed L-049	1955	1.57	1.35
32	Lockheed L-749	1958	1.85	1.79
33	Lockheed L-749	1961	2.26	2.15
34	Lockheed L-749	1964	2.40	2.16
35	DC-6	1948	1.57	1.20
36	DC-6	1952	1.76	1.43
37	DC-6	1959	1.32	1.31
38	Convair 240	1949	1.74	1.44
39	Convair 240	1951	1.96	1.62
40	Convair 240	1953	2.14	1.82
41	Convair 240	1956	1.74	1.70
42	Convair 240	1960	2.24	2.22
43	Boeing 377	1950	2.44	1.80
44	Boeing 377	1952	2.56	2.04
45	Boeing 377	1954	2.07	1.54
46	Boeing 377	1957	1.83	1.81

39

Table 3-1

(*continued*)

	Aircraft	Year of Observation	Direct Operating Expenses Including Depreciation	Excluding Depreciation
47	Boeing 377	1959	1.71	1.64
48	DC-6B	1953	1.72	1.29
49	DC-6B	1955	1.68	1.39
50	DC-6B	1960	1.73	1.45
51	Convair 440	1954	1.75	1.31
52	Convair 440	1955	1.79	1.40
53	Convair 440	1957	1.88	1.44
54	Convair 440	1960	1.87	1.59
55	DC-7	1954	2.07	1.50
56	DC-7	1955	1.89	1.43
57	DC-7	1957	2.02	1.51
58	DC-7	1961	2.45	1.70
59	Lockheed L-1049G	1957	1.96	1.57
60	Lockheed L-1049G	1958	2.12	1.69
61	Lockheed L-1049G	1960	2.51	1.86
62	Lockheed L-1049G	1963	2.28	1.90
63	DC-7C	1958	1.63	1.22
64	DC-7C	1959	1.79	1.42
65	DC-7C	1962	2.45	1.79
66	Lockheed L-1649	1958	2.83	2.13
67	Lockheed L-1649	1959	2.34	1.83
68	Lockheed L-1649	1960	2.83	1.92

Source: R. E. Miller and D. Sawers, *The Technical Development of Modern Aviation* (1968).

[a] 1937 data are originally from E. P. Warner, *Technical Development and Its Effect on Air Transportation* (1938). The 1937 data here are adjusted upward by a factor of 1.46, the ratio of the price corrected 1938 figure for the Boeing 247 to the price corrected 1937 Warner figure for the Boeing 247. Warner's figures are uniformly and inexplicably low. The correction, if anything, appears too small.

expenses, including and excluding depreciation, as shown in Table 3-1. The 68 observations cover 20 types of aircraft for 1932, 1937–1942, 1948–1964. Except in the cases of the Lockheed "Vega," the Boeing 80A, and the Lockheed L-10 "Electra," each aircraft type is represented by at least two observations. All data are given in current dollars and, for years after 1938, are from only the domestic trunk airlines operating the various aircraft.

Tables 3-2 and 3-3 provide the reported direct operating costs for jet and turboprop aircraft operated by domestic trunk airlines. Only three turboprop aircraft are involved, even when the Vickers-Armstrong "Viscount" 745s and 812s are separated. Cost data are available for nine general types of jet aircraft, but for only 1965 in four cases and for only 1964 and 1965 in another.

Table 3-2

Cents per Seat Mile of Direct Aircraft Operating Expenses for a Sample of Jet Aircraft, 1959–1965

| | | | Direct Operating Expenses | |
	Aircraft	Year of Observation	Including Depreciation	Excluding Depreciation
1	SUD-210	1961	2.29	1.27
2	SUD-210	1962	2.35	1.60
3	SUD-210	1963	2.23	1.53
4	SUD-210	1964	2.40	1.71
5	SUD-210	1965	2.57	1.86
6	DC-8	1960	1.53	1.15
7	DC-8	1961	1.42	1.07
8	DC-8	1962	1.31	1.00
9	DC-8	1963	1.18	.92
10	DC-8	1964	1.23	.96
11	DC-8	1965	1.15	.93
12	Boeing 707	1959	1.77	1.45
13	Boeing 707	1960	1.55	1.30
14	Boeing 707	1961	1.47	1.17
15	Boeing 707	1962	1.30	1.06
16	Boeing 707	1963	1.24	.95
17	Boeing 707	1964	1.22	.94
18	Boeing 707	1965	1.30	1.01
19	Boeing 720	1961	1.51	1.23
20	Boeing 720	1962	1.46	1.20
21	Boeing 720	1963	1.28	1.08
22	Boeing 720	1964	1.28	1.08
23	Boeing 720	1965	1.27	1.05
24	Boeing 727	1964	1.46	1.04
25	Boeing 727	1965	1.43	1.11
26	Convair 990	1965	1.68	1.26
27	Convair 880	1965	1.67	1.36
28	BAC-111	1965	1.59	1.22
29	DC-9	1965	2.07	1.39

Source: R. E. Miller and D. Sawers, *The Technical Development of Modern Aviation* (1968), *Aviation Week and Space Technology* (May 2 and 21, 1966).

Operating Costs and Embodied Technology: A Priori Considerations

There are pronounced differences in characteristics among aircraft of much the same vintage as well as substantial changes in aircraft characteristics over time. These differences and changes appear in total engine power, seating capacity, aircraft weights, wing loadings, power loadings, speeds, and cruise distances. Many other differences in characteristics are not shown, including those in such fundamental factors as methods and materials used in airframe construction, navigational and flight control equipment, airfoil design, and propulsion systems.

The variables selected to summarize differences and changes in aircraft

Table 3-3

Cents per Seat Mile of Direct Operating Expenses for a Sample of Turboprop Aircraft.

	Aircraft	Year of Observation	Direct Operating Expenses Including Depreciation	Excluding Depreciation
1	Viscount-745	1956	1.72	1.22
2	Viscount-745	1957	1.73	1.29
3	Viscount-745	1958	1.74	1.35
4	Viscount-745	1959	1.95	1.53
5	Viscount-745	1960	1.94	1.50
6	Viscount-745	1961	2.05	1.59
7	Viscount-745	1962	1.97	1.60
8	Viscount-745	1963	2.07	1.68
9	Viscount-745	1964	2.08	1.73
10	Viscount-745	1965	2.38	1.98
11	Lockheed L-188	1960	2.26	1.73
12	Lockheed L-188	1961	2.29	1.67
13	Lockheed L-188	1962	1.96	1.46
14	Lockheed L-188	1963	1.99	1.47
15	Lockheed L-188	1964	2.04	1.53
16	Lockheed L-188	1965	1.70	1.26
17	Viscount-812	1964	1.88	1.51
18	Viscount-812	1965	1.98	1.60

Source: R. E. Miller and D. Sawers, *The Technical Development of Modern Aviation* (1968), *Aviation Week and Space Technology* (May 10, 1965; May 9, 1966).

technology and to explain their relationships with operating costs are:
1. gross weight per seat;
2. wing loading;
3. power loading;
4. aircraft range design; and
5. model age of the aircraft.

In terms of *partial* relations, it is anticipated that costs per seat mile vary directly with gross weight per seat. The less the required amount of weight transported per seat, the lower should be the cost per seat, other things remaining equal.

Historically, as well as among a cross-section of aircraft, other things do not, of course, remain the same. There has been a slight upward trend in weight per seat over time and, as will be noted below, very significant positive association between aircraft range and weight per seat. Aircraft range has a pronounced upward trend over time. Costs per seat tend generally to fall. Hence, failure to identify properly the effects of weight per seat of costs could yield statistical estimates suggesting an inverse relation between costs and gross weight per seat.

Wing loading—gross take-off weight per square foot of wing area—is without question a direct measure of very important changes in airfoil technology. It probably is also an indirect or proxy indicator of parallel changes in the technology of other aspects of the airframe. Prior to the mid-1930s, wing loads for transport aircraft ranged generally between 14 and 18 pounds per square foot. The DC-3 and its contemporaries had wing loads between 20 and 30 pounds; post-World War II piston-engined transports, between 50 and 90 pounds. The jets were introduced with wing loads in excess of 100 pounds, though the shorter range jets as well as the earlier piston-engined aircraft designed for shorter ranges have considerably lower wing loads than their longer range counterparts.

While materials and construction methods have set limits to maximum wing load designs, these are incidental to the anticipated relations between wing loads and operating costs. Underlying the changes in wing loading are changes in airfoil technology which, in addition to increasing lift, reduced parasite drag. The changes in wing design were such that the wing load data reflect improvements in boundary layer airflows over wings, with extensions of the relative amount of wing area over which there are smooth laminar airflows rather than drag-creating turbulent flows. As a result, the higher wing loads generally are associated with less power loss in overcoming drag and, consequently, it is anticipated that wing loading should be inversely related to operating costs.

The attention to reducing wing drag was accompanied by efforts to reduce drag in other parts of the airframe. Coincidentally, the low drag wings developed in the late 1920s and early 1930s had cross-section profiles with thicker center sections than did earlier wings. This promoted the use of wing sections for space in which to retract landing gear, to place fuel tanks and to position engines. At the same time, there were changes in joining techniques, engine mountings, and many other parts of the aircraft that reduced drag and increased efficiency which, if quantified, would be highly correlated with the wing load variable.

The inclusion of the power load variable was predicted more on curiosity concerning possible relations between it and costs than on effects anticipated from *a priori* considerations. With the assumption of a static technology, the safe conclusion would be that relations between costs and power loads are nonmonotonic. Application of additional power relative to airframe weight would be expected to yield diminishing returns phenomena, with average costs first falling and then rising with respect to power loads. Actually, the power loads of piston-engined aircraft tended to fall somewhat over time. Total power rose relative to gross aircraft weight, even while the power loss from drag per unit of aircraft weight fell. Engine developments resulted in more power per pound of engine weight which, together with less drag, yielded the possibility of higher payload-distance or higher weight-distance units (for example, seat miles or ton miles) per unit of power. Thus, if the dynamic trend tendencies prevail in the data, a positive association between costs and power loads would be expected. Cross-section data *could* yield a negative association if aircraft at particular points in time do not cluster around the power load yielding minimum costs with the engine airframe technologies of that period.

The aircraft range design variable is used as a very crude proxy for the effects of stage lengths on operating costs. It is assumed that, among aircraft of the same period, those designed for longer ranges typically fly longer stage lengths than do the others. Because some costs vary with flying time and because the block speeds of particular aircraft tend to vary directly with stage lengths, the partial effect of stage length on seat mile operating costs is negative. Hence, observations of the costs of operating aircraft are affected by stage length, with those operating over longer distances tending, for this reason alone, to have lower costs per seat mile. If the dichotomy between long and short range design proxies for differences in the stage lengths for which different aircraft are used, this variable should also be negatively related to costs per seat mile.

The model age of the aircraft is measured by the number of years from the year of first service to that of the cost observation. Except for most unusual conditions of purchases and sales of aircraft by the carriers, the average age of aircraft of a particular type in the fleet varies directly with the model age of the aircraft. If, following the assumptions of static theories of replacement, operating costs (excluding depreciation) tend to rise with age, a positive relation between these costs and model age would be expected. This positive relation is not that anticipated for aircraft use—at least for a number of years following first use. The development process for aircraft themselves is clearly a learning process. So is the process of putting them into fleet use. Operating costs, it is expected, tend to fall over time for any widely used aircraft. Initially, it is used with a low utilization rate, but this gradually rises as the intervals between inspection and overhaul become longer. Initially, the maintenance and repair of the aircraft entail experimentation and learning, but these tend to become routinized. In addition, changes are made in the aircraft even as it is used over time. Retrofits of improvements made in the later manufacture of the same type are made on existing equipment, including in some cases the use of new engines as well as airframe modifications. Finally, aircraft are often reequipped with larger numbers of seats in the years after their first introduction. All of these factors should tend to cause lower operating costs per seat mile as model age rises.

Statistical Estimates: Piston-Engined Aircraft

The operating cost data in Table 3-1 were converted to 1954 dollars by use of the implicit GNP deflator. This index presumably captures the effects of economywide changes in productivity and factor prices on costs. Deflation by this index removes the influences of such economywide changes on seat mile costs, but it retains in the data the influences of productivity and factor prices specific to the production of seat miles of air transportation. Deflation by an index related directly to air transportation costs would tend to remove these specific effects and, hence, the effects of aviation technology on seat mile costs. It is the latter, of course, on which attention focuses.

The use of the gross weight per seat, wing loading, power loading and model age variables in the regression followed directly from considerations discussed above. The range design variable, because of the cross-sectional aspects of the regression model, considers each aircraft relative to its contemporaries and the typical inuse ranges for which it was designed. It was entered in the form of a dummy variable, with unit values for aircraft intended for short-range use and with zero values for aircraft intended for long-range use. The only cases in which the selection of values for this variable was at all questionable was in the pre-World War II period. The choice among the early aircraft was to assign zero only to the DC-3. It was specifically designed for the needs for American Airlines for a transcontinental sleeper transport and had a significantly longer full payload range than did others of its vintage. While the DC-2 could and did fly nonstop from Chicago to New York, it was not designed for this purpose and could not do so with a full payload. With full payload, the range of the DC-2 was similar to that of the Boeing 247, the Ford and Stinson Trimotors, the Boeing 80A and the Lockheed L-10 "Electra." Piston-engined aircraft designated for short-range design after the DC-3, including some not in the cost sample, are the Lockheed L-12, L-14, and L-18, the Convair 240, 340, and 440, and the Martin 202 and 404.

The initial regressions which were attempted showed relatively large underestimates for the seat mile costs for the three observations of trimotor aircraft (the Ford and the Boeing 80A) and for the one observation of a single-engined aircraft (the Lockheed "Vega"). A dummy variable was introduced for the trimotors and another for single-engined aircraft. The use of these dummies increased the coefficient of determination significantly. It did not significantly change the estimated value for the other regression coefficients. Both the trimotors and the "Vega" are the only aircraft in the sample which are not of the smooth, all metal, low wing, airframe construction which began with the Boeing 247. While the estimates here suggest a difference between the costs of trimotor and single-engined planes, there is but one observation for the latter.

The basic cost estimating regression for the piston-engined aircraft is:[2]

$$\ln \hat{C}_{it} = 2.0869 + .9382(\ln S_i) - .7364(\ln W_i) + .1838(\ln H_i)$$
$$(.1187) \qquad (.0669) \qquad (.2041)$$
$$+ .3779(R_i) - .0117(M_{it}) + .4167(T_i) + .8504(O_i) \qquad (3.1)$$
$$(.0757) \qquad (.0049) \qquad (.1070) \qquad (.1736)$$
$$\bar{R}^2 = .894$$

where

$\hat{C}_{it}$ = estimated operating costs, *excluding depreciation*, expressed as cents per seat mile $\times$ 10^2, for the ith aircraft type in the tth year

---

[2] All logarithmic expressions are in natural logarithms.

S_i = gross take-off weight per seat, expressed as pounds, for the ith aircraft type

W_i = gross take-off weight per square foot of wing area, expressed as pounds $\times$ 10, for the ith aircraft type

H_i = gross take-off weight per horsepower, expressed as pounds $\times$ 10, for the ith aircraft type

R_i = range design variable for the ith aircraft type

M_{it} = model age of the ith aircraft type in the tth year

T_i = trimotor dummy variable for the ith aircraft type

O_i = single-engine dummy variable for the ith aircraft type

Multicollinearity did not arise as an important problem in this combined cross-sectional and time series sample. The highest simple correlation is between gross weight per seat and the range design dummy variable. This correlation is $-.688$, showing, as would be expected, that longer range aircraft require higher weight per seat than do the shorter range craft. Despite this negative simple correlation, the partial effect of range on costs per seat mile is significantly positive. With the unit-zero convention adopted for the range variable, this indicates that longer range designs, with the weight per seat mile effects held constant, are associated with lower operating costs. This conforms with the expectations derived from *a priori* considerations.

Two other simple correlations coefficients between the independent variables exceed $|.60|$. The coefficient between gross weight per seat and wing loading is .651. That between wing loading and range is $-.604$. All of the involved variables show t ratios which are significant well beyond the one percent level.

The signs of the regression coefficients are uniformly those expected. The estimates are that each one percent increase in weight per seat is associated with a .94 percent increase in operating costs per seat mile, *ex* depreciation. Each one percent increase in wing loading is associated with a $-.74$ percent decrease in these costs. Gross weight per horsepower shows a positive effect on costs per seat mile, but it is not significant at the five percent level. Each additional year of model age is associated with a decrease in the *ex* depreciation operating costs of slightly more than one percent. In all, nearly 90 percent of the variance in operating costs per seat mile, excluding depreciation, is explained.

The combination of cross-sectional and time series observations renders the Durbin-Watson Statistic formally useless for analysis of the residuals from the predicted cost values. The Durbin-Watson ratio, for the ordering of the observations given in Table 3-1, is 1.18, but serial correlation may occur in this format either because the costs of a particular type of aircraft tend generally to be overestimated or underestimated by the regression or because its costs do not follow closely the estimated amount of decrease with respect to model age. Inspection of the residuals shows that all of the estimates of the operating costs of the Boeing 247, Boeing 307, and Lockheed L-04, are somewhat below the actual values. No other patterning in the residuals is apparent.

Direct operating costs per seat mile, with depreciation included, were estimated using the estimated values for operating costs, *ex* depreciation, as one of the variables. It was hypothesized that these "full" direct costs per seat mile would be a percentage of variable (that is, *ex* depreciation) direct cost, with the percentage being larger the greater was investment per seat and smaller the older was the average age of the aircraft. This amounts to assumptions that depreciation charges vary directly with the amount of investment and inversely with the age of the equipment.

No direct observations of investment per seat mile were available. Gross weight per seat mile was introduced as a proxy, eliminating among other things the problem of deflating capital costs. Neither were observations available for the average age of aircraft in the fleets. For this, model age was substituted, though it is clear that this tends to overstate the average age for those types the use of which grows over the years as compared with those put into the fleets in a given year and not acquired in subsequent years.

The regression equation for full direct operating costs is:

$$\ln \hat{C}'_{it} = .1866 + 1.0126(\ln \hat{C}_{it}) + .0103(\ln S_i) - .0185(M_{it})$$
$$\phantom{\ln \hat{C}'_{it} = .1866 + 1.0126} (.0502) \phantom{(\ln \hat{C}_{it}) +} (.0924) (.0052) \qquad (3.2)$$
$$\bar{R}^2 = .882$$

where $\hat{C}_{it}$ is the estimated cost per seat mile, including depreciation, for the *i*th type of aircraft in the *t*th year and the remainder of the nonmenclature is that given above. The highest value among the simple correlation coefficients is $+.439$. This correlation is between log $\hat{C}_{it}$ and log S_i and is expected because of the relations found in the regression for variable direct operating costs.

Gross weight per seat mile proves not to be significant in explaining depreciation. The remaining variables have the anticipated signs and are significant beyond the one percent level.

Statistical Estimates: Jet Aircraft

The statistical estimates of operating costs per seat mile for jet aircraft could not be done in a manner fully parallel to that used for piston-engined aircraft. After the deflation to 1954 dollars, it was apparent that the seat mile costs, *ex* depreciation, for the SUD 210 "Caravelle" have tended to rise with model age. Data for the Boeing 727 were available for only two model years; for the Convair 990, Convair 880, BAC-111, and Douglas DC-9, for only one model year. Indeed, in the case of the DC-9, the data cover only two weeks of use in late 1965, immediately after its introduction. This left only the SUD 210, DC-8, Boeing 707, and Boeing 720 with cost data for five or more years and it seemed possible that, among them, the behavior of costs with respect to model age was not uniform.

The first step in estimation was to run separate regressions of price-corrected costs, *ex* depreciation, on model age for the four types with five or more cost observations.

The results of these are:

$$\hat{C}_{210,t} = 107.80 + 8.60(M_{210,t})$$
$$(2.63) \tag{3.3}$$
$$\bar{R}^2 = .719$$
$$\ln \hat{C}_{\text{DC-8},t} = 4.6927 - .0554(M_{\text{DC-8},t})$$
$$(.0093) \tag{3.4}$$
$$\bar{R}^2 = .874$$
$$\ln \hat{C}_{707,t} = 4.8884 - .0840(M_{707,t})$$
$$(.0134) \tag{3.5}$$
$$\bar{R}^2 = .864$$
$$\ln \hat{C}_{720,t} = 4.7831 - .0589(M_{720,t})$$
$$(.0088) \tag{3.6}$$
$$\bar{R}^2 = .916$$

where $\hat{C}_{it}$ and M_{it} are defined as above for each of the types. Within each type of aircraft, model age explains a large fraction of the reported cost variances. In the case of the SUD 210 "Caravelle," which has apparently experienced increasing operating costs, the regression on the log transform of costs fit less well than did that on the natural numbers.

These regressions leave to be explained the differences in absolute levels of costs, model year held the same, among the jet aircraft. This explanation was attempted by computing the $\hat{C}_{it}$ value at $M_{it} = 1$ for the SUD 210, DC-8, 707, and 720 and, with rather arbitrary assumptions, estimating similar values for the Boeing 727, BAC-111, Convair 880 and 990, and the DC-9. The actual C_{it} value for the DC-9 and the BAC-111 in 1965, corrected for price level only, were used for this purpose. In the cases of the Boeing 727 and the Convair 990, the 1964 and 1965 price-corrected actual values were used, respectively, and it was assumed from the 707, DC-8, and 720 experience that operating costs for these aircraft fell by five percent per model year. For the Convair 880, which is reputed to have had poorer cost performance, it was assumed that costs fell by only three percent per model year.

This procedure yielded "observations" for the nine jet types in their respective first model years. For these types, however, gross weight per seat, wing loading, power loading, and range design were highly intercorrelated. Even were this not true, the use of the number of independent variables required to introduce them in a regression including these variables would have put quite a burden on nine observations. Consequently, an approach similar to that in regression 3.1 was abandoned.[3] Nothing beyond the steps indicated above

---

[3] The samples of jet and turboprop operating costs were separated from that of piston-engined planes for a technical reason. Pounds of thrust cannot be converted on a fixed ratio

seemed possible for estimating costs *ex* depreciation. Full costs, including depreciation, were estimated by use of the costs, *ex* depreciation, corrected statistically only for model age, for the DC-8, SUD 210, Boeing 707, and Boeing 720. Actual observations of costs *ex* depreciation, corrected only for price level, were used for the other jet aircraft.

The results for operating costs, including depreciation are:

$$\ln \hat{C}'_{it} = .3385 + 1.1419(\ln \hat{C}_{it}) - .0126(M_{it})$$
$$\phantom{\ln \hat{C}'_{it} = .3385 + 1.1419} (.0974) \phantom{(\ln \hat{C}_{it}) -} (.0095) \qquad (3.7)$$
$$\bar{R}^2 = .883$$

Of the 29 observations of jet aircraft, only 15 are for model years beyond two and these relate to the DC-8, 707, 720, 880, 990, and SUD "Caravelle." Save for the latter, these are long range craft and have the higher gross weight per seat values, which leads to high positive correlation between gross weight per seat and model year. The sample of costs is thus inadequate to measure the effects of weight per seat or, indeed, other technical characteristics on full direct operating costs.

Statistical Estimates: Turboprop Aircraft

Only three types of turboprop aircraft have appeared in the trunk line fleets. This small number, the fact that two of the three are different versions of the same aircraft and the short time period over which cost observations are available made it impossible to trace the effects of any variables other than model age on their operating costs.

The Viscount 745s and, based on two observations only, the Viscount 812s have had increasing operating costs with respect to model age. The estimating equation for direct operating cost per seat mile, *ex* depreciation, for the 745 is:

$$\hat{C}_{745,t} = 107.99 + 4.09(M_{745,t})$$
$$\phantom{\hat{C}_{745,t} = 107.99 +} (.53) \qquad (3.8)$$
$$\bar{R}^2 = .865$$

The same equation for the Lockheed L-188 is:

$$\hat{C}_{188,t} = 167.02 - 8.49(M_{188,t})$$
$$\phantom{\hat{C}_{188,t} = 167.02 -} (1.78) \qquad (3.9)$$
$$\bar{R}^2 = .830$$

In neither case does a log transformation of the cost variable improve the fit. Variable direct costs per seat mile for the Viscount 745 have tended to rise by

---

to horsepower. Letting h = thrust horsepower, t = thrust, and v = airspeed in miles per hour, an approximate conversion formula is:

$$h = \frac{t(v)}{375}.$$

That is, one pound of thrust equals one thrust horsepower at 375 miles per hour but, given thrust, horsepower equivalents of jet engines tend to vary directly with airspeed over relevant speed ranges. See J. V. Casamassa, *Jet Aircraft Power Systems* (1950), pp. 105–106.

four-hundredths of a cent each year while those for the L-188 "Electra" have tended to fall by over eight-hundredths of a cent. Variable costs per seat mile were not estimated statistically for the Viscount 812.

Gross weight per seat for all three models of turboprops are nearly the same —1,344 pounds for the 745, 1,330 pounds for the L-188, and 1,394 pounds for the 812. Wing loadings are different—70.0 pounds, 86.9 pounds, and 75.3 pounds, respectively—but the small number of models and the nonuniform behavior of costs make statistical estimates of the effects of these variables very unreliable.

Costs per seat mile, including depreciation, were estimated from the $\hat{C}_{it}$ values for the 745 and the L-188 and, representing the best estimates in this case, the actual $\hat{C}_{it}$ values for the 812. The result is:

$$\hat{C}'_{it} = 39.996 + 1.093(\hat{C}_{it}) - 2.291(M_{it})$$
$$\phantom{\hat{C}'_{it} = 39.996 + } (.150) \phantom{(\hat{C}_{it}) - } (.719) \tag{3.10}$$
$$\bar{R}^2 = .752$$

Again, the log transformation of cost variables failed to improve the fit. For all three aircraft, full direct costs per seat mile tend to be approximately forty-hundredths of a cent over variable direct costs, less about two-hundredths of a cent for each model age year.

The Viscounts and, among the jets, the SUD 210 "Caravelle" are the only aircraft types which seem clearly to have experienced increasing costs per seat mile over their model years of life. Both are of foreign manufacture, which could presumably affect maintenance costs. The SUD 210s have been operated only by United Airlines. The 745s were acquired by Capital Airlines, but have been operated by United since the merger of Capital into United in 1961. It is conceivable that the accounting system used by United with respect to these craft may be involved. The limited data available on the intensity of use and the stage lengths for which these aircraft have been used provide no clue as to why costs might rise over time. The clearest fact is that the SUD 210s and Viscount 745s are among the few aircraft appearing in trunk line fleets which were acquired by particular lines in essentially one lump order, with no subsequent reorderings or acquisitions by other lines. After initial deliveries were made, the lines gradually reduced rather than increased the numbers of these aircraft in the fleets.[4]

VII. The Effects of Technological Change on Operating Costs

The next chapters will utilize these cost estimates to analyze the demand for aircraft by the domestic trunk lines. Both the total demand and the relative demand for particular planes, it will be shown, have been significantly as-

[4] Continental, however, did purchase Viscount 812s about three years after Capital bought its 745s.

Table 3-4

Estimated Operating Costs per Seat Mile for Aircraft Used by Scheduled Domestic Air Carriers (cents per seat mile, 1954 dollars).

Aircraft	Year First Available for Service	Operating Costs, Including Depreciation, in First Year Available for Service
Fokker "Super Universal"	1928	13.40
Hamilton "Silver Streak"	1928	12.13
Fairchild 71	1928	12.82
Ford 4-AT	1928	9.50
Fokker 10A	1928	11.80
Fokker F-14	1929	17.24
Bellanca "Pacemaker"	1929	12.80
Travel Air 6000B	1929	12.40
Stinson SM-6B	1929	10.89
Lockheed "Vega" (Wasp)	1929	10.28
Ryan "Brougham"	1929	12.22
Boeing B-40-B4	1929	29.14 [a]
Flamingo	1929	11.71
Ford 5-AT-C	1929	7.92
Curtiss "CO Transport"	1929	9.75
Boeing 80A	1929	10.81
Fairchild "Pilgrim 100"	1930	12.19
Consolidated "Fleetster"	1930	12.10
Boeing 221	1930	20.10 [a]
Northrop "Alpha"	1930	10.84
Fokker F-32	1930	6.55
Stinson 6000A	1930	8.31
Curtiss "Kingbird D-2"	1930	9.39
Lockheed "Orion"	1931	10.90
Stinson U	1932	9.43
Boeing 247	1933	7.78
Curtiss "Condor T-32"	1933	7.30
Douglas DC-2	1934	6.81
Stinson A	1934	7.92
Lockheed L-10	1934	4.70
Douglas DC-3	1936	3.28
Lockheed L-12	1936	5.95
Lockheed L-14	1937	4.77
Boeing 307	1940	3.22
Lockheed L-18	1940	4.74
Douglas DC-4	1946	2.35
Lockheed 049	1946	2.84
Douglas DC-6	1947	2.17
Lockheed 749	1947	2.51
Martin 202	1947	2.53
Convair 240	1948	2.51
Boeing 377	1949	2.44
Douglas DC-6B	1951	1.99
Martin 404	1951	2.38
Lockheed 1049	1951	1.84

Table 3-4 (*continued*)

Aircraft	Year First Available for Service	Operating Costs, Including Depreciation, in First Year Available for Service
Convair 340	1952	2.58
Lockheed 1049C	1953	1.86
Douglas DC-7A	1953	1.80
Vickers "Viscount" 745	1955	1.62
Douglas DC-7C	1956	2.31
Convair 440	1956	2.22
Lockheed 1649	1957	2.39
Lockheed L-188	1959	2.10
Boeing 707-120	1959 [c]	1.70
Douglas DC-8	1959	1.41
Convair 880	1960	1.73
Boeing 720	1960	1.54
SUD 210 "Caravelle"	1961	1.66
Boeing 720 B	1961	1.43
Convair 990	1962	1.55
Boeing 727	1964	1.14
BAC-111	1965	1.55
Douglas DC-9	1965	1.55 [b]

[a] Cost estimate is high because aircraft was used primarily for mail to which no costs are allocated.

[b] Based on actual costs covering only two weeks of operation in December 1965.

[c] The 707–120 was introduced into domestic service on December 10, 1958. In the cost estimates, 1959 is taken as its first model year.

sociated with the appearance of new types of aircraft. Cost differences at any given time do affect the relative demands for new planes and, hence, have a direct impact on market structure. Further, it will be argued that the most successful of the new varieties of aircraft over the years have been those which combined new technologies in ways which yielded cost and other performance advantages. Sharp increases in the share of the market held by particular manufacturers, that is, have been associated with the development of planes which, as compared with former models, are better in a number of significant ways.

The treatment of the cost data in the chapters to come will not highlight the important long term effects of changes in aircraft technology on operating costs. Table 3-4 presents the estimated operating costs for all aircraft used by the domestic trunk carriers between 1932 and 1965.[5] These show the magnitude of cost changes as new planes have been developed. The typical early

[5] Costs for aircraft not in the samples used in the regressions above are derived from the regression results and the technical characteristics of the planes.

single-engined planes had operating costs, expressed in 1954 dollars, of well over ten cents per seat mile. The trimotors and other multiengined planes of their period brought these costs down to roughly eight or nine cents.

Operating costs fell rapidly with the introduction of the all metal, low wing monoplane transport in 1933. Cost per seat mile for the DC-3 were about three cents in 1936. The DC-4 and the Lockheed 049/649/749 series lowered costs again; stretched versions of these—in the DC-6, DC-6B, DC-7A, and Lockheed 1049 models—attained costs of less than two cents per seat mile. The first successful jets pushed costs down to perhaps one and one-half cents and later models, down to slightly over one cent by 1965.

Even this summary recount is suggestive of the associations between operating costs and the changes in market shares shown in the tables of Chapter 2. The planes for which there are obvious downward breaks in operating costs are the same as those involved in the large or increasing market shares.

4

The Aggregate Market for Trunk Line Commercial Aircraft

Introduction

Changes in aircraft technology, we have seen, have resulted in great reductions in aircraft operating costs and, hence, have directly affected the supply of air transportation. Because the new aircraft types have both altered the character of air transportation and permitted reductions in fares, the demand for air travel has also been affected by technology. From the interactions of the supply of and demand for air travel, a demand for aircraft has presumably been generated.

This chapter constructs a model of these interrelations in an effort to isolate the economic and technological factors that explain the overall demand by the trunk lines for new planes. Neglecting a great many of the details, the general model is:

$$PM_t = f_1(P_t, Y_t, q_{1t}, \ldots, q_{mt}) \tag{4.1}$$
$$SM_t = f_2(PM_t, \pi_t) \tag{4.2}$$
$$NA_t = f_3(SM_t, t_{1t}, \ldots, t_{nt}) \tag{4.3}$$

where

PM_t = passenger miles of trunk line air transportation demanded during time period t

P_t = price per passenger mile during time period t

Y_t = income during time period t

q_{it} = qualitative aspects of air transportation relative to time period t (for example, speed, safety) ($i = 1, \ldots, m$)

SM_t = seat miles of trunk line air transportation supplied during time period t

π_t = anticipated rate of return in supplying SM_t

NA_t = number of new aircraft added to fleet during time period t

t_{jt} = technical characteristics of new aircraft and of aircraft in existing fleets (e.g., speed, passenger capacity) ($j = 1, \ldots, n$).

Thus, the overall demand for new planes in given years is formulated as a derived demand. It depends upon the demand for air travel, the long-term profitability of supplying that service, and the characteristics of new and existing aircraft. The model is formulated as a recursive system and is solved with minor modifications by the ordinary least squares technique. For reasons to be explained in the conclusions of the chapter, this type of derived demand model fails to explain well the variance in overall trunk line aircraft purchases.

Demand for Passenger Miles of Trunk
Line Transportation

The years prior to 1947 present some statistical and some factual problems calling for separation of the analysis into two time periods. Some attention is given to the character of passenger demand and the supply of seat miles for the whole period 1932–1965, but no effort is made to move from these to estimating equations for the demand for new aircraft. The primary reason for this is that at least until 1934 the major carriers had common ownership with aircraft manufacturers. This resulted, as is developed in more detail in Chapter 5, in something of a captive demand which influenced both the choice of particular aircraft and the aggregate number of planes in the fleets.

There are additional problems relating to the earlier years. A number of nonrandom events occurred that drastically affected air carrier demand and supply. These are difficult to quantify for inclusion in the statistical analysis and yet are of such importance that without explicit consideration only small portions of the variance in demand and supply can be explained. Chief among these nonrandom disturbances are:

(1) The Black Committee investigations in 1934 of the administration of the McNary-Watres Act by former Postmaster General Brown and related events of that year. Air mail contracts were cancelled and the Army Air Corps carried the mail between February 9th and June 1st. The commercial carriers reduced their flight schedules during this period. Moreover, the highly publicized death of nine Army pilots and passengers and the extremely bad weather in this interval very probably reduced passenger demand for the commercial carriers.

(2) A series of Senate investigations relating to safety. These grew from the crash of a TWA DC-2 in 1935 in which Senator Cutting lost his life. The circumstances brought to light by the investigations led to a bitter controversy about safety and the responsibilities of the government and the carriers. The startling facts, abetted by a high accident rate in 1936 and 1937, seem clearly to have affected passenger demand in the latter year.[1]

(3) The absorption into the armed forces in the early months of World War II of more than half of the aircraft in the domestic trunk line fleet. This undoubtedly forced a contraction of supply and very probably resulted in unsatisfied demand in at least 1942 and 1943.

(4) The following release by the military of numbers of aircraft beginning in 1943, but affecting mainly the years 1945 and 1946.

There are events of a similar nature but of much smaller magnitude in subsequent years. In 1948, for example, the grounding of DC-6s after two inflight fires and crashes seems to have affected demand directly and also, because of the number of DC-6s in the fleets of American and United Air Lines, to have caused the supply of seat miles to be less than it otherwise would have been. Similarly, a number of planes were absorbed and subsequently

---

[1] For additional details, see D. R. Whitnah, *Safer Skyways* (1966), pp. 116–136.

released by the armed forces for the Pacific Airlift in the years of the Korean War. In 1958, strikes involving Western, Capital, TWA, Eastern and American reduced supply and, because of service suspensions, make the observed value of passenger miles a poor indicator of actual passenger demand.

The disturbances after 1947 are not so large as to require their inclusion as variables in the statistical estimates. Hence, separate estimates are made for the 1947–1965 period. These are not affected by the arbitrary methods used to account for the disturbances in the estimates for the entire period from 1932 to 1965.

1932–1965

The underlying data for the passenger mile demand estimations are given in Table 4-1. Passenger miles for the years 1932–1937 are very slightly different from those provided for the domestic trunk carriers in the *Handbook of Airline Statistics*. This is because of differences in the identities of the carriers included there and here. Passenger miles for these years were estimated by a simple ratio method. The numbers in Table 4-1 come from the ratio of numbers of aircraft included in Chapter 2 in the fleet concentration data to total fixed-wing aircraft in service and the 1938 ratio of seat miles per aircraft for planes in the trunk line fleets to seat miles per aircraft for planes in scheduled service but not in the trunk line fleets.[2]

Revenue per passenger mile data for the years 1932–1937 are not available for trunk carriers alone. Those given in Table 4-1 for these years are those reported for all scheduled domestic carriers less .05 cents, the difference between revenue per passenger mile for the trunk lines and that for all domestic carriers in 1938.

The number of fatal accidents given is for all United States scheduled carriers, domestic and international. Their inclusion in the demand model is predicated not on the notion that accidents reduce the supply of seat miles and, hence, of passenger miles, but rather on a hypothesis that the public's fear of flying is related to current fatal accidents. Fatal accidents are typically reported in newspaper headlines and the resulting increase in fear may affect domestic passenger demand regardless of whether the accidents occurred to domestic or international carriers.

A constant dollar Gross National Product figure was used as the income item for the passenger demand estimation. Another variable is simply time, the inclusion of which in the ratio form of estimation utilized tends to account for linear changes in the annual rate of change in the dependent demand variable.

---

[2] The differences between those estimates and those in the *Handbook* are, in millions of passenger miles, −0.1, −0.4, +0.3, −6.9, +1.3, and −1.2 for the years 1932, 1933, 1934, 1935, 1936, and 1937, respectively.

Table 4-1

Passenger Miles, Revenue per Passenger Mile, and Number of Fatal Accidents, 1932–1965

Year	Revenue Passenger Miles, Domestic Trunk Lines (000,000)	Revenue Per Passenger Mile, Domestic Trunk Lines (cents)	Number of Fatal Accidents All U.S. Scheduled Air Carriers
1932	126.9	6.05	17
1933	173.1	6.05	9
1934	188.2	5.85	10
1935	272.5	5.65	8
1936	389.5	5.65	10
1937	406.1	5.55	6
1938	475.6	5.12	8
1939	679.8	5.07	3
1940	1,047.1	5.03	3
1941	1,377.2	5.01	5
1942	1,405.8	5.24	5
1943	1,617.1	5.32	3
1944	2,161.0	5.32	4
1945	3,336.3	4.93	9
1946	5,903.1	4.62	11
1947	6,016.3	5.04	8
1948	5,840.2	5.73	6
1949	6,570.7	5.75	4
1950	7,766.0	5.54	6
1951	10,210.7	5.59	9
1952	12,120.8	5.54	8
1953	14,279.6	5.43	6
1954	16,234.6	5.37	4
1955	19,205.7	5.32	9
1956	21,643.1	5.28	4
1957	24,499.5	5.25	5
1958	24,435.7	5.58	6
1959	28,127.2	5.80	10
1960	29,233.2	6.01	12
1961	29,534.8	6.19	5
1962	31,827.8	6.35	5
1963	36,383.8	6.07	5
1964	41,658.4	6.01	9
1965	48,987.0	5.94	7

Source: *Handbook of Airline Statistics* (1965); *Air Transport Facts and Figures* (1966); *Historical Statistics of the United States.*

A dummy variable was introduced with unit value for the years in which a substantially new form of long-haul aircraft was introduced into service and with a zero value for other years. The years of unitary value are 1933 (for the Boeing 247), 1934 (for the DC-2), 1936 (for the DC-3), 1940 (for the Boeing 307), 1946 (for the DC-4 and Lockheed L-049 "Constellation"), and 1959 (for the Boeing 707 and DC-8).

The final variable is an artificial one whose purpose is to eliminate the effects of large, historically traceable, nonrandom disturbances. The values assigned to this variable are subjective, with the ultimate choice of values being governed by the arbitrary criterion of effects on the t ratios for the other variables. By repetitive runnings of the regressions, values for this variable were selected which tended to maximize the t ratios of the other independent variables. While the years of its use at other than zero values and the sign of the effect can be defended by real events, the exact values used have none other than a pragmatic defense. These values are given in Table 4-2. The historical events to which they relate are explained above.

Table 4-2

Values for the Artificial Disturbance Variable
in 1932–1965 Passenger Demand Regression

Year	Value
1934	-50
1937	-50
1942	-50
1943	-20
1944	$+10$
1945	$+35$
1946	$+60$
1948	-10
1950	-10
1951	$+10$
1958	-10

The variables in the passenger demand equation are highly correlated with time and so with each other. Regressions based on the straight natural or logarithmic equation forms yield coefficients of determination approaching unity and unreliable estimates of regression coefficients. To avoid this collinearity problem, the demand equation was expressed in terms of year-to-year changes. To transform the equation into an approximation of a logarithmic form and, at the same time, to circumvent the difficulties presented by the log form when some changes are negative, ratios of the values of the passenger demand, price, and income variables in a given year to their values in the previous year were used.

The regression for passenger mile demand for the years 1932–1965 yielded:

$$\frac{PM_t}{PM_{t-1}} = 1.513 - \underset{(0.259)}{1.227} \left(\frac{P_t}{P_{t-1}}\right) - \underset{(.00033)}{.00052}(F_t)$$

$$+ \underset{(0.229)}{1.039} \left(\frac{Y_t}{Y_{t-1}}\right) + \underset{(.032)}{.108}(NP_t) - \underset{(.0012)}{.0079}(t) \qquad (4.4)$$

$$+ \underset{(.0006)}{.0071}(E_t)$$

$$\bar{R}^2 = .90$$
$$D - W = 2.59$$

where, in addition to the nomenclature set out above, F_t is the number of fatal accidents during time t, NP_t is the dummy variable representing the introduction of a significantly new long-haul aircraft, t is time, and E_t is the variable for exogeneous influences. The highest simple correlation among the independent variables is $+.45$, between F_t and NP_t.

In this form, the coefficients of the price and income terms are elasticities with respect to year-to-year changes in demand. Both the income and price elasticities are significant at the five percent level and, with appropriate signs, slightly in excess of unity. All the other variables have the anticipated signs and, except for the fatal accident variable, each is significant at at least the five percent level.

The price variable is uncorrected for price level and for the prices of possible substitutes. Because of the ratio expression, most of the trend and a great deal of the cyclical variation in price is removed. Use of price level corrected prices yielded a slightly lower and statistically somewhat less significant elasticity coefficient. The use of air revenue passenger fares relative to rail pullman or average rail passenger fares, or the use of either of the latter as an additional variable, did not improve the fit. Several simple lagged distributions of the price effect over two years were attempted, but these also failed to improve the fit.

It was possible to find a significant fatal accident effect with a more complicated index of a fear factor arising from fatal crashes. The fear factor index was made by weighting domestic accidents more heavily than foreign and by weighting current year accidents more heavily than previous year accidents. This form of weighting has appeal on *a priori* grounds. Year-to-year ratios of this index proved to be correlated with income, however, and their use reduced but did not eliminate the significance of the income effect. The accident death rate per 100 million passenger miles had no explanatory value.

The new plane effect is an influence of technology on passenger demand. It was introduced into the passenger mile regression estimate after other, more obvious indications of technological change proved to be of no significant explanatory value. Average airborne speed and air speed relative to train speed, for example, were tested on the hypothesis that they would be reciprocal measures of the time cost of travel. Seating capacity per plane, alone and as an interaction factor with air speed, was tried. None of these other measures reflecting technological change produced significant results.

1947–1965

The demand estimates obtained for the 1947–1965 period are based on the same data and, while somewhat different in particular form, yield results essentially consistent with those for the longer period. No arbitrary variables for nonrandom disturbances were used.

The demand estimating equation that appears best of the several attempted is:

$$\frac{PM_t}{PM_{t-1}} = 1.114 - \underset{(0.308)}{1.372} \left(\frac{P_t}{P_{t-1}}\right) + \underset{(.372)}{.848} \left(\frac{Y_t}{Y_{t-1}}\right)$$

$$+ \underset{(.336)}{.610} \left(\frac{Y_{t-1}}{Y_{t-2}}\right) - \underset{(.009)}{.019}(F_{t-1} + F_{t-2}) - \underset{(.012)}{.016}(VA_t) \quad (4.5)$$

$$- \underset{(.021)}{.021}(t) \qquad \bar{R}^2 = .763$$
$$D - W = 2.50$$

In this equation, VA_t refers to the weighted average version age of the new aircraft being added to the fleets. For example, the version age of the DC-6 is one in 1947 and two in 1948; that of the DC-6B, one in 1951, two in 1952. This variable was intended to play the same role in this regression as the NP_t dummy played in the regression for the whole period. The version age coefficient is significant at the 10 percent level and has the expected sign. Passenger demand tends to be somewhat greater during years when aircraft of newer version ages are being added than in years when the versions are of older vintages.

The other variables are those defined above. Price elasticity is estimated at very nearly the same level as in regression (4.4). Income has greater explanatory value—using the magnitude of the corrected coefficient of determination as the criterion—when it is introduced as two separate variables. One is the ratio of current income to the previous year's income; the other, the ratio of previous year's income to income in the year prior to that. The number of fatal accidents seems significant in annual data for this period only when accidents over the two years past are aggregated. Even here, the effect is very small. Time, which was highly significant for the 1932–1965 period, is much less significant from 1947 to 1965.

The highest intercorrelation among the independent variables in equation (4.5) is $-.55$. This is between the price and fatal accidents variables. No other simple correlation coefficients among the variables exceeds $|.33|$.

The Supply of Seat Miles of Trunk Line Transportation

Unlike most supply-demand models of markets, the units supplied by the trunk carriers are not identical with those demanded by air line passengers. In particular flights, seat miles may on occasion equal passenger miles but, in the aggregate, seat miles supplied exceed passenger miles demanded. The ratio of the latter to the former is the load factor.

No formal tests of the independence of the error terms of the equations of the model were made. Thus, it may be true that the model is not fully recursive. The fact that the supply units are different from the demand units does reduce somewhat the problems of interdependence among the equations, however. In addition, less formal statistical checks indicated that, with the year-to-year ratios used in the demand and supply expressions, the system does indeed appear recursive. Year-to-year changes in price which are significantly associated with changes in passenger miles demanded are not significantly correlated with year-to-year changes in seat miles supplied. The load factor, which in a loose sense measures the excess of supply over demand, is also unassociated with price changes in any near-current period. Thus, neither seat miles supplied nor the load factor seems to affect demand indirectly through price.

1932–1965

The underlying hypothesis is that seat miles are supplied by the carriers in response to their own estimates of passenger demand. The latter, it is assumed, include the effects of price, income, new aircraft, and time trends, but not the effects of the large nonrandom disturbances discussed above. Neither are random disturbances considered in the carriers estimates. Both of these are of a nature such that they cannot be anticipated and, hence, seat mile supply decisions are assumed to be made initially without their being affected by either of these types of disturbances.

These considerations lead to the use of a planned passenger mile variable in the supply regressions. The planned passenger mile variable is simply the estimated passenger mile figure from the demand regressions in most years. This agrees with the hypothesis that seat miles are supplied on the basis of anticipations concerning the significant variables affecting demand, and that small, random disturbances do not enter the supply reaction. The large disturbances of the period up to 1947 do require use of a different planned demand variable for the years in which the disturbances occur. In these years, the planned passenger mile demand is the estimated value plus a correction factor equal to the value of the arbitrary variable in the 1932–1965 demand regression multiplied by the coefficient of that variable. It estimates, that is, what demand might have been predicted to be had the large disturbances not occurred. The supply function for the 1932–1965 period uses this planned demand as one of the independent variables. To account for possible direct effects of the large nonrandom disturbances on supply, the function incorporates another artificial variable of the same kind as is in the demand regression.

In the general formulation of the model given in (4.1), (4.2), and (4.3), above, the rate of return appears in the supply equation. The obvious rationale for this is that the supply response to passenger demand may be conditioned by the profits or rate of return on capital realized in providing the service. A number of problems arise if profits or rates of return are introduced directly into the supply regression. One is that such data are not available for all of the carriers for years prior to 1938. Another is that profits reported in particular years are affected by events peculiar to those years and, hence, fail to reflect the *ex ante* profit considerations which presumably govern supply decisions. In particular, reported profits, especially when the fleets were small, vary with aircraft accident losses and the carriers' insurance programs and accounting methods.[3] Reported profits are also affected by depreciation policies and the age distribution of the aircraft being operated. These considerations led to a search for a proxy for the profits variable.

The rate of return on current operations is a conceptually appropriate profitability measure. For air carriers, this rate can be calculated as operating income (excluding capital gains and losses and income from other sources, as a percent of net worth plus long-term debt. These data are available for the domestic trunk carriers from 1938. It was hypothesized, following Schumpeterian arguments, that long-run shifts in the cost structure associated with technological changes and trends in factor prices would be reflected in trends in output prices. If this is correct, short-run variations in profits would be explained by short-run variations in the intensity of equipment use and short-run variations in price.

The intensity of flight equipment utilization is provided by the load factor, the ratio of revenue passenger miles purchased to revenue seat miles flown. Price, for this purpose, is not identical to revenue per messenger mile, the traveler's measure of average price, because of various transportation excise taxes in effect since October 1941. Net sellers' price was computed by subtracting from revenue per passenger mile the estimated amounts of such taxes per passenger mile in each year.

Short-run operating costs, it was assumed, vary directly but less than proportionately with the load factor. Some cost items, such as flight crew pay, are fixed with respect to the load factor while others, such as those incident to baggage and passenger handling, tend to vary directly with the load factor. It was assumed also that there was some longer-run ideal load factor beyond which there may be increases in the per unit operating costs associated with more intensive equipment utilization. Finally, it was assumed that costs may not respond instantaneously to variations in load factors. Short-run increases in the load factor might be accommodated by using existing personnel and facilities more intensively and at a lower per passenger cost than would be sustainable over a longer period. Short-run decreases in the load factor might result in higher per passenger costs than would prevail over a longer period because of the inability quickly to reduce personnel and facilities.

These assumptions were tested and the following estimating equation resulted:

$$\pi_t = 265.55 + 59.00(\ln U_t) - .66|U^* - U_t|$$
$$(12.49) \qquad (.20)$$
$$+ 75.62(\ln U_t - \ln U_{t-1}) + 7.74(P'_t) \qquad (4.6)$$
$$(13.80) \qquad (3.87)$$
$$\bar{R}^2 = .757$$
$$D - W = 1.23$$

[3] A. J. Gellman, *The Effect of Regulation on Aircraft Choice* (unpublished Ph.D. dissertation. Massachusetts Institute of Technology, 1968), pp. 183–184.

In this equation, $\hat{r}$ is the estimated rate of return on current operations during time t, U_t is the load factor at time t, U^* is an approximation of the ideal utilization rate, and P'_t is the net sellers' price per passenger mile. The ideal rate was set at 66, the mean of the observed load factors in the period 1938–1965. The simple correlation between P'_t and log U_t is $-.70$. No other correlation among the independent variables exceeds $|.39|$.

Each variable is significant beyond the five percent level and has the anticipated sign. More sophisticated treatment of the non-linearity in the cost function and of the location (possibly shifting with time) of the ideal load factor would undoubtedly produce a more complete explanation of the variance in the rates of return on operations. The results from (4.6) were regarded as sufficient to justify the use of some form of the load factor variable as a proxy for cost in the seat mile supply estimates.

The estimated seat mile supply equation for the 1932–1965 period is:

$$\frac{SM_t}{SM_{t-1}} = -.478 + \underset{(.095)}{.937} \left(\frac{PM^*_t}{PM_{t-1}}\right) + \underset{(.011)}{.048}(U_{t-1})$$

$$+ \underset{(.333)}{.242} \left(\frac{P'_t}{P'_{t-1}}\right) + \underset{(.0010)}{.0090}(E'_t) \qquad (4.7)$$

$$\bar{R}^2 = .867$$
$$D - W = 2.24$$

where SM_t is the estimated number of seat miles supplied at time t, PM^*_t is the "planned" passenger miles, U_t is the load factor, P'_t is the sellers' net price per passenger mile, and E'_t is the other artificial variable used to account for large, unanticipated and non-random events which affect supply.

The coefficient showing the partial effects of planned passenger miles on seat miles is highly significant. For each one percent increase in planned passenger miles at t over passenger miles at $t - 1$, seat miles increase by approximately 94 percent. On a priori grounds, it could be argued that this should equal 100 percent if all observations of the load factor were at the ideal level and if the revenue structure were such that increments to seat miles always provided positive incremental profits. These conditions did not prevail. The actual load factor in fact averages less than 62 for the entire period 1932–1965. There are years of negative average (and, presumably, negative incremental) rates of return. Moreover, short-term increases in seat miles which are less than proportional to the increases in passenger miles contribute to short-term returns. All of these lend credence to an empirical result of a response of less than 100 percent.

The load factor used in the seat mile regression is that of the previous year. This captures the essence but not the detail of using the complicated relations shown in equation (4.6) between rate of return and the load factor. The lower is the load factor at $t - 1$, the greater is the increase in rate of return on current operations from increasing seat miles offered less than proportionately with the increase in planned passenger miles at time t over passenger miles at $t - 1$.

The artificial variable for exogeneous influences is significant. Although this variable covers the same historical occurrences as does that for the passenger mile demand regression, its values are not exactly equivalent. The events affected supply and demand differently. In 1937, for example, seat miles rose by 21 percent over 1936 whereas passenger miles rose by only 4 percent. Planned passenger miles for 1937 are estimated at 34 percent over actual passenger miles in 1936. Thus, as would be expected, the 1937 safety inquiry apparently had a relatively small effect on seat miles supplied as compared with its effect on passenger miles demanded. Conversely, the absorption of aircraft into the military in 1942 and during the Korean airlift had a relatively larger impact on seat miles than on passenger miles; the increase in the load factor in each instance reflects this difference. The predicted seat miles from (4.7) were converted to planned seat miles following the manner used for passenger miles with the same exogenous events being treated as unanticipated.

The price factor proves not to be significant in (4.7). Over time, it must be true that price affects supply because of its bearing on profits. Price in the current period, however, seems not to influence current period supply significantly. This is a condition required for recursiveness in this case and the price variable was retained in the equation to demonstrate its lack of significance.

1947–1965

The seat mile supply response in the 1947–1965 period fits the same general explanation as that given for the entire period. Supply appears to arise in response to changes in passenger demand, with the load factor conditioning the degree of response. The best statistical form of the 1947–1965 supply is somewhat different from that for 1932–1965, however.

In the 1947–1965 period, there is a significant downward time trend in the load factor. This is not apparent in a linear or logarithmic trend fit for the full 1932–1965 period. During the 1932–1946 years the load factor was rising. In view of the downward movement for the later period, a logarithmic time trend was fitted and deviations from it were used in place of the load factor itself. The results are:

$$\frac{SM_t}{SM_{t-1}} = .445 + .647 \left(\frac{PM^*_t}{PM_{t-1}}\right) + .028(U'_{t-1})$$
$$(.127) \qquad\qquad (.019)$$
$$+ .061(U'_{t-2}) - .003(t) \qquad\qquad (4.8)$$
$$(.018) \qquad (.001)$$

$$\bar{R}^2 = .691$$
$$D - W = 2.59$$

where U'_{t-1} and U'_{t-2} represent the absolute deviations of the load factor from its time trend in the year past and two years past, respectively.

In this form, the partial effect of changes in passenger miles demanded on seat miles supplied appears smaller than it does in (4.7). This is because the removal of trend from the measures of the load factor leaves in the coefficient of the passenger demand variable the effect of the generally declining load factor. The annual percentage increase in seat miles changes less than proportionately with the changes in the percentage increase in passenger miles. Time periods of relatively high load factors (that is, positive deviations from trend) tend to induce larger seat mile responses in subsequent periods but, over the whole period, the declining load factor tends to reduce the seat mile supply response. No significant current or lagged effect of price changes on supply were found.

Table 4-3 gives the actual and planned seat miles supplied, passenger miles demanded and load factors as derived from equations (4.4) and (4.7). Table 4-4 gives the same results from equations (4.5) and (4.8). The results of (4.4) and (4.7) are affected by the arbitrary values assigned to represent exogeneous and nonrandom disturbances. Those of (4.5) and (4.8) give a somewhat poorer statistical fit. Yet, either alone or together the sets of supply and demand estimations are adequate to give a picture of the nature of year-to-year variations in passenger mile demand and seat mile supply. The former depends primarily on price, income, safety, and the newness or novelty of aircraft types being introduced into the fleets. The latter is primarily a response to passenger demand conditioned by utilization rates in recent past periods.

Trunk Line Demand for Aircraft

The demand for aircraft can be viewed in two ways. One is as demand in a Wicksellian sense—demand to hold a stock of aircraft. The other is demand in the more usual sense—demand for a flow of newly produced aircraft which, apart from possible purchases of used planes, are gross increments to the stock. A major problem with the formulation of the Wicksellian type of demand for aircraft is that it may be tautological. Take, for example, the expression:

$$S_t = \frac{SM_t}{(V_t)(C_t)(H_t)} \tag{4.9}$$

where S_t is the stock, or average number, of planes in the fleet during the tth year, SM_t is the seat miles during the year, and V_t, C_t, and H_t are, respectively, the average velocity, average seating capacity, and average annual hours of use of the planes in S_t. This form is an identity if the variables are consistently

Table 4-3

Actual and Planned Seat Miles, Passenger Miles and Utilization Rates, 1932–1965

	Seat Miles (000,000)		Passenger Miles (000,000)		Load Factor	
Year	Actual	Planned	Actual	Planned	Actual	Planned
1932	300.1	—	126.9	—	42.3	—
1933	369.0	370.0	173.1	170.0	46.9	45.9
1934	363.3	517.0	188.2	260.0	51.8	50.3
1935	558.3	487.0	272.5	265.0	48.8	54.4
1936	683.4	787.0	389.5	406.0	57.0	51.6
1937	825.5	888.0	406.1	522.0	49.2	58.8
1938	944.7	974.0	475.6	516.0	50.3	53.0
1939	1,209.6	1,219.0	679.8	647.0	56.2	53.1
1940	1,809.4	1,706.0	1,047.1	993.0	57.9	58.2
1941	2,330.6	2,461.0	1,377.2	1,466.0	59.1	59.6
1942	1,949.7	2,913.0	1,405.8	1,763.0	72.1	60.5
1943	1,838.5	1,930.0	1,617.1	1,574.0	88.0	81.6
1944	2,418.1	2,500.0	2,161.0	2,167.0	89.4	86.7
1945	3,784.5	3,845.0	3,336.3	3,242.0	88.2	84.3
1946	7,490.4	7,154.0	5,903.1	5,738.0	78.8	80.2
1947	9,152.4	9,063.0	6,016.3	6,493.0	65.7	71.6
1948	9,980.2	10,250.0	5,840.2	6,377.0	58.5	62.2
1949	11,117.7	11,577.0	6,570.7	6,891.0	59.1	59.5
1950	12,385.6	14,009.0	7,766.0	8,608.0	62.7	61.4
1951	14,672.0	14,987.0	10,210.7	9,708.0	69.7	64.8
1952	18,068.1	17,900.0	12,120.8	12,151.0	67.1	67.9
1953	22,114.8	22,404.0	14,279.6	14,788.0	64.7	66.0
1954	25,623.3	25,437.0	16,234.6	16,136.0	63.4	63.4
1955	29,978.6	31,004.0	19,205.7	19,482.0	64.1	62.8
1956	33,752.6	34,776.0	21,643.1	22,087.0	64.1	63.5
1957	39,838.2	39,153.0	24,499.5	24,889.0	61.5	63.6
1958	40,695.0	41,033.0	24,435.7	24,745.0	60.0	60.3
1959	45,793.2	48,427.0	28,127.2	29,078.0	61.4	60.0
1960	49,153.6	47,167.0	29,233.2	28,408.0	59.5	60.2
1961	52,525.0	52,595.0	29,534.8	31,279.0	56.2	59.5
1962	59,736.8	56,727.0	31,827.8	32,489.0	53.3	57.3
1963	67,601.3	66,905.0	36,383.8	36,920.0	53.8	55.2
1964	75,242.4	71,657.0	41,658.4	40,022.0	55.5	55.9
1965	88,593.0	81,261.0	48,904.3	46,240.0	55.2	56.9

defined. The denominator, $(V_t)(C_t)(H_t)$, reduces to SM_t/S_t. The variables in the denominator, nonetheless, represent on a fleetwide basis the very technological characteristics that must be considered in explaining aircraft demand.

This difficulty cannot be wholly escaped so long as these variables are retained as weighted averages relating to the entire fleet. Consequently, while the formal identity of (4.9) is avoided in the regression of the stock size of the fleet on seat miles supplied and the technical characteristics of the aircraft, the regression equation is close enough to an identity to render moot the

Table 4-4

Actual and Planned Seat Miles, Passenger Miles and Utilization Rates, 1947–1965

Year	Seat Miles (000,000)		Passenger Miles (000,000)		Load Factor	
	Actual	Planned	Actual	Planned	Actual	Planned
1947	9,152.4	9,101.0	6,016.3	6,209.0	65.7	68.2
1948	9,980.2	9,976.0	5,840.2	5,956.0	58.5	59.7
1949	11,117.7	10,948.0	6,570.7	6,593.0	59.1	60.2
1950	12,385.6	12,463.0	7,766.0	8,030.0	62.7	64.4
1951	14,672.0	14,417.0	10,210.7	9,412.0	69.7	65.3
1952	18,068.1	18,105.0	12,120.8	12,100.0	67.1	66.8
1953	22,114.8	21,953.0	14,279.6	14,557.0	64.7	66.3
1954	25,623.3	25,565.0	16,234.6	16,279.0	63.4	63.7
1955	29,978.6	30,030.0	19,205.7	19,157.0	64.1	63.8
1956	33,752.6	35,165.0	21,643.1	22,452.0	64.1	63.8
1957	39,838.2	38,073.0	24,499.5	23,353.0	61.5	61.3
1958	40,695.0	41,750.0	24,435.7	24,084.0	60.0	57.7
1959	45,793.2	45,782.0	28,127.2	27,294.0	61.4	59.6
1960	49,153.6	49,640.0	29,233.2	30,546.0	59.5	61.5
1961	52,525.0	53,332.0	29,534.8	29,701.0	56.2	55.7
1962	59,736.8	59,826.0	31,827.8	30,953.0	53.3	51.7
1963	67,601.3	67,025.0	36,383.8	36,920.0	53.8	55.1
1964	75,242.4	77,471.0	41,658.4	42,205.0	55.5	54.5
1965	88,593.0	86,227.0	48,904.3	48,823.0	55.2	56.6

question of the appropriate number of degrees of freedom. In short, the statistical significance of none of the coefficients can be tested.

The stock regression for the entire 1932–1965 period is:

$$\frac{S_t}{S_{t-1}} = 2.97 + \underset{(.075)}{.696} \left(\frac{SM_t}{SM_{t-1}}\right) + \underset{(.081)}{.027} \left(\frac{SM^*_{t+1}}{SM_t}\right)$$

$$- \underset{(0.373)}{1.351} \left(\frac{V_t}{V_{t-1}}\right) - \underset{(.257)}{.577} \left(\frac{C_t}{C_{t-1}}\right) - \underset{(.098)}{.740} \left(\frac{H_t}{H_{t-1}}\right) \quad (4.10)$$

$$+ \underset{(.049)}{.378} (E'_t)$$

$$\bar{R}^2 = .869$$
$$D - W = 2.55$$

The velocity (V_t), seating capacity (C_t) and hours of use (H_t) data are those given in Table 4-5. They are not independently defined. The fleet data, however, are those pertaining to the stock at the end of the year, not the average number for the year. Because of this, the regression contains a variable representing planned seat miles for the coming year as well as one giving seat miles in the year past. This form allows for the effects of fleet expansion in anticipation of increases in seat miles, but—with the caveats from above—the effect did not appear significant. The E''_t variable in this case reflects the disturbance

Table 4-5

Overall Characteristics of Trunk Line Fleets, 1932–1965.

Year	Seats Per Aircraft	Average Airborne Speed	Thousands of Revenue Miles Per Aircraft Per Year	Thousands of Airborne Hours Per Aircraft Per Year
1932	6.9	109	114	1,046
1933	8.0	116	129	1,112
1934	9.3	127	113	890
1935	10.6	142	157	1,106
1936	11.3	149	209	1,403
1937	13.1	153	254	1,660
1938	13.9	153	279	1,824
1939	14.7	153	321	2,098
1940	16.5	155	351	2,265
1941	17.6	160	380	2,375
1942	17.9	159	427	2,686
1943	18.3	154	568	3,688
1944	19.0	156	575	3,686
1945	19.7	153	607	3,967
1946	25.3	169	590	3,491
1947	30.3	170	457	2,688
1948	33.1	176	426	2,420
1949	36.3	184	412	2,239
1950	39.7	188	414	2,202
1951	41.8	192	499	2,599
1952	45.0	199	474	2,382
1953	48.6	207	505	2,440
1954	53.0	216	523	2,421
1955	54.5	220	567	2,577
1956	55.5	223	587	2,632
1957	57.0	228	616	2,702
1958	59.3	233	570	2,446
1959	63.0	239	593	2,481
1960	71.1	256	574	2,242
1961	80.5	284	559	1,968
1962	88.2	314	603	1,920
1963	92.5	329	688	2,091
1964	95.6	343	745	2,172
1965	95.8	362	824	2,276

Source: World Airline Record (1952), *Handbook of Airline Statistics* (1965), *Air Transport Facts and Figures* (1966).

effects of absorptions and releases of aircraft by the government during World War II and the Korean War. The regression is not formally tautological, but no reliance can be put on the coefficients.

The trunk line demand for new aircraft expressed in terms of additions of new aircraft to the fleets is the most relevant for present purposes. It is also very difficult to explain statistically. Variables used in a number of attempted regressions include the supply of planned seat miles, the load factor, various lagged distributions of actual and planned seat miles and of the load factor, the passenger capacity, and cruising speeds of planes being added (in absolute terms, relative to planes in the existing fleets and relative to the aircraft being replaced), the model age of aircraft being added, the version age of aircraft being added, the same age measures for aircraft being replaced, and some interaction terms for model and version ages. Even comparisons of the average operating costs of aircraft being added with those of aircraft being replaced failed to be of significant explanatory value.

For the most part, then, variables of the kind described with reference to equation (4.3) and defined more specifically immediately above proved not to be statistically significant. Because the data are for calendar year and because deliveries of new planes have tended to cluster heavily in the first 12 calendar months after the initial delivery, another variable reflecting the proportion of these twelve months which occurred in a given calendar year was computed, with a dichotomy between aircraft designed for long range and nonlong range uses. The nonzero values of this variable for each plane, based essentially on the date of first use by a domestic trunk carrier, are given in Table 4-6.[4]

Based on the value of the coefficient of determination, after excluding regressions in which there was obvious multicollinearity, and correcting for degrees of freedom, the best equation found is:

$$\frac{NP_t}{S_{t-1}} = -.515 + \underset{(.164)}{.418} \left(\frac{SM^*_t}{SM_{t-1}}\right) + \underset{(.041)}{.054} \left(\frac{SM_{t-1}}{SM_{t-2}}\right)$$
$$+ \underset{(.035)}{.019(MA'_t)} + \underset{(.020)}{.017(NLR_t)} + \underset{(.018)}{.061(NNLR_t)} \qquad (4.11)$$
$$\bar{R}^2 = .491$$

where the dependent variable is the ratio of the estimated number of new planes added during one year to the stock of planes in the fleet at the end of the preceding year, MA'_t is the average model age of aircraft being taken out of service during the year, NLR_t is the sum of the percentages of the first twelve months of deliveries of long-range planes in a given year, and $NNLR_t$ is the sum for nonlong range planes. The regression in (4.11) applies only to the period 1947–1965. Because of the effect of the war years on new deliveries and the large exogenous disturbances in the few observations of the prewar period, a similar equation was not fit for the entire 1932–1965 period.

Table 4-7 gives the actual and predicted additions of new aircraft as derived from equation (4.11). The year with the largest absolute deviation is 1957, when 179 aircraft were actually added and for which the estimated additions

---

[4] *Handbook of Airline Statistics* (1965), Part VII, Item 7, "Introduction of New Aircraft Types Into U.S. Airline Service."

Table 4-6

Distribution of First Year Deliveries of New Models and Versions of Aircraft to Trunk Line Carriers among Calendar Years.

Aircraft	Range	Distribution of First Year Deliveries
DC-6	Long	1947 = 67%; 1948 = 33%
DC-6B	Long	1951 = 75%; 1952 = 25%
DC-7	Long	1953 = 20%; 1954 = 80%
DC-7C	Long	1956 = 36%; 1957 = 64%
B-707	Long	1959 = 100%
B-720	Long	1960 = 44%; 1961 = 56%
B-720B	Long	1961 = 80%; 1962 = 20%
L-647/749	Long	1947 = 25%; 1948 = 75%
L-1049	Long	1951 = 20%; 1952 = 80%
L-1049C	Long	1953 = 20%; 1954 = 80%
L-1049G	Long	1955 = 95%; 1956 = 5%
L-1649	Long	1957 = 80%; 1958 = 20%
CV-880	Long	1960 = 62%; 1961 = 38%
CV-990	Long	1962 = 79%; 1963 = 21%
DC-8	Long	1959 = 35%; 1960 = 65%
CV-240	Non-Long	1948 = 60%; 1949 = 40%
CV-340	Non-Long	1952 = 25%; 1953 = 75%
CV-440	Non-Long	1956 = 70%; 1957 = 30%
M-202	Non-Long	1947 = 35%; 1948 = 65%
M-404	Non-Long	1951 = 33%; 1952 = 67%
DC-9	Non-Long	1965 = 5%; 1966 = 95%
V-745	Non-Long	1955 = 42%; 1956 = 58%
V-812	Non-Long	1958 = 91%; 1959 = 9%
L-188	Non-Long	1959 = 95%; 1960 = 5%
S-210	Non-Long	1961 = 85%; 1962 = 15%
BAC-111	Non-Long	1965 = 67%; 1966 = 33%

amount to but 114. This was a year in which 12 DC-7Cs, 58 DC-7Bs, and 25 L-1649 "Constellations" were among the new planes added to the fleets. These aircraft, it will be pointed out in the next chapter, were acquired primarily because of rivalry among transcontinental carriers for two-way, nonstop traffic from coast-to-coast. Their operating costs were higher than those of preceding models of the same manufacturers. Their performance was superior primarily with respect to range. It has been argued that these purchases in particular and postwar trunk fleet aircraft purchased in general resulted from an uneconomic form of nonprice competition.[5] Whatever the reason, the fact that so small a portion of the total variance in annual additions to the fleets can be statistically explained within the context of a recursive market model indicates that aircraft demand arises from sources other than those covered by the statistical model. And this model is one which emphasizes variables based on rather conventional economic reasoning.

[5] A. J. Gellman, *Effect of Regulation.*

Table 4-7

Actual and Estimated Additions of New
Aircraft by Domestic Trunk Lines,
1947–1965.

| | Additions of New Aircraft | |
Year	Actual	Estimated
1947	105	109
1948	115	89
1949	58	65
1950	51	31
1951	63	62
1952	148	121
1953	127	125
1954	75	99
1955	55	96
1956	125	117
1957	179	114
1958	82	48
1959	166	166
1960	97	125
1961	125	154
1962	66	94
1963	23	62
1964	119	99
1965	135	149

A Suggested Alternative Explanation of
Changes in the Annual Demand for Aircraft

If equation (4.11) or another similarly specified variant of it had explained
a large proportion of the variance in the demand for aircraft, the weight of the
evidence therefrom could have been interpreted as being against the acceptance of the main hypothesis of this book. If the demand for aircraft can be
explained by passenger demand and by variables representing rational and
controllable change in variables describing the state of technology, then
technology would itself appear as an endogeneous aspect of the market
process.

What is seen in the data of Table 4-7 is something different from this. The
details of Chapters 5 and 6 are necessary to appreciate fully the process involved, but a preliminary view from these summary data can be presented
here. The 1947 additions are largely of DC-6s and the new L-649/749 "Constellations." These were the two successes among a substantial number of
aspiring manufacturers of new, larger, and longer ranged aircraft. The 1948
additions, beyond carry-on deliveries of the DC-6s and L-749s, are of Convair
240s and Martin 202s. These, and later versions, were the successful entrants
into the shorter-range end of the market. Again, other manufacturers attempted somewhat similar planes and failed.

The 1947–1948 cases are illustrative. Successful major types of new aircraft appear discontinuously over time—not precisely at the times predicated on the carriers preferences but rather as technological developments have permitted cost reductions or other performance improvements. The success of one plane may lie principally in speed; of another, in operating costs; of another, in range or passenger capacity. No single variable captures the effects of technology on the demand for aircraft.

It will be shown in the next two chapters that relatively low operating costs are a necessary condition for a plane to capture a large share of the transport market over a number of years. Low operating costs alone, however, are not sufficient to assure that a plane receives a large share of demand. A number of aircraft types have had large sales for a year or so only to demonstrate in use that their operating costs were higher or some other performance aspect was inferior to that anticipated when orders were placed. It is these intermittant technological successes and technological mistakes which cause much of the variance in annual aircraft demand and in market shares. They cannot easily be captured in a statistical model of demand.

5

Entry and Aircraft Technology: The Misses and Near Misses

Introduction

The influence of technology on market structure that is hypothesized in the first chapter results from attempts by new or existing firms to adapt to changes in the scientific and technical environment. Some succeed, others fail; and so long as entry does not offset failures of established firms, market structure changes. Thus, any attempt at verification should, if possible, include the record of failures or, as they were called in the conclusion of the previous chapter, the mistakes made in the process of change. Innovation involves not only the replacement of older products and processes by newer ones; it involves also a selection of which among the new alternatives are chosen and which are not.

In most industrial histories, data on unused variants of an innovation are lacking. Their failure to be used is reflected in an absence of information. The history of the commercial aircraft industry suffers from this also. There are undoubtedly many attempted aircraft the nature and technical details of which cannot be traced. But, there are also many planes that were designed for commercial use from the late 1920s through the 1950s which failed to gain carrier acceptance and for which a good deal of information can be gathered. The data relevant to these aircraft allow an analysis of the differences between them and other aircraft that were ordered and operated by carriers.

Appendix Table B-2 gives the characteristics of 62 aircraft types developed and available for order between 1927 and 1960. None of these appeared in the trunk line fleets after 1931. Only those types with passenger seating capacity in excess of four and ostensibly designed for commercial passenger transport use are included in the table. Each aircraft listed for years prior to 1942 is believed to have existed in an actual flying model. Most of the types shown for years up to 1938 received Approved Type Certificates from the Bureau of Air Commerce. This form of certification required air worthiness tests for the aircraft and the approval of facilities for production of the type. Thus, aircraft that got only as far as drawing board models as well as others that were conceived of in firms technically incapable of manufacturing them are excluded.

Twenty-nine of the 62 aircraft types were first available during the years through 1933, the year the Boeing 247 was introduced. The latter represents the first "modern airliner," with smooth duralumin and alclad all-metal airframe, multiple engines mounted on the wings, retractable landing gear, wing deicing equipment and, in the 247-D version of 1934, controllable pitch propellers and low-drag engine cowlings. From then through 1941, a total of only 20 aircraft are shown, 14 of which were multiengine types. Six of the latter were the products of Bellanca, Stinson, Douglas, Curtiss-Wright, Lockheed [1] and Consolidated—manufacturers some of whose previous models had been adopted by the trunk carriers. The other eight multiengine types were made by manufacturers whose models had not previously been in trunk line use.

Following World War II, only 13 additional types appear. Four of these were developed by manufacturers who previously had had no commercial transport aircraft in the fleets. The Hughes H-4 was an outgrowth of the Navy-financed Mars flying boat project and a counterpart of the Hercules flying boat proposed for transoceanic service. No flying version of the H-4 was produced. The two Chase aircraft and the Stroukoff YC-134A originated from Chase's development of the YC-122 and C-123B military transports. Lockheed, Beech, Hughes, and Douglas each made unsuccessful attempts to develop a short-range aircraft to serve as a replacement for the DC-3. No jet appears, though many must have been carried through at least the early design phases by some manufacturers—particularly, by Lockheed.

While the distinction between aircraft used and not used by the domestic trunk carriers is itself unambiguous, comparisons of the used and the not-used requires some care. A plane not used at one point in time may serve as a direct prototype for another which is subsequently used. No such cases are believed to be involved in the listings of Appendix Table B-2. In other cases, certain specific models of a type of aircraft may be used, while others are not. This is true, for example, of some of the variants of the Ford and Stinson Trimotors. To the extent allowed by available data, the comparisons of this chapter are based on the particular models that either appear or fail to appear in the fleets.

Beyond these problems, some of the aircraft that appear in the fleets were acquired in very small numbers and may have been regarded as mistakes of acquisition from a cost or performance point of view. Once acquired, however, the relevant cost comparison is that between variable (that is, *ex* depreciation) direct operating costs for those in the fleet and full (that is, including depreciation) direct operating costs for possible replacements. Differences in performance characteristics, of course, still obtain in full measure. These near misses are discussed in both this and the next chapter.

Cost Comparisons: Single Engined Aircraft

Despite an apparent preference by airline passengers for multiengined planes as early as the late 1920s, 222 of the 374 planes in the 1932 total trunk line fleet were single engined. The exact years of their acquisition are

---

[1] Allan H. Lockheed's Alcor Duo-6 was his personal entry attempt, not that of the Lockheed Aircraft Company.

not known, but it is likely that the dates correspond closely to the years in which the aircraft first became certificated and available for airline purchases.[2]

Table 5-1 gives the estimated direct operating costs of the single engined planes in the trunk line fleets between 1932 and 1936 along with alternatively available single engined planes which were not in the fleet in these years. Some of the latter may, of course, have been utilized by these carriers in earlier years. The cost estimates are based on the regression equations in Chapter 3.

Nineteen single engined Fokkers remained in the 1932 fleets. At least 14 of these were the "Super Universals" of 1928 vintage. These were being operated by Western Air Express, National Parks Airways, and Transcontinental and Western Airlines. Additional 1928 single engined aircraft in the 1932 fleets were nine Hamilton H-47 "Silver Streaks," operated by Northwest Airlines, and 20 Fairchild 71s, 17 of which belonged to American Airways and three of which were operated by Pennsylvania Air Lines.[3] One newly developed plane of the same year, the Bellanca CH, was not in the 1932 fleet. Table 5-1 shows that its estimated operating costs, as of its first model year, were above those of its contemporary and used rivals—though only insignificantly above those of the "Super Universal."

The cost differences seem adequate to explain the choice of the Hamilton and Fairchild over the Bellanca. The Hamilton, beyond its cost advantage, was one of the early all-metal, corrugated duralumin aircraft and had a somewhat faster cruising speed than did the others. But the selection of the "Super Universal" obviously is not explained by cost differences. The primary reason for its use lies in the common control of Western Air Express and Fokker established in 1928. Western Air Express continued as the major buyer for new Fokker planes until its consolidation with T.A.T.-Maddux in 1930.[4]

Of the 1929 models in the 1932 fleets, the cost differences fail to explain the adoptions of the Boeing B-40-B4 and the Fokker F-14; the cost differences fail also to explain the nonuse of the Cessna CPW-6 and, perhaps, the Thaden T-1. The first Boeing 40 was eliminated from a government production contract in a Post Office competition of 1925.[5] The 40A, a later version, was designed in 1927 specifically for an airmail competition in which Boeing Air Transport was the successful bidder. The B-40C and B-40-B4 were built for and nearly exclusively used by Boeing Air Transport. They carried four pas-

---

[2] The rapidly expanding volume of air traffic and successive introduction of lower cost aircraft underlie this view. To the extent that cost criteria governed aircraft use, purchases for expansion should have tended to cluster each year in new types with lower full costs, with the older types being retained or sold depending on their variable operating costs.

[3] *Aviation* (August 1932), pp. 344–347.

[4] See P. M. Bowers, "The American Fokkers," Part 3, *Journal of the American Aviation Historical Society* (Fall 1967). General Airlines, later to become Western Airlines, and sometimes called Western Air Express after 1930, continued as a separate firm after the 1930 consolidation.

[5] See *Pedigree of Champions*, second edition (The Boeing Company, 1963), pp. 40–41.

Table 5-1

Estimated Operating Costs of Single Engined Aircraft Used by Domestic Trunk Lines and
of Similar Aircraft Available but Not Used, 1932–1936
(Cents Per Seat Mile, 1954 Dollars)

	USED		NOT USED
Aircraft and Year First Available	Estimated Operating Costs Per Seat Mile, Including Depreciation	Aircraft and Year First Available	Estimated Operating Costs Per Seat Mile, Including Depreciation
1928		*1928*	
Fokker "Super Universal"	13.40	Bellanca CH	13.49
Hamilton H-47	12.13		
Fairchild 71	12.82		
1929		*1929*	
Fokker F-14	17.24	International F-18	16.06
Bellanca "Pacemaker"	12.80	Thaden T-2	13.06
Travel Air 6000B	12.40	Buhl GA-8(A)	14.41
Stinson SM-6B	10.89	Cunningham-Hall PT-6	16.16
Lockheed Vega-"Wasp"	10.28	Cessna CPW-6	12.84
Ryan "Brougham" B-7	12.22	C-R "Thrush J"	13.99
Boeing B-40-B4	29.14		
Flamingo G-2H	11.71		
1930		*1930*	
Fairchild 71A	12.68	Bellanca "Skyrocket"	12.37
Fairchild "Pilgrim 100"	12.19	Curtiss-Wright 6-B	13.19
Consolidated "Fleetster 17"	10.10	Bellanca "Airbus"	15.16
Boeing 221	20.10		
Northrop "Alpha"	10.84		
1931		*1931*	
Lockheed "Orion"	10.90	Bellanca "Aircruiser"	15.31
		Shamrock 3-6PW-300	9.86
		Curtiss-Wright CW-A6-A	12.44
		Simplex W-6	11.99
1932		*1932*	
(None)		Bellanca "Skyrocket F-2"	14.51
1933		*1933*	
(None)		Chamberlin C-82	10.47
		Solar M-S-2	14.52
1934		*1934*	
Vultee V-1-A	7.14	General GA-43A	10.96
		Northrop "Delta 1-A"	7.16
		Bellanca "Aircruiser" [a]	12.43
1935		*1935*	
(None)		Bellanca "Sr. Skyrocket"	15.84
		Bellanca "Sr. Pacemaker"	11.90
1936		*1936*	
(None)		Fairchild C-31	13.66

[a] A larger, heavier aircraft than the 1932 model of the same name.

sengers instead of the two carried by the 40A, but retained the principal function of providing a 1,000-pound mail and express payload. This was the equivalent of about four additional passengers so that, with a prorating of passenger costs and mail costs, the seat mile costs of the B-40-B4 would be perhaps half the indicated figure. It is true, nonetheless, that the B-40-B4 had relatively high costs, even with such a prorating. As late as 1932 only four of the 57 B-40-B4s in the total fleet were owned by airlines other than United, the successor company to Boeing Air Transport. Hence, an element of captive demand is suggested here as in the Fokker case.

The account of the Fokker F-14 is similar to that of the "Super Universal." Its use is explicable largely because of the Fokker-Western Air Express affiliation. Western purchased the original models and these were transferred to the newly established TWA at the time of the T.A.T.-Maddux-Western merger of 1930.[6] Only three F-14s were involved and TWA apparently retained them until the end of 1932. The F-14 was Fokker's last single-engined plane intended for commercial use.

Specific reasons for the failure of Thaden T-1 and the Cessna CPW-6 to gain acceptance are unknown, though the records do indicate possible explanations. Neither received an Approved Type Certificate, but this could have been due to either decisions by the companies not to seek such certification or to characteristics of the aircraft. The latter is a distinct possibility. Each of the planes was very small for the number of passengers to be carried.[7] Cessna moved from the CPW-6 to its DC-6 series, which were of about the same size but which had only four seats, including that of the pilot. The Thaden T-1, in addition to its size relative to planned passenger seats, was something of an experimental plane with all-metal construction in both frame and skin.

Among the 1930 single engined aircraft, estimated cost differences suggest that the Boeing 221 should not have gained use and that the Bellanca "Skyrocket" should have. The 221 is something of a special case. The 221 was a smooth, all metal, low wing design with retractable gear and an antidrag cowling. These should have made it more efficient than most of its contemporaries. Nonetheless, it was very heavy relative to its passenger capacity and had problems with the engine and propeller combination and the lack of a controllable-pitch propeller.[8] Only two were made. Both were substantially modified. Both were operated only by Boeing Air Transport and, later, by United Air Lines, the successor to Boeing Air Transport. While the cost estimates may be somewhat high, the 221, was not really a successful entrant. It was an error in acquisition from a cost standpoint, if not in terms of speed and range, and its use

[6] Correspondence with Peter M. Bowers.

[7] This is the reason, of course, the cost estimates derived here are as low as they are.

[8] See *Pedigree of Champions*, p. 31. The 221 may be compared to the Vultee V-1-A of 1934, which had many of the construction features of the 221. The Vultee weighed a bit more, carried nine rather than six passengers, and had a greater range and substantially higher wing loading. Its estimated costs, even using the single engine dummy variable, do not appear nearly so high as those for the 221.

seems accounted for only by the common ownership of the manufacturer and carrier.

The Bellanca "Skyrocket" was the CH-400, used for round-the-world and transoceanic competitions and for several sensational aviation stunts of the period.[9] In dimensions and performance, it was much like the Fairchilds and Stinsons. Bellanca, however, had a very poor record in efforts to gain acceptance for his aircraft, perhaps due to the retention of unusual design features developed in the early 1920s.[10]

The record of single-engined aircraft after the planes of 1930 is principally one of a few manufacturers continuing to develop such planes and of the domestic carriers acquiring only multiengined aircraft. The exceptions are the Lockheed "Orion," a 1931 design of which 12 planes remained in the 1932 fleets and the Vultee V-1-A of 1934. Both were quite special aircraft. The "Orion," like the "Vega," was of wood and plywood monocoque construction. But it had a low wing, hydraulically operated retractable landing gear and high wing loading for its time. It had a top speed of 215 miles per hour and cruised at 180 miles per hour or above. It had no equals among contemporary planes—multiengined as well as single—for high speed mail and passenger service.

The Vultee was acquired in only small numbers, mainly by American Airlines. It carried one or two fewer passengers than the Boeing 247 and the DC-2, but had quite comparable operating costs. In addition, it was considerably faster than any other commercial plane of the mid-thirties and had an exceptionally long range. Its smaller size and single engine account for its limited use. A number of lines retained the "Orions" and the Vultees for high-speed services up to 1936 and 1937.

The Northrop "Delta" is the only one among the last of the single engined commercial aircraft that approached the Vultee in performance. It rivaled the multiengined planes in operating costs. The "Delta" had a longer range than the Vultee, but it was smaller and slightly slower. The fact that it was not adopted by trunk carriers is explained just as is the limited demand for the Vultee. Presented with the need to emphasize safety in promoting air travel, the carriers were no longer interested in the single engined design.

The estimated costs of these planes suggest that technical changes which would create improved performance, higher capacity, and cost reductions within the single engine configuration had largely run their course by 1930. Operating costs for the 1931 through 1936 designs, excepting the "Orion" and the Vultee, are about the same as those of the earlier designs, excepting the Boeing 221 and B-40-B4. Lower costs and improved characteristics came from the switch to multiengined aircraft. So did a radical change in the structure of the market.

[9] See F. E. Ezquerro, "Bellanca's History Making Aircraft," *Journal of the American Aviation Historical Society* (Spring 1965), pp. 42–46.

[10] Additional comment is made on Bellanca aircraft in the concluding section of this chapter.

Cost Comparisons: Multiengined Aircraft
Prior to the Boeing 247

Paralleling the development of single engined aircraft from 1928 through 1932 was a series of early multiengined planes. Table 5-2 gives estimates of their costs.

In 1932, 63 Ford Trimotors, 28 Fokker F-10s, 26 Stinson Trimotors, 12 Boeing 80As, 9 Fokker F-32s, 9 Curtiss-Robertson "Kingbirds," and 5 Curtiss Condor COs remained in the fleets. Of these, the Fokker F-10s, the Boeing 80As, and the two Curtiss-affiliated planes have relatively high costs. The F-10, like the "Super Universal" and the F-14, was developed for Western Air Express, Fokker's parent company. Western was the only airline customer for the original model. Western purchased 10 new F-10As, a modification of the F-10, and subsequently acquired eight used F-10As from other fleets. Pan American and Universal Airlines (earlier Robertson Airlines, later merged into American Airlines) were apparently the only other commercial carriers to buy new F-10As.[11] Airlines operating them in 1932 were American (14),

Table 5-2

Estimated Operating Costs of Multiengined Aircraft Developed Prior to 1933 and Used by Domestic Trunk Lines and of Similar Aircraft Available but Not Used
(Cents Per Seat Mile, 1954 Dollars)

USED		NOT USED	
Aircraft and Year First Available	Estimated Operating Costs Per Seat Mile, Including Depreciation	Aircraft and Year First Available	Estimated Operating Costs Per Seat Mile, Including Depreciation
1928		*1928*	
Ford 4-AT	9.50	General 101-A	8.94
Fokker 10A	11.80		
1929		*1929*	
Ford 5-AT-C	7.92	Keystone K-47-D	14.28
Curtiss Condon CO	9.75	Keystone "Patrician"	7.78
Boeing 80A	10.81	Air Transport T-6	9.33
		Bach 3-CT-9	8.15
1930		*1930*	
Fokker F-32	6.55	Ogden "Osprey"	9.47
Stinson 6000A	8.31		
Curtiss-Robertson "Kingbird D-2"	9.39		
1931		*1931*	
(None)		Curtiss-Wright "Kingbird D-3"	10.00
1932			
Stinson U	9.43		

[11] Bowers, *American Fokkers*, p. 187.

Eastern (3), TWA (4), Transamerican (2), and General (later Western Airlines) (5). American had retained the F-10As originally acquired by Universal. TWA and General presumably shared the original Western Air Express fleet after the T.A.T.-Maddux and Western Air Express merger of 1930. Transamerican, a short-lived small carrier, and Eastern seem to have purchased second- and third-hand F-10As. In sum, the tie between Western and Fokker seems an important factor in the use of the F-10A, as it was in the use of other Fokker models.

Only 15 Boeing 80As (including four converted Boeing 80s and one converted 80B) were manufactured.[12] By 1932, twelve remained in the trunk line fleets, all of them operated by United. Again, the Boeing 80A owes its use to the orders of the parent Boeing Air Transport.[13]

The original airline demand for the Curtiss Condor CO and the Curtiss-Robertson D-3 may again reflect the close affiliations between carriers and certain manufacturers. Both are found in only the Eastern Air Transport fleet of 1932. Eastern was a subsidiary of North American Aviation Corporation, whose president was C. M. Keys. Keys was also president of the affiliated Curtiss Aeroplane and Motor Company, which controlled Curtiss-Wright, Curtiss-Robertson, and other aircraft manufacturers.[14]

Given the ties between manufacturers and carriers, the failure of the General 101-A, the Bach 3-CT-9, the Air Transport T-6, and the Ogden "Osprey" to gain acceptance perhaps needs little explanation. Indeed, even the early demand for the Fords came from the Ford-controlled Stout Airlines. The General 101-A, however, was much smaller and somewhat slower than were the multiengined planes actually used by the lines. In addition, it was a bimotor plane, which at the time would have been regarded as a disadvantage.[15] The Keystone K-47-D was very costly to operate. The "Patrician" was the largest airliner available in 1929. While the Fords and Fokkers were covered with metal and had cantilever wings, the "Patrician" was cloth-covered and had externally braced wings. This method of construction was probably its main disadvantage.[16]

[12] P. M. Bowers, *Boeing Aircraft Since* 1916 (1966), pp. 122–126.

[13] Richard Caves, *Air Transport and Its Regulators* (1962), p. 100, observes that, "Before United Air Lines was freed of its corporate ties to Boeing, it had suffered severely from its lack of freedom in equipment purchases. . . ." The reference is primarily to the subsequent period of the Boeing 247, but the cost estimates given here suggest that it was true prior to 1933 as well.

[14] R. E. G. Davies, *A History of the World's Airlines* (1964), pp. 48–49, and H. L. Smith, *Airways* (1942), p. 386.

[15] In its 1932 request to Douglas which led to the DC-1 and DC-2, TWA stipulated a trimotor because of its beliefs concerning passenger views on safety.

[16] The "Patrician" does not appear in any of the scheduled carriers' fleets in 1930's. It was used at least experimentally by Transcontinental Air Transport and Colonial Air Transport in 1929, however. See *Aircraft Year Book* (New York, 1930), pp. 35, 305. *Aviation* (November 1934), pp. 347–349, shows that Delta owned some Keystone aircraft in that year. All available evidence indicates that these were neither K-47's nor "Patricians" and that Delta's passenger service was conducted with Stinsons.

The Air Transport T-6 was a very small trimotor with no distinct advantages to offset its size disadvantage. The low-cost Bach 3-CT-9 could accommodate only 9 passengers. While this includes the use of the copilot's seat, the practice of using this seat for passengers was not uncommon in 1929. With this load, the Bach had lower estimated operating costs per seat mile than any of the early multiengined planes save for the Ford 5-AT series and the Fokker-32s.

The Ogden "Osprey" was so small, slow, and underpowered that its failure to find use among the trunks is not difficult to understand.

Cost Comparisons: A Digression on the
Early Single and Multiengined Aircraft

All the estimates of costs in Table 5-1 utilize the value found for the coefficient of the dummy variable for single-engined aircraft in the regression equations of Chapter 3. This is based on a single cost observation for the Lockheed "Vega" in 1932. Similarly, the values of Table 5-2 use the effect estimated for the early trimotors, which is based on two observations for Ford and one for the Boeing 80A. The data within each of these tables are internally consistent regardless of errors in the coefficients for the dummies, but comparisons between them depend on the relative sizes of the dummy coefficients being reasonably correct.

The "Vega," Table 5-1 shows, had lower operating costs than any of the single-engined planes used by the carriers except for the Consolidated "Fleetster 17" and the Vultee. While the average estimated cost of all single engined planes used is 13.13 cents per seat mile, that of the "Vega" is only 10.28 cents.[17] The average estimated costs of the Ford 5-AT-C (weighted twice) and the Boeing 80A is 8.8 cents; that of all the used multiengine aircraft in Table 5-2 is 9.12 cents. Thus, for the single engined planes, the sample value used in the cost regression is .78 of the average of all such planes which were used and, for multiengined, the sample value is .97 of the average for all such planes. Assuming no interaction between the effects of single and multiengined planes and the other effects estimated in the regression, it follows that the coefficients for the dummy variables should, if anything, be underestimated for the single engined aircraft relative to the multiengined.

This raises questions as to why the single engined planes were initially acquired and subsequently retained in the fleets. The two types of 1928 trimotors that remained in the 1932 fleets had average estimated seat mile operating costs of 10.65 cents, the three types of single engined, 12.78 cents. The lowest estimated costs among the single engined planes is higher than the highest costs among the trimotors. Similar averages for 1929 and 1930 single engined and multiengined planes are 9.07 cents versus 14.59 cents and 8.08

[17] All cost data are in 1954 dollars and as of the first model year unless otherwise indicated.

cents versus 12.74 cents. Even considering the effects of the extremely high and equally weighted values estimated for the Boeing B-40-B4 and Boeing 221 on the averages for the single engined planes, the multiengined planes appear to have had significantly lower operating cost per seat mile. In addition, the operating costs for the multiengined planes were tending to fall over time and their performance characteristics were, for the most part, better in all respects than were those of single engined planes.

The acquisition of the single engined aircraft can be appreciated when differences between seat mile and passenger mile operating costs are considered. The retention of these planes in the fleets can be appreciated when these differences and the difference between full and variable operating costs are considered. As late as 1932, the weighted average number of seats per aircraft used in scheduled domestic service was 6.6.[18] In the same year, the load factor was only 42 percent. That is, something less than three passengers were carried on an average plane mile of service. Even in 1932, many routes did not generate adequate passenger demand to justify the use of larger planes. A Ford Trimotor with fifteen-seat capacity and full operating costs of, say, 7.5 cents per seat mile would have had full costs of 22.5 cents per passenger mile if it experienced an average load of only five passengers on a given route. A Fokker "Super Universal," carrying the same five passengers, would have had full operating costs per passenger mile of roughly 13 cents. The Fokker's costs would be higher per seat mile but lower per passenger mile.

While data for the pre-1932 period are inadequate to present a formal analysis of passenger load and routes, it is safe to conjecture that the 1928, 1929, and 1930 passenger demand conditions justified the acquisition of single engined planes even more than did the 1932 situation. Indeed, after 1930, the trunk carriers acquired few, if any, single engined aircraft other than the Lockheed "Orion" and the Vultee V-1-A. These had definite performance advantages over the slower, multiengined planes. The carriers did, however, retain large numbers of previously acquired single engine planes that possessed no such performance advantages. The variable operating costs (that is, cost *ex* depreciation) of these planes was considerably lower than their full costs and lower than the full costs of multiengined replacements. For example, the variable operating costs per seat mile of the Fokker "Super Universal" in 1932 are estimated at 11.43 cents. This is not so low that, with the same load factor, it would not have been less costly to replace the Fokkers with some of the trimotors. But on many routes the load factor of larger planes would have been lower than that for planes such as the Fokker. A comparison of the *variable* passenger mile cost of the single engined planes with the *full* passenger mile costs of possible multiengined replacements would in many cases have shown the former to be more efficient.

The growth in passenger demand, which itself was shown in Chapter 4 to be positively related to the introduction of new planes, and the progressively

[18] *Handbook of Airline Statistics* (1965), p. 85.

lower costs of the multiengined aircraft after the late 1920s signalled the effective end of the market for new single engined planes. Through time, the advantage of even retaining single engined planes tended to disappear. Some manufacturers, nonetheless, continued the mistake of developing and attempting to market such planes to airline customers at least through 1936.

Cost Comparisons: Multiengined Aircraft After 1932

Table 5-3 provides estimates of the operating costs for a number of aircraft which were acquired and for others which were available but were not acquired by the trunk carriers in particular years from 1933 through 1965. The Air Mail Act of June 12, 1934, required that airlines competing for mail contract awards be separated from aircraft manufacturers. In the previous April, American, Eastern, and TWA had appeared in new corporate forms at air mail contract award meetings because the firms involved in the previous spoils conferences had been barred.[19] Of the aircraft shown in Table 5-3, however, the Boeing 247, the Curtiss "Condor" T-32 and the DC-2 were developed by manufacturers with direct or indirect airline affiliates and prior to the 1934 separation. Moreover, despite the formal separation of ownership after 1934, some planes were developed jointly by particular airlines and manufacturers and there is some evidence that favoritism and discrimination in the acceptance of orders and in delivery dates continued for many years.

The exclusive initial uses of the Boeing 247 by United and of the DC-2 by TWA are explicable in terms of the relations between the carriers and the manufacturers. New 247s were never delivered to any domestic commercial carrier other than United and its related companies. The other carriers who eventually used them received them through sales or lease from United.[20] At least the first 21 DC-2s went to TWA, but American and Eastern had numbers of them prior to the introduction of the DC-3 by American in 1936.

The "also rans" in the multiengined, modern airliners developed after 1932 do not appear until 1935. Many of those appearing as potential entrants were built by the same manufacturers as the earlier single engined and multiengined planes shown in Tables 5-1 and 5-2. A number of these continued to concentrate, it appears, on the development of the older types even after the Boeing 247 and the DC-2 were in service. Yet none of these, with the possible exception of the Stinson A Trimotor, was successful. The Stinson A, while retaining the welded steel frame and fabric-covered construction, was an unusually streamlined and modern-looking craft.

The Allan H. Lockheed "Alcor Duo-6" entry was small and constructed of

---

[19] Davies, *World's Airlines*, p. 130.

[20] V. D. Seely, "Boeing's Pacesetting 247," *Journal of the American Aviation Historical Society* (Winter 1964), pp. 244, 254–270.

Table 5-3

Estimated Operating Costs of Multiengined Aircraft Developed After 1932 and Used by Domestic Trunk Lines and of Similar Aircraft Available but Not Used (Cents Per Seat Mile, 1954 Dollars)

Year	Principal Multiengined Aircraft Acquired	Estimated Operating Costs of Acquired Aircraft	Multiengined Aircraft Newly Available But Not Acquired	Estimated Operating Costs of Unacquired Aircraft
1933	Boeing 247	7.78	(None)	
	Curtiss Condor T-32	7.30		
1934	DC-2	6.81	(None)	
	Stinson A	7.92 [a]		
	Lockheed L-10A	4.70		
1935	DC-2	6.61	Alcor Duo-6	6.45
	Lockheed L-10B	4.70	Bellanca "Air Transport"	5.11
			Burnelli UB-14	5.53
1936	DC-3	3.28	Stinson B	7.38
	Lockheed L-10B	4.56	Kinner "Invader"	6.48
	Lockheed L-12	5.95	Crusader AG-7	n.a.
1937	DC-3	3.19	Air Transport B-6	5.81
	Lockheed L-14	4.77		
	Beech 18	5.57		
1938	DC-3	3.09	Air Transport B-8	4.35
	Lockheed L-14	4.63	Barkley-Grow T8P-1	3.73
1939	DC-3	3.00	(None)	
	Lockheed L-10B	4.17		
1940	DC-3	2.91	Burnelli CB-34	4.47
	Lockheed L-18	4.74	Douglas DC-5	5.18
	Boeing 307	3.22	Curtiss-Wright Transport	3.88
			Lockheed L-144	2.92
			Consolidated "Landplane"	n.a.
1941	DC-3	2.83		
	Lockheed L-18	4.60		
1946	DC-4	2.35	Lockheed 75-72 "Saturn"	2.76
	Lockheed L-049	2.84	Hughes "Feederliner"	n.a.
			Douglas DC-8	2.87 [b]
			Consolidated CV-37	2.00
			Republic RC-2 "Rainbow"	3.06
1947	DC-6	2.17	Hughes H-4	n.a.
	L-749	2.51	Lockheed "Constitution"	n.a.
	Martin 202	2.53		
	DC-4	2.28		
1948	CV-240	2.51	Beech "Twin-Quad"	n.a.
	DC-6	2.11	Douglas DC-9	n.a.
	Martin 202	2.46		
	Lockheed L-749	2.43		

Table 5-3 (Continued)

Year	Principal Multiengined Aircraft Acquired	Estimated Operating Costs of Acquired Aircraft	Multiengined Aircraft Newly Available But Not Acquired	Estimated Operating Costs of Unacquired Aircraft
1951	DC-6B	1.99	Chase YC-122	3.21
	Martin 404	2.38		
	Lockheed L-1049	1.84		
	Boeing 377	2.39		
1952	Martin 404	2.31	Chase C-123B	2.49
	CV-340	2.58		
	DC-6B	1.93		
	Lockheed L-1049	1.72		
1953	CV-340	2.50	Douglas R4D-8	2.11
	Lockheed L-1049C	1.86		
	DC-7A	1.80		
	DC-6B	1.88		
1958	DC-7C	2.23	Stroukoff YC-134A	n.a.
	Viscount 812	1.57 [c]		
	Martin 404	1.92		
	Lockheed L-1649	2.37		
1959	Lockheed L-188	2.10	Convair 600	n.a.
	Boeing 707	1.70		
	DC-8	1.41		
1960	Convair 880	1.73	(None)	
	Boeing 720	1.54		
1961	SUD 210	1.66	(None)	
	Boeing 720-B	1.43		
1962	Convair 990	1.55	(None)	
1964	Boeing 727	1.14	(None)	
1965	BAC-111	1.55	(None)	
	DC-9	1.55 [d]		

[a] Arbitrary estimate. The "A" was a trimotor, with drag creating struts and non-retractable landing gear. It incorporated, however, many other features of the then modern airfoil and frame.

[b] The Douglas DC-8, of 1946, and the DC-9, of 1948, have no relations to the subsequent jet aircraft of the same designations.

[c] Estimated from 1958 operating costs of Viscount 745 and 1965 ratio of Viscount 745 and 812 operating costs.

[d] Based on two weeks of operation in December, 1965.

wood and plywood. Its estimated operating costs, while roughly equivalent to those of the larger, faster DC-2, were well above those of the slightly larger and faster Lockheed L-10 series. The Bellanca "Air Transport" attempt was for a sesquiplane—a design with full upper wing and an upward-slanting short lower wing which served also as the main strut. It seems to have promised relatively low operating costs, but it had, aside from its unusual appearance, wood frame and fabric wings and a steel tube and fabric fuselage. If the unusual design and the existence of the more efficient L-10s were not enough to prevent its adoption, the more rigid safety inspections of the 1930s would have been.[21] The "Condor" T-32 and the Stinson A gained limited use prior to the availability of more efficient, all-metal, low-wing planes. The "Air Transport," coming almost two years later, did not have this time advantage.

The 1935 Burnelli UB-14 was the result of over a decade of development work on aircraft with airfoil-shaped fuselages.[22] It promised operating costs as low as those of the DC-2, but it was a most unusual plane. The UB-14 was slightly larger and considerably more costly to operate than the L-10. It was constructed of duralumin, with twin monocoque boomtype fuselages aft of the passenger cabin and a twin vertical rudder assembly. While offered for sale at least through 1938, none of the trunk lines acquired the type.

Table 5-3 shows that the operating costs per seat mile for the DC-3—in long range use—were well below those of any other contemporary aircraft.[23] Successful entry after 1938, to the extent that it depended on the development of a plane with seat mile costs as low as those of the DC-3, required a larger jump in cost-reducing technology than had previously been the case. And exits from the market had been exceeding entrants in the previous period.

The Air Transport B-6 and B-8 seem to have been aimed more at the short-stage length market. Both were made of wood, steel tube, and fabric and both were relatively small. In appearance, there was a resemblance between them and some of the earlier Stinsons. Neither seems to have yielded a cost or performance advantage.

The 1938 Barkley-Grow T8P-1 was a duralumin aircraft. Its estimated costs were below those of the L-10, but well above those of the DC-3 in longer-range operation. Since it had only eight places, including seats for pilot and copilot, it was considerably smaller than even the L-10. The T8P-1 was constructed with an unusual wing with multiple, thin sheet-metal spars. It had a retractable landing gear, but otherwise looked much like the Beech 18 or Lockheed 12. It had no obvious performance advantages.[24]

Lockheed, notably successful with the L-10s, had less success with its immediately subsequent designs. Only three L-12s were acquired by the trunk lines. Nine L-14s were used by 1938, all by Northwest Airlines which thereafter sold them. The L-18 of 1940 was acquired in only small numbers by United, Continental, Mid-Continent, and National. One Beechcraft 18, a plane quite similar in appearance to the L-12 but with much higher operating

---

[21] Wood construction in commercial aircraft had been discouraged by safety standards as early as 1930. See *Handbook of Airline Statistics* (1965), p. 505, under the discussion of the Fokker F-32.

[22] C. H. Gibbs-Smith, *The Aeroplane: An Historical Survey* (1960), indicates that Burnelli had developed a biplane with a life-augmenting fuselage as early as 1924.

[23] In the next section it is shown that the operating costs per passenger mile for the Lockheed L-10 for passenger loads of 10 or less were probably less than those for the DC-3.

[24] See *The Aircraft Year Book* (1938), pp. 155–157.

costs, was acquired by TWA in 1937. Its only other use by trunk lines was in 1943 and 1944 when the World War II shortage of planes existed.

From 1940 on, attempts at entry by substantially new firms were rare. Aircraft manufacturers other than the few which by then produced nearly all United States transport and bomber aircraft disappeared from the list of those supplying potential new types of commercial planes. This is discussed further in Chapter 6. Some transports came quite directly from the development of military planes. The Boeing 307, for example, was developed from the 299 bomber, which eventually became the B-17. The 307, the first four-engined land-type transport in domestic use, "differed from early production B-17s mainly in the fuselage." [25] Only ten were made. Their advantages over the DC-3 were in size, speed, and range. The 307 was also the first commercial plane with a pressurized cabin. The operating costs of the 307s were relatively high, however.

Other generally unsuccessful planes were developed by experienced transport producers. Douglas' DC-5, a small, tricycle-geared, high wing monoplane, presumably intended for short-stage lengths and feederlines, had high estimated operating costs. KLM and the U.S. Navy bought a few models; no United States commercial carrier bought any. The 1940 Curtiss Transport entry was a larger, longer-range plane which became the CW-20, or C-46, cargo plane. Its having but two engines was a disadvantage even at the time of its appearance. The military was again the main purchaser.

Some of these developments—successful and unsuccessful—were supported by the carriers. The latter had demonstrated interest in larger, four-engined aircraft for long-range use well before the appearance of the Boeing 307 and the CW-20, but the development of the desired types was lengthy. Their use in commercial transport service was ultimately postponed by World War II. The form which the carriers' interest took adversely affected the ability of some manufacturers to enter this market. For example, the success of the DC-3 led five domestic carriers to provide financial support to Douglas for the DC-4. The prototype—called the DC-4E—had a tricycle undercarriage and three vertical fins and rudders. It first flew in June 1938. It had accommodations for 40 passengers but was rejected by the carriers, probably because of high costs associated with the drag of a wing with a low loading and with the high gross weight per seat. United and American continued their support even after the failure of the DC-4E version. Quantity production of the final version of the DC-4 planes was begun in 1940 without another prototype. The final DC-4 involved a wing load of 50.1 pounds rather than the 30 pounds of the DC-4E. The 50 pound load is about twice that of the DC-3. The DC-4 was typically equipped with 54 seats, more than double those in the DC-3. It was not pressurized. But, whatever the aircraft's characteristics, other potential entrants were undoubtedly impeded by the carriers' ties with the Douglas project.

[25] See *Pedigree of Champions*, p. 46.

TWA, which was initially in the consortium backing the Douglas DC-4, joined Pan American in support of a Lockheed transport. The Lockheed L-144 was one of the results. Though the L-144 would apparently have had low cost relative to all existing planes except the DC-3, it was inferior for long-range use to the rival DC-4 then being developed by Douglas. The much larger Lockheed L-049, the first of the "Constellations," was the aircraft ordered by TWA and Pan American, but the partially assembled planes were requisitioned by the government as C-69s after December 7, 1941.

The pre-1941 development of the L-049 with support from carriers as large as TWA and Pan Am suggests that the Douglas' dominance of the new aircraft market might have been broken even had World War II not occurred. The pattern of cooperative development arrangements between the lines and aircraft manufacturers could hardly have fostered attempts at entry by a large number of manufacturers, however. For a limited period, the war did have just such an effect. The principal attempts were by Consolidated, Hughes, Martin, and Republic, all of which had large production volumes of military aircraft during the war. Hughes, Consolidated, and Martin, along with Lockheed and Douglas, developed short-range and intermediate range designs even while surplus DC-3s (C-47s) flooded the postwar market for used aircraft. The Lockheed "Saturn" had a wing load of only 35.9 pounds; the Douglas "DC-8," 35.9 pounds. The planes were very different in size, but both promised high operating costs relative to DC-3s and DC-4s. Thus, the most successful prewar commercial aircraft manufacturers contributed unsuccessful short-range entries in the immediate postwar period. Martin and Consolidated (then Convair) developed the 202 and CV-240, with wing loads of 46.2 and 49.6 pounds, respectively. These had operating costs below those of the DC-3 even in short-range use.[26]

Consolidated, Hughes, Republic, and Boeing were the major aspirants in supplying new types of long-range aircraft, but Douglas and Lockheed, with the DC-8 and L-749 and their successor models, were the only manufacturers to achieve substantial use by the domestic fleets. The projected Consolidated-Vultee CV-37 was an enormous aircraft, with gross weight and passenger capacity exceeding those of the Boeing 707 and the DC-8. The CV-37 was based on the XC-99 military transport and was to be powered by six pusher-type engines. The planned horsepower of these engines was greater than that of any piston engine ever successfully developed for commercial transports. The CV-37 concept was, in short, beyond the technical capabilities of the time to produce an efficient aircraft of this size. The same is true of the even larger H-4 described by Hughes Aircraft in the same year.

[26] Note that the 1946 cost estimate for the DC-3 assumes short-range operation. This conforms with the uses then made of that plane. The 1947 estimate of DC-3 short-range operating costs, *ex* depreciation, is 3.10 cents per seat mile as against full operating costs of 2.53 cents per seat mile for the Martin 202. Where passenger loads were light, however, the DC-3 would still have had lower costs per passenger mile than did the Martins and Convairs. It was still being used by trunk lines as late as 1965.

The Republic RC-2 "Rainbow" was ordered by Pan American and American Airlines, but none was delivered for commercial use. While the plane promised greater speed and longer range than the DC-6 or the L-749, its great weight per seat indicates that it would have been very costly to operate. To a lesser extent, the same advantages and disadvantages marked the Boeing 377. This aircraft came from the development of the B-29 bomber and the C-97 military cargo plane. A total of fifty-six 377s were manufactured, with a maximum of only sixteen appearing in any year in the domestic trunk line fleets.

Between the introduction of the DC-6B and the L-1049 in 1951 and the use of jets in late 1958, only the Chase and Stroukoff attempts at entry appear from other than the established commerical aircraft manufacturers. None of the Chase-Stroukoff planes offered cost or quality advantages over existing planes. After transfer of the Chase C-123B design to Fairchild in 1953, the plane was procured in quantity as a troop carrier by the Tactical Air Command. TAC also acquired a trial batch of YC-122s.

The last of the long-range piston-engined planes to be added to the fleets, the DC-7C and the Lockheed L-1649, are notable because of their operating costs. Rather than reducing operating costs over previous models they tended to cause them to rise.[27] In terms of entry by existing producers with variants of older models, the last stretch of each of the types was not notably successful.

The Boeing 707 and the DC-8 produced a sharp reduction in full operating costs per seat mile. The only other domestic entries or attempts at entry were the Convair 880 and 990, with crudely estimated first year operating costs of 1.73 cents in 1960 and of 1.55 cents in 1962, respectively.[28] Neither of the Convair models seems to have operatings costs as low as those of the Boeing 707 or DC-8 in the same calendar year. Both of the Convairs went out of production shortly after initial orders were filled.

Technical Change and Entry into the Market for Commercial Aircraft

No attention has as yet been paid to the primary sources of the changes in technology represented by the changes in costs and operating characteristics of the aircraft surveyed. Nonetheless some conclusions concerning the effects of these on successful entry into the market can be suggested. Attention focuses first on the rather small number of successful new aircraft which were

[27] See Caves, *Air Transport*, pp. 150, 310, and Gellman, *Effect of Regulation*, pp. 387–403. Gellman notes that the domestic operators of the planes—Braniff, Northwest, and TWA—were aware of the higher costs prior to ordering them. The range performance of the planes was the important consideration for the carriers.

[28] For reasons discussed in Chapter 3, the estimates of costs for these planes are more uncertain than are those for others. If it had been assumed in Chapter 3 that the operating costs of the 880 fell as rapidly as those of either the 707 or DC-8, the estimates of its 1960 costs would be even higher, since the cost estimate for that year is a backward extrapolation.

introduced and used in quantity by the domestic carriers. Differences among them are the principal subject of the next chapter; differences between them and the unsuccessful planes are important here.

Aircraft whose quantity use seems predicated solely on ownership relations between manufacturers and particular carriers rather than on cost and performance are omitted from consideration. Aside from these, the obvious planes which fall in the successful category up to 1965 are the Ford Trimotors, DC-2, DC-3, Lockheed L-10, DC-4, DC-6 and DC-6B, Lockheed L-049, 649, 749 and 1049, Boeing 707 and 720, DC-8 and the Boeing 727. The history in each of these cases shows that the seat mile operating costs of the aircraft when it was introduced were substantially below those of aircraft in use for the same purpose and, except for the ties between Douglas and Lockheed from 1947 to 1955 and between Douglas and Boeing from 1958 on, below those of other planes being contemporaneously developed. In some but not all of these cases, the operating costs, including depreciation, of the new and successful planes were lower than the operating costs, excluding depreciation, of the planes then in use in the fleets. The cost effects, supplemented in most instances by other performance improvements and by the demonstrated effect of new types of planes on passenger demand, were such that the new aircraft were demanded for replacement of existing models as well as for fleet expansion. The really successful entries, that is, embodied something of a quantum leap in technology. They have not typically arisen from innovations incorporating slight and continuous technical improvements and yielding only small reductions in costs. Another characteristic of these aircraft is that their operating costs tend to fall through at least substantial parts of their model life. Indeed, in no instance was there evidence that the operating costs of the planes with major market success tended to rise except, as discussed below, when attempts were made to stretch successful versions to achieve, in at least some dimensions, improvements in performance.

These factors create obstacles to successful entry and consequent tendencies for market concentration. While it is undoubtedly true that particular aircraft have been added to the fleets because of noncost aspects of performance and because of the influence of new equipment on passenger demand, the record over the years is strong in suggesting that, in the absence of favorable cost behavior, none or only a few of any new type of aircraft is demanded.[29]

The data also suggest that to enter the market in any depth the manufacturer of a new model cannot simply duplicate the basic technology of then successful planes. The duplication of a technology embodied in existing aircraft would yield a new plane with operating costs at least equal to and likely higher than those of the planes then in the fleets. Duplication by the entering manufacturer is unlikely to be so complete that the reduction in costs arising from the learning involved in the use of the existing planes can be captured. Effective entry—entry that leads to acquisitions of quantities of the new type

---

[29] *Cf.* Caves, *Air Transport*, Chapter 13, and the analysis that follows.

—seems to require a major change in technology which creates substantial cost advantages and, undoubtedly, other performance advantages for the carriers using the new type.

Tending to offset this obstacle to entry is an apparent proclivity on the part of the once successful manufacturers to remain too long with the basic technology of their original success. The Ford Trimotor, for example, was being modified to accommodate new engines and to offer different passenger compartments through at least August of 1931. The underlying technology of the originally successful 1926 version and the Stout designs on which it was based were not fundamentally changed. Much the same is true of the only slightly less successful Stinson aircraft. The Stinson trimotors continued in development until 1934; the single engined Stinson transports evolved into the Reliant series sold in the market for private aircraft. Not until 1936 did Stinson attempt a two-engined, low-wing monoplane, and this was a failure in the commerical aircraft market.

Douglas stretched the DC-2 to the DC-3 with unparalleled success. After World War II an attempt was made to market the "Super DC-3" and other new aircraft with wing loads and performance attributes not distinctly different from those of the DC-3 technology. None was commercially successful.

The progression from the DC-4 to the DC-7 is more remarkable. The DC-4 grew from design efforts which began in 1936.[30] After failure with the DC-4E, the DC-4 of 1942 was conceived. It was stretched to the DC-6 with design work apparently beginning in 1944. This was subsequently stretched again to the DC-6B and ultimately to the DC-7A, 7B, and 7C. The changes have been lauded as the "kind of phenomenal accomplishment that is possible using the same wing and fuselage of an airplane design that has been laid down with a sharp eye on the future." [31] The result, however, was a slowing in the rate at which the newer Douglas models lowered operating costs, with the last of the group actually having higher rather than lower seat mile costs. Sticking to the DC-4 and DC-6 technology by Douglas opened an opportunity for others to introduce more substantial innovations.

Lockheed, though somewhat less dramatically, followed the same pattern with the L-049 to L-1649 series. The stretching was carried on to the point that Lockheed was left with no commercial aircraft production after 1960.[32] The Lockheed case is less clear, perhaps, because of the introduction of the L-188 "Electra" turboprop shortly after the L-1649, but even that plane did not embody such new technologies as to produce the cost and performance characteristics essential to a lengthy period of market success. Lockheed had attempted much the same thing with the L-10. Modifications in the form of the L-12, L-14, and L-18 were made, yet none was as successful as the original L-10.

[30] See "Design Growth," *The Aircraft Yearbook* (1951), p. 257.
[31] *Ibid.*
[32] At this writing, Lockheed is attempting to re-enter the market with the L-1011 jumbo-jet.

The record of the misses and near-misses shows the tendency for some firms to adhere to given technologies despite market evidence signalling the need for change. The Bellanca history is an obvious case.[33] Guiseppi Bellanca was responsible for several important aerodynamic innovations of the early 1920s. He was successful in producing several models which, for the time, were held to be remarkably efficient and reliable. One was considered by Lindbergh for his transoceanic solo flight. The same plane, piloted by Clarence Chamberlin and carrying one passenger, crossed the Atlantic two weeks after the Spirit of St. Louis and flew 300 miles further to land in Germany.

Bellanca, however, seems to have been unwilling or unable to deviate from the features of his early planes which, no matter how efficient and reliable by the standards of 1927, were small and decidedly ungainly in appearance relative to other planes a year or so later. The "Pacemaker" of 1929 and 1930 did find some buyers among commercial carriers. This plane was followed by the "Skyrocket" (1930), the "Airbus" (1930), the "Aircruiser" (1931), the "Aircruiser" (1934), the "Sr. Skyrocket" (1935), the "Sr. Pacemaker" (1935), and the "Air Transport" (1935). None found commercial success. The last was Bellanca's only multiengined entry and came nearly a decade after the trimotors had been introduced and five years after the carriers had all but given up the acquisition of any single engined planes.

The possibility of entry by a particular manufacturer into the commercial market is not independent of demand in other markets. For example, fourteen of the Bellanca "Airbus" C-27s were purchased as military transports. Many other actual and potential entrants into the commercial aircraft market were similarly aided by orders from the government, including Beechcraft, Boeing, Cessna, Chase, Douglas, Stinson (Stinson Division, Aviation Manufacturing Corporation; later Stinson Division of Consolidated Vultee), Convair, Curtiss, Fairchild, Fokker, Lockheed, Northrop, Republic, and Vultee.[34] Procurement of aircraft technologically related to commercial transports and procurement in the form of military research and development contracts has also had the effect of increasing the probability of entry into the commercial transport market. This is a subject treated in more detail in Chapter 7. The tendency in recent years for the government to procure fewer types of aircraft, to procure smaller numbers of the selected types, and to divert research and development from manned aircraft to rockets and aerospace projects has lowered the probability of new model entry from other than the existing producers of military and commercial planes. An unsuccessful attempt at entry into the commercial market which is not offset by orders for technically related military aircraft or by technically related military research and development carries such drastic financial penalties that further attempts are effectively foreclosed.

[33] See F. E. Ezquerro, "Bellanca."

[34] F. G. Swanborough, with P. M. Bowers, *United States Military Aircraft Since 1909* (1963).

Aircraft Choice and Technology: The Hits and Near Misses

Introduction

The problems inherent in producing new types of aircraft for the trunk line market, it is contended, create forces tending toward high market concentration and changing relative positions of leading firms. The quantum leaps in technology that have characterized the differences between successive generations of aircraft have meant that some firms—by failing to leap far enough, by attempting to leap too far, or by leaping in what proved to be wrong directions or at wrong times—have failed or sustained losses in market position. In the absence of offsetting factors such as military R and D and aircraft procurement, both of which have maintained the economic viability and technical capabilities of a number of firms, the tendency toward concentration would have been more obvious.

It has been true thus far that more than one firm has survived each of the technological leaps. The Ford, Stinson, and Fokker trimotors shared the pre-1932, multiengined market. Boeing, Douglas, and Lockheed produced the 247, DC-2, and L-10 reasonably contemporaneously. The DC-4, DC-6, and DC-7 were rivaled by the Lockheed 049, 749, 1049, and 1649 series. The 707 and the DC-8 entered the jet market at roughly the same time. The one rather clear exception to there being two or more producers of aircraft of approximately the same technical and cost characteristics is the case of the DC-3.

This chapter examines the factors that have affected the numbers of new aircraft types acquired by the domestic trunk carriers. The objective is to provide, insofar as possible, explanations for the year-to-year changes in concentration and, with such explanations, to indicate the importance of technological change in the changing market. Emphasis in the previous chapter was on the failures and mistakes among new aircraft; emphasis here is on the successful ones.

The Period Prior to World War II

As noted previously, up to 1934 many new transport aircraft were produced by firms under common control with the carriers. This led, it appears, to the use of some planes—especially Fokkers, Boeings, and Stinsons—that would presumably not otherwise have been used or, at least, would have been used in smaller numbers if the carriers had been more free to select among alternatives. The common control up to 1934 results in there being little purpose in formal statistical analysis of aircraft choices made prior to at least that year. The influences arising from the interlocking relationships, as the data in the previous chapter indicate, tended to override the influences of cost or performance advantages.

From 1936 until the United States entered World War II, the DC-3 dominated the market for new commercial planes. The extent of this dominance is shown in Table 6-1. Aside from ten L-10 "Electras" and three L-12s, all delivered in 1936 but undoubtedly ordered prior to the introduction of the DC-3, only 29 aircraft other than DC-3s were added to the trunk line fleets after the appearance of the latter and up to World War II. Consequently, statistical analysis of this period would be largely meaningless. Whatever the aircraft characteristics used to compare the DC-3 with others—cost, size, speed— that characteristic would appear statistically significant in explaining the Douglas market share so long as the DC-3 differed from other aircraft with respect to this characteristic.

Table 6-1

Estimated Deliveries of Newly Produced Aircraft to Domestic Trunk Carriers, 1936–1941.

Year	Total Deliveries of New Aircraft	Deliveries of Particular Types						
		DC-3	L-10	L-12	L-14	L-18	Beechcraft 18	B-307
1936	42	29	10	3	—	—	—	—
1937	54	47	—	—	6	—	1	—
1938	24	21	—	—	3	—	—	—
1939	41	40	1	—	—	—	—	—
1940	112	95	—	—	—	12	—	5
1941	36	35	—	—	—	1	—	—
Total	309	267	11	3	9	13	1	5

The DC-3 was not at the time of its appearance the largest or the fastest or the longest-ranged aircraft the carriers had ever used. Neither was it the only all-metal, low-wing plane with retractable gear, variable-pitch propellers and other modern equipment. It was, rather, among the largest and fastest and longest-ranged planes. It was, more importantly, an aircraft which combined other desirable technical characteristics in a way which resulted in much lower operating costs per seat mile than were those of any other plane up to that time. Its seat mile costs were, in fact, so much lower than those of alternative aircraft that even with a relatively low load factor its passenger mile costs were often lower than those for other planes.

Estimates of the seat mile operating costs for different stage lengths for the DC-3 and for other planes in use at the time of its introduction are shown in Table 6-2. Because stage length data are unavailable for years prior to 1948, the overall mean value used in preparing the cost estimates in Table 6-2 was found by an extrapolation to 1936 of a regression of the ratio of passenger trip length to flight stage length on time for the years 1948 through 1964.[1] The resulting estimate for 1936 is 144 miles.

[1] Passenger trip length is the weighted average number of miles from origin to destination (one way) for each passenger trip. Stage length is the number of miles between each sched-

Table 6-2

Estimated Direct Operating Costs, Excluding and Including Depreciation, of Multiengine Aircraft in 1936 Trunk Line Fleets (Cents Per Seat Mile, 1954 Dollars).

Aircraft Type		Stage Length (miles)							
		100	*200*	*300*	*400*	*500*	*600*	*700*	*800*
DC-2	(Ex. Dep)	4.89	4.14	3.89	3.79	3.71	—	—	—
	(Inc. Dep)	6.47	5.72	5.47	5.37	5.29	—	—	—
DC-3	(Ex. Dep)	3.04	2.53	2.38	2.29	2.24	2.20	2.18	2.16
	(Inc. Dep)	3.91	3.40	3.25	3.16	3.11	3.07	3.05	3.03
B-80A	(Ex. Dep)	5.88	5.16	4.93	4.80	—	—	—	—
	(Inc. Dep)	7.42	6.70	6.47	6.34	—	—	—	—
B-247D	(Ex. Dep)	5.70	4.76	4.44	4.30	4.20	—	—	—
	(Inc. Dep)	7.41	6.47	6.15	6.01	5.91	—	—	—
L-10B	(Ex. Dep)	3.54	2.96	2.77	2.67	2.60	—	—	—
	(Inc. Dep)	4.70	4.12	3.93	3.83	3.76	—	—	—
L-12B	(Ex. Dep)	5.36	4.40	4.11	3.95	3.83	3.77	3.73	—
	(Inc. Dep)	6.98	6.02	5.73	5.57	5.45	5.39	5.35	—
Stinson A	(Ex. Dep)	7.65	6.52	6.11	5.90	5.83	5.75	—	—
	(Inc. Dep)	9.94	8.81	8.40	8.19	8.12	8.04	—	—
Condor T-32	(Ex. Dep)	4.70	4.02	3.77	3.67	3.59	—	—	—
	(Inc. Dep)	6.33	5.65	5.40	5.30	5.26	—	—	—
Ford 5-AT	(Ex. Dep)	5.91	5.22	5.02	4.92	4.83	—	—	—
	(Inc. Dep)	8.00	7.31	7.11	7.01	6.92	—	—	—

The costs of the particular aircraft for different stage lengths are based on the regression equations of Chapter 3, with additional assumptions concerning the stage length of the individual aircraft to which the underlying cost observations pertain. To allow for the fact that longer-range aircraft can be used for short-stage lengths but that short-range aircraft cannot be used for stage lengths in excess of their maximum ranges, it was assumed that the mean stage-length at which costs for particular planes are observed in any year are to the mean stage-length of all planes in that year as the square of the range of the particular plane is to the mean of the squares of the ranges of all planes. From this assumption it was estimated that, in 1936, the stage lengths underlying the cost estimates of particular planes given in Chapter 3 are those given in Table 6-3.

Using these assumed stage lengths and the cost estimates of Chapter 3 as the base, the seat mile costs of operating the types at different stage lengths were estimated by assuming that seat mile costs, excluding depreciation, for

uled takeoff and landing. The regression is $\hat{y} = .0312 - 3.988(t)$, $R^2 = .95$, where y is the ratio of average trip length (.238) to average stage length and t is time, 1932 = 0.

each type tend to be constant per hour of operation for the type. Then, assuming time lost in each stage in climb, descent and taxiing amounted to 0.26 hours and that actual distance flown equalled 1.02 times the reported stage length,[2] the figures in Table 6-2 can be calculated.

The remarkable thing about the DC-3—and large errors in the cost estimates and the assumptions concerning stage lengths would be required to alter this—is that it had lower costs per seat mile at all stage lengths than did any other aircraft of the time, new or old. Its seat mile costs, including depreciation, were lower than the same costs, excluding depreciation, for all planes except the Lockheed L-10. Thus, ignoring differences in load factors, it appears that the DC-3 would have been purchased as promptly as possible to replace all planes except the L-10.

Table 6-3

Estimated Mean Stage Length of Aircraft
Types in Use in 1936 Trunk Line Fleets.

Aircraft Type	Estimated Mean Stage Length
DC-2	105 miles
DC-3	269
B-80A	89
B-247D	105
L-10	105
L-12	216
Stinson A	173
Condor T-32	105
Ford 5-AT	128

Loads, however, varied greatly among the carriers in 1936, as shown in Table 6-4. Continental Airlines (Varney Air Transport at that time) averaged only 1.6 passengers per flight on its sole route between Pueblo and El Paso. It continued to operate a Lockheed "Vega" through 1937 and purchased three, six-place Lockheed L-12s in 1936. The line later bought L-14s and L-18s; it did not acquire DC-3s until 1944. Similarly, National Airlines, operating 237 route miles between Jacksonville and St. Petersburg, averaged only 1.8 passengers per flight in 1936. It had a fleet of six aircraft. Between 1936 and 1941, National acquired L-10s and L-18s. It is the only domestic trunk carrier never to have operated the DC-3.

American Eastern, TWA, and United were the first carriers to purchase the 21 passenger DC-3. Table 6-5 shows that all 76 DC-3s in service at the end of 1937 were operated by these lines. In 1938, three DC-3s were delivered to Western Airlines. In 1939, Braniff, Colonial, Pennsylvania-Central, and Northwest received the aircraft for the first time.

[2] W. C. Mentzer and H. E. Nourse, "Some Economic Aspects of Transport Aircraft Performance," Part II, *Journal of the Aeronautical Sciences* (May 1940), p. 302, is the source for these parameters.

The tendencies for the quantities of DC-3s purchased and for the years in which they were first acquired to vary with the number of passengers per flight are obvious.[3] This reflects the high cost per passenger mile of operating the 21 passenger DC-3s on routes with low passenger demand. Estimates of these costs for the DC-3, DC-2, L-10, L-12, and B-247D for 100 mile and for 500 mile stage lengths and for passenger loads varying from two to the capacities of the aircraft are given in Table 6-6. At capacity—where passenger miles and seat miles are identical—the passenger mile costs given are those of Table 6-2. The costs shown for the other passenger levels increase proportionately with the decrease in the assumed load factor.

The cost advantages of the DC-3 relative to other planes appear more limited in Table 6-6 than they do in Table 6-2. The plane was developed specifically for the long-range operations of American Airlines, as a replace-

Table 6-4

Passengers per Flight, Seats per Plane, Estimated Load Factors and Fleet Sizes of Domestic Trunk Carriers, 1936.

	Passengers per Flight [a]	Seats per Plane	Estimated Load Factor	Planes in Fleet
Big Four				
American	8.0	14.9	.54	63
Eastern	7.5	17.4	.43	25
TWA	9.1	13.0	.70	36
United	6.9	12.5	.55	46
Other Trunk Carriers				
Braniff	4.3	9.1	.47	13
Chicago & Southern	3.6	8.3	.43	6
Continental	1.6	5.8	.28	4
Delta	3.2	9.5	.34	4
Inland	2.1	9.6	.22	5
Mid-Continent	2.5	8.5	.29	8
National	1.8	12.0	.15	6
Northeast	3.5	12.0	.29	6
Northwest	4.9	10.0	.49	12
Penna-Central	5.5	12.0	.46	10
Western	5.3	10.0	.53	11
Total [b]	6.4	11.3	.57	260

[a] Passenger miles per plane mile.
[b] Includes National Parks Airways which is not shown separately.
Source: Aviation (April 1937), p. 77.

[3] There is significant statistical association between the number of DC-3s owned in 1941 and the number of passengers carried per flight in 1936. The coefficient is determination is +.66, but the distributions of the variables are distinctly nonnormal.

Table 6-5

Number of DC-3s in Fleets of Domestic Trunk Line Carriers, 1936–1941.

	1936	1937	1938	1939	1940	1941
American	20	29	30	44	76	79
Eastern	2	5	10	15	34	40
TWA	0	13	19	22	24	29
United	7	29	35	35	50	54
Brandiff	0	0	0	3	8	11
Chicago & Southern	0	0	0	0	5	6
Colonial [a]	—	—	—	2	4	4
Continental	0	0	0	0	0	0
Delta	0	0	0	0	1	5
Inland	0	0	0	0	0	0
Mid-Continent	0	0	0	0	0	0
National	0	0	0	0	0	0
Northeast	0	0	0	0	0	3
Northwest	0	0	0	7	13	11
Penna-Central	0	0	0	6	13	18
Western	0	0	3	3	4	7
Total	29	76	97	137	232	267

[a] Operations began in 1939.

ment for the 16-passenger Condor II. It appears, however, that the lower costs of the DC-3 came not from whatever design differences gave the DC-3 greater range. Rather, the lower costs came from the design changes which permitted the comfortable carrying of additional passengers.[4] Only as the number of passengers carried in the DC-3 exceeds the capacities of alternative new aircraft do the estimated passenger mile costs of the DC-3 fall below those of the other planes.[5]

The rapid increase in passenger demand—in part because of the introduction of the DC-3—provided the reason for the adoption of the plane by the smaller lines in the years after 1936. By 1947 for example, Braniff's route mileage was 1.27 times that of 1938; its 1947 revenue passenger miles amounted to 14.78 times those of 1938. For Continental Airlines, the similar numbers are 3.1 and 44.61. In 1947, Braniff's fleet consisted of 17 DC-3s, 10 DC-4s, and 5 DC-6s. Continental's fleet still consisted of only 12 DC-3s. But it is clear that without increases in passenger demand over their routes and concomitant higher load factors, none of the carriers except the "Big Four" would have found the DC-3 the most economical equipment to use.

[4] The greater width of the DC-3 fuselage, rather than giving it greater drag than the DC-2, provided an unanticipated reduction in drag. This was due in part to then unknown aerodynamic attributes of fuselages with circular cross-sections.

[5] In this connection, it may be noted that the sleeper DST, with 14 berths, and the deluxe, 14-seat "Sky Lounge" versions of the DC-3 operated at high costs. Extra charges were made for these services.

Table 6-6

Estimated Direct Operating Costs per Passenger Mile of Selected Aircraft in 1936 Trunk Line Fleets (Cents Per Passenger Mile, 1954 Dollars).

| | | Cost Per Passenger Mile [a] | |
Aircraft	*Number of Passengers*	*100 Mile Stage Length*	*500 Mile Stage Length*
New [a]			
DC-3	2	41.06	32.66
	5	16.42	13.06
	10	8.21	6.53
	15	5.47	4.35
	21	3.91	3.11
L-10B	2	23.50	18.80
	5	9.40	7.52
	10	4.70	3.76
L-12B	2	20.94	16.35
	5	8.38	6.54
	6	6.98	5.45
In Use [a]			
L-10B	2	17.70	13.00
	5	7.08	5.20
	10	3.54	2.60
DC-2	2	34.23	25.97
	5	13.69	10.39
	10	6.85	5.19
	14	4.89	3.71
247D	2	28.50	21.00
	5	11.40	8.40
	10	5.70	4.20

[a] Costs for new aircraft include depreciation; those for aircraft in use exclude depreciation.

The data in Table 6-6 suggest the reasons for the retention of particular other aircraft types by the trunk operators after 1936. American, the first line to receive DC-3s, did not begin to eliminate its DC-2s until 1939. The DC-2s were used on routes of lower passenger demand, for which its costs per passenger mile were lower than those of the DC-3. As demand grew, fewer of these routes existed.[6] Eastern, Braniff, and TWA, the only other lines with substantial members of DC-2s, also retained the bulk of their DC-2 fleets until 1939 or 1940. United was somewhat quicker to sell its 247s with their number falling from 44 in 1935 to 33 in 1936, 24 in 1937, 17 in 1938 and 15 in

[6] The costs given in Table 6-6 do not reflect any costs analogous to out-age costs of inventory. These may be an important consideration. If demand for a particular scheduled flight were Poisson-distributed with mean of 10 passengers, demand would exceed the 14 passenger limit of the DC-2 more than eight percent of the time.

1940. A small number of these were sold to Pennsylvania-Central and to Inland, but most were sold to companies other than the domestic trunk carriers. The Lockheed L-10, for which passenger mile costs for loads up to 10 passengers were the lowest of any plane of the period, had greater use in 1939 than in 1935. Thereafter, however, its use by the trunk carriers fell quickly.

By 1941 the growth in trunk line passenger demand gave Douglas and the DC-3 nearly all of the demand for new trunk line aircraft. The same growing demand, however, had created the vision of still larger and, for routes of high traffic density, still less costly aircraft. But this vision was one which Douglas, with the prolonged and eventually unsuccessful DC-4E development, had difficulty turning to reality.

The Period 1947–1965

As noted above, the lack of comparable alternatives to the DC-3 makes it impossible to assess the relative significance of its separate characteristics to its market success. In the period after 1947, when three or more domestic manufacturers were represented in the gross additions to the fleets in every year except 1965, a number of comparable aircraft models were simultaneously available to the carriers. For this period, somewhat more formal estimates of the demand for new aircraft and the market shares of particular manufacturers can be attempted.

In Chapter 4 it was found that only about one-half of the variance in the number of new planes added each year to the trunk line fleets could be explained by factors such as seat miles to be supplied and the model ages and technical characteristics of new and replaced aircraft. Here the purpose is to ascertain whether, within the total demand for new aircraft, the relative costs and performance characteristics of various planes explain large proportions of the variance in market shares over the years. Again, only about one-half of the variance could be explained.

Based on the size of the corrected coefficient of determination, with highly intercorrelated independent variables excluded, the best estimating equation found was:

$$ln\,(NP_{it}) = 1.020 + .550\,(ln\,NP_t) + .004\,(C_{it}) - 1.059\,(C'_{it})^2$$
$$\qquad\qquad\quad (.164) \qquad\quad (.164) \qquad\quad (.295)$$
$$- .061\,(MA_{it}) + 1.137\,(NLR_{it}) + 2.102\,(NNLR_{it}) - 1.240\,(I_i) \quad (6.1)$$
$$(.034) \qquad\quad (.335) \qquad\qquad (.375) \qquad\qquad (.297)$$
$$R^2 = .480$$

where

NP_{it} = the estimated number of new aircraft of the ith type put into service in the tth year.

NP_t = actual number of new aircraft of all types put into service in the tth year.

C_{it} = seat mile operating costs, including depreciation, of the ith type of plane in the tth year relative to the seat mile operating costs, excluding depreciation, of the plane being replaced, expressed as a percent.

C'_{it} = seat mile operating costs, including depreciation, of the ith type of plane in the tth year relative to the same costs of the closest alternative plane available in the same year, expressed as a percent.

MA_{it} = model age of the ith plane in the tth year.

NLR_{it} = the fraction of the first twelve months of deliveries of the ith type of long-range plane which occurred in the tth year (Table 16, Chapter 4).

$NNLR_{it}$ = the fraction of the first twelve months of deliveries of the ith type of nonlong-range plane which occurred in the tth year (Table 16, Chapter 4).

I_i = dummy variable for the ith type plane; unity for foreign manufacture, zero for domestic.

The regression, which is based on 105 observations, shows that the deliveries of particular planes are significantly related to the total deliveries of all planes. This is, of course, expected where the number of types added each year is so small. The seat mile operating costs of the added planes relative to those being replaced does not appear significant.[7] Indeed, the mean of the C_{it} variable is 1.08, indicating that on the average new aircraft were added before the operating costs of new planes, with depreciation, were as low as the operating costs, *ex* depreciation, of aircraft which were replaced by the new.

The finding that operating costs of new planes relative to those being replaced is unimportant in explaining the demand for particular planes is consistent with the findings of Chapter 4 that the averages of these costs do not add significantly to the explanation of total demand. And these findings are not contradictory to the conclusion of Chapter 5 that effective entry requires technological change which creates substantial cost advantages. In the first place, most of the demand for new aircraft has not been for pure replacement purposes but rather for the purpose of capacity expansion. Seat miles supplied by the trunk carriers, it will be recalled, rose from 7,490 million in 1946 to 88,593 million in 1965, and for expansion it is full costs, not cost less depreciation, which are relevant. In addition, the cost relatives in equation

---

[7] Types of aircraft being replaced were identified from the fleet records of the individual carriers adding and retiring aircraft.

(6.1) include those for aircraft which were among the near misses. Among the highest C_{it} values, for example, are those for the small additions of DC-7Cs in 1957 and 1958. Most of the DC-7Cs purchased for domestic use were taken by Northwest as replacements for DC-4s. The C_{it} values of 141 and 138 for the DC-7Cs in these two years reflect this fact. But in the three years 1956–1958, only 24 DC-7Cs were delivered to the domestic trunk carriers. For comparison, the C_{it} value for the DC-6 in 1947 is 101; for the DC-6B in 1951, 97; for the DC-8 and 707 in 1962, 86, and 95, respectively; for the 727 in 1964, 93.[8] Large numbers of the planes were added in these years. A weighted average C_{it} would be less than 100.

The important costs—those which do help to explain the relative shares of new planes each year and, hence, help to explain the near miss phenomena —are those in the C'_{it} variable. This appears more significant in the squared form, showing that the influence of cost differences among alternative new aircraft tends to become greater as the cost difference increases. That is, viewing demand in terms of market shares and relative operating costs of new planes, demand tends to become more elastic with respect to costs as the cost ratios depart from unity. As relative operating costs rise above unity, the market share falls more than proportionately, and vice versa.

The model age effect is of an absolutely small magnitude but is statistically significant at nearly the five percent level. The big effect of age of model on demand appears in the NLR_{it} and the $NNLR_{it}$ variables, which account for the distribution of first year sales among calendar years. The size of the co-efficients for these shows that, beyond the first year of sales, only small numbers of many of the aircraft types are sold. Where this is not the case, the C'_{it} values are nearly uniformly low.

Version age and an interaction term between version age and model age proved to have less explanatory value than does model age. High intercorrelations among the three age variables prevent the inclusion of more than one of them in the same regression.[9]

Foreign manufacture—for the Viscount 745 and 812, the SUD 210 and the BAC-111—has a significant and fairly large negative effect on demand. Attempts were made to find whether manufacture by Douglas, Boeing, or Lockheed irrespective of other variables, has a significant effect on the demand for particular aircraft. No such effect is apparent for overall purchases

---

[8] In the first years of their use, the DC-8s and 707s largely replaced DC-6Bs, which were not capable of nonstop, coast-to-coast flights from east to west with full passenger loads. For these years, the C_{it} values exceed 100. After this, the DC-8s and 707s replaced DC-7s and Lockheed 1049Gs and 1649s, resulting in much lower C_{it} values.

[9] There is some evidence, however, that the effects on demand of new versions of the same basic model tend to fall as the number of versions rises over time. If the NLR_{it} and $NNLR_{it}$ variables are divided by the version number, their significance is greater and $\bar{R}^2$ is larger. The division procedure is obviously arbitrary, but nonetheless shows that stretching tends to yield progressively smaller demand results.

by all carriers for the entire period. Attention is given below to the possibilities of certain carriers having proclivities to purchase from one or another of the manufacturers. Attention is also given to the possibility that aircraft of Douglas manufacture had a smaller share than the factors in the regression would indicate for the years after 1958.

The actual and predicted demands for particular aircraft are shown in Table 6-7. The predicted values are those from regression (6.1), adjusted in each year by the ratio of the sum of the estimated purchases to total actual purchases in that year. This adjustment makes the sum of predicted values in each year equal to actual purchases, but leaves relative shares unaffected.

A few of the major discrepancies between actual and predicted values merit discussion. No dummy was included in the regression to account for groundings and crashes. The DC-6 was grounded on November 12, 1947, because of a number of on-board fires and fatal crashes. The low actual deliveries in 1949 and 1950 cover a period in which the DC-6s were being modified to prevent the fires and in which the larger DC-6B was being developed. Similarly, the L-049 "Constellation" was grounded because of fires on July 12, 1946. The Martin 202 was grounded on August 29, 1948, on November 12, 1950, and on March 17, 1951, because of structural failures. The low 1948 deliveries of the "Constellation" and the virtual end of deliveries of the 202 after 1948 reflect these events.

Other factors are clearly involved. The 202 was an unpressurized aircraft, a disadvantage compared with the Convair 240. The high predicted relative to actual sales of the 202 in 1940 compared to those of the 240 seem to indicate the effect of this technological difference. Martin attempted a 303 pressurized model, but plans for this were dropped when United cancelled its order in September of 1947.[10] Again, these influences are not in the regression estimates.

The initial orders for 65 of the Martin 404s were placed in a joint offer by TWA and Eastern. The price was reported to be less than adequate to cover Martin's production costs.[11] The predicted sales of the 404 are less than the actual, but not by so much as might be expected. The Convair 340 was not available for delivery until a few months later and this, rather than price or operating cost differences, appears to be the more important factor.

In the same vein, the predicted values for deliveries of the DC-8 are consistently higher than the actuals; those of the Boeing 707 are typically lower. The latter was available nearly a year in advance of the former. The DC-6B, the actual deliveries of which far exceed the predicted, was available some eight months prior to the L-1049 Constellation, where the reverse relation between predicted and actual deliveries obtains. There is thus the suggestion

[10] *New York Times* (January 3, 1946), p. 34; (September 30, 1947), p. 30; (December 15, 1947), p. 41.
[11] Richard Caves, *Air Transport and Its Regulators*, p. 104.

Table 6-7

Actual and Predicted Deliveries of New Aircraft, 1947–1965.

Year	DC-6 Actual	DC-6 Predicted	DC-6B Actual	DC-6B Predicted	DC-7 and 7B Actual	DC-7 and 7B Predicted	DC-7C Actual	DC-7C Predicted	DC-8 Actual	DC-8 Predicted
1947	78	56	—	—	—	—	—	—	—	—
1948	25	20	—	—	—	—	—	—	—	—
1949	1	13	—	—	—	—	—	—	—	—
1950	5	17	—	—	—	—	—	—	—	—
1951	2	9	28	21	—	—	—	—	—	—
1952	4	10	18	13	—	—	—	—	—	—
1953	—	—	21	9	16	19	—	—	—	—
1954	—	—	5	8	45	27	—	—	—	—
1955	—	—	5	6	16	12	—	—	—	—
1956	—	—	28	16	18	18	4	12	—	—
1957	—	—	48	22	58	36	12	24	—	—
1958	—	—	4	8	37	18	8	6	—	—
1959	—	—	—	—	—	—	—	—	18	34
1960	—	—	—	—	—	—	—	—	38	29
1961	—	—	—	—	—	—	—	—	12	14
1962	—	—	—	—	—	—	—	—	8	12
1963	—	—	—	—	—	—	—	—	2	5
1964	—	—	—	—	—	—	—	—	8	10
1965	—	—	—	—	—	—	—	—	13	15
TOTAL	115	125	157	103	190	130	24	42	99	119

Table 6-7 (continued)

Year	DC-9 Actual	DC-9 Predicted	L-647/749 Actual	L-647/749 Predicted	L-1049 Actual	L-1049 Predicted	L-1049C/G Actual	L-1049C/G Predicted	L-1649 Actual	L-1649 Predicted
1947	—	—	18	17	—	—	—	—	—	—
1948	—	—	6	16	—	—	—	—	—	—
1949	—	—	19	6	—	—	—	—	—	—
1950	—	—	31	8	—	—	—	—	—	—
1951	—	—	10	5	5	14	—	—	—	—
1952	—	—	5	7	19	43	—	—	—	—
1953	—	—	4	6	—	—	8	22	—	—
1954	—	—	—	—	—	—	7	32	—	—
1955	—	—	—	—	—	—	24	21	—	—
1956	—	—	—	—	—	—	10	11	—	—
1957	—	—	—	—	—	—	8	16	25	36
1958	—	—	—	—	—	—	8	9	4	8
1959	—	—	—	—	—	—	—	—	—	—
1960	—	—	—	—	—	—	—	—	—	—
1961	—	—	—	—	—	—	—	—	—	—
1962	—	—	—	—	—	—	—	—	—	—
1963	—	—	—	—	—	—	—	—	—	—
1964	—	—	—	—	—	—	—	—	—	—
1965	4	17	—	—	—	—	—	—	—	—
TOTAL	4	17	93	65	24	57	65	111	29	44

(continued)

Table 6-7 (Continued)

Year	B-727 Actual	B-727 Predicted	M-202 Actual	M-202 Predicted	M-404 Actual	M-404 Predicted	CV-240 Actual	CV-240 Predicted	CV-340 Actual	CV-340 Predicted
1947	—	—	9	32	—	—	—	—	—	—
1948	—	—	15	42	—	—	69	37	—	—
1949	—	—	—	—	—	—	28	21	—	—
1950	—	—	9	13	—	—	6	13	—	—
1951	—	—	—	—	18	14	—	—	24	18
1952	—	—	—	—	78	57	—	—	74	57
1953	—	—	—	—	4	14	—	—	18	8
1954	—	—	—	—	—	—	—	—	2	7
1955	—	—	—	—	—	—	—	—	8	10
1956	—	—	—	—	—	—	—	—	3	14
1957	—	—	—	—	—	—	—	—	—	—
1958	—	—	—	—	—	—	—	—	—	—
1959	—	—	—	—	—	—	—	—	—	—
1960	—	—	—	—	—	—	—	—	—	—
1961	—	—	—	—	—	—	—	—	—	—
1962	—	—	—	—	—	—	—	—	—	—
1963	—	—	—	—	—	—	—	—	—	—
1964	88	84	—	—	—	—	—	—	—	—
1965	79	57	—	—	—	—	—	—	—	—
TOTAL	167	141	33	87	100	85	103	71	129	114

Table 6-7 (Continued)

Year	L-188 Actual	L-188 Predicted	B-377 Actual	B-377 Predicted	B-707 Actual	B-707 Predicted	B-720 Actual	B-720 Predicted	B-727B Actual	B-727B Predicted
1947	—	—	—	—	—	—	—	—	—	—
1948	—	—	—	—	—	—	—	—	—	—
1949	—	—	10	18	—	—	—	—	—	—
1950	—	—	—	—	—	—	—	—	—	—
1951	—	—	—	—	—	—	—	—	—	—
1952	—	—	—	—	—	—	—	—	—	—
1953	—	—	—	—	—	—	—	—	—	—
1954	—	—	—	—	—	—	—	—	—	—
1955	—	—	—	—	—	—	—	—	—	—
1956	—	—	—	—	—	—	—	—	—	—
1957	—	—	—	—	—	—	—	—	—	—
1958	—	—	—	—	—	—	—	—	—	—
1959	96	91	—	—	50	32	—	—	—	—
1960	11	6	—	—	12	7	22	26	—	—
1961	15	13	—	—	—	—	24	35	33	26
1962	—	—	—	—	16	8	11	10	7	11
1963	—	—	—	—	14	5	1	3	1	4
1964	—	—	—	—	14	8	1	7	6	7
1965	—	—	—	—	19	15	2	9	6	10
TOTAL	122	110	10	18	125	75	61	90	53	58

(continued)

Table 6-7 (Continued)

Year	CV-440 Actual	CV-440 Predicted	CV-880 Actual	CV-880 Predicted	CV-990 Actual	CV-990 Predicted	V-745 Actual	V-745 Predicted	V-812 Actual	V-812 Predicted
1947	—	—	—	—	—	—	—	—	—	—
1948	—	—	—	—	—	—	—	—	—	—
1949	—	—	—	—	—	—	—	—	—	—
1950	—	—	—	—	—	—	—	—	—	—
1951	—	—	—	—	—	—	—	—	—	—
1952	—	—	—	—	—	—	—	—	—	—
1953	—	—	—	—	—	—	—	—	—	—
1954	—	—	—	—	—	—	8	9	—	—
1955	11	—	—	—	—	—	46	19	—	—
1956	20	39	—	—	—	—	5	7	—	—
1957	—	24	—	—	—	—	7	3	14	30
1958	—	—	—	—	—	—	1	3	1	6
1959	—	—	—	—	—	—	—	—	—	—
1960	—	—	14	29	—	—	—	—	—	—
1961	—	—	24	17	—	—	—	—	—	—
1962	—	—	6	6	15	15	—	—	—	—
1963	—	—	1	3	4	3	—	—	—	—
1964	—	—	2	3	—	—	—	—	—	—
1965	—	—	—	—	—	—	—	—	—	—
TOTAL	31	63	47	58	19	18	67	41	15	36

Table 6-7 (Continued)

| | SUD-210 | | BAC-111 | | |
Year	Actual	Predicted	Actual	Predicted	Total
1947	—	—	—	—	105
1948	—	—	—	—	115
1949	—	—	—	—	58
1950	—	—	—	—	51
1951	—	—	—	—	63
1952	—	—	—	—	148
1953	—	—	—	—	127
1954	—	—	—	—	75
1955	—	—	—	—	55
1956	—	—	—	—	125
1957	—	—	—	—	179
1958	—	—	—	—	82
1959	—	—	—	—	166
1960	—	—	—	—	97
1961	17	20	—	—	125
1962	3	4	—	—	66
1963	—	—	—	—	23
1964	—	—	—	—	119
1965	—	—	12	12	135
Total	20	24	12	12	1914

that, by itself, being the first manufacturer capable of delivering a plane of improved performance dimensions has a favorable effect on sales.[12]

This points to one of the deficiencies of the NLR_{it} and $NNLR_{it}$ variables. The variable does not distinguish between new planes which have the possible advantage of being the first of their type and those which are not first. An even more glaring deficiency of the variable, however, is that it does not distinguish between new planes which are in the near miss and hit categories. Actual deliveries of the near misses cluster more in the first twelve months than do those of the hits. The predicted deliveries of Table 6-7 reflect this only to the extent that the hits have lower relative operating costs than do the near misses. Noncost performance advantages that add to market success are not incorporated in the estimates.

Table 6-8 gives the actual and predicted shares of the market gained by particular manufacturers from 1947 to 1965. There is a suggestion in the data of Table 6-8—though not one which shows to be statistically significant— that Douglas lost a preferred market position in the transition from piston-engined to jet aircraft. The predicted shares for Douglas DC-6s through 1958 are generally below the actual shares. The predicted shares after 1958— reflecting deliveries of DC-8s—are well above the actual. Predicted shares of

[12] Note, however, that subsequent stretched versions of the Lockheeds were generally available prior to comparable Douglas models. There is no clear evidence in the results here that this had favorable and differential effects on Lockheed sales. Predicted sales exceeded actual for both manufacturers.

Table 6-8

Actual and Predicted Shares of Aircraft Deliveries by Particular Manufacturers, 1947–1965.

Year	Douglas		Boeing		Lockheed		Convair	
	Actual	Predicted	Actual	Predicted	Actual	Predicted	Actual	Predicted
1947	74.3%	53.3%	0.0%	—	17.1%	16.2%	0.0%	—
1948	21.7	17.4	0.0	—	5.2	13.9	60.0	32.2%
1949	1.7	22.6	17.2	31.0%	32.8	10.3	48.3	36.2
1950	9.8	33.3	0.0	—	60.8	15.6	11.8	25.5
1951	47.6	47.6	0.0	—	23.8	30.2	0.0	—
1952	14.9	15.5	0.0	—	16.2	33.8	16.2	12.2
1953	29.1	22.0	0.0	—	9.4	22.0	58.3	44.9
1954	66.7	46.7	0.0	—	9.3	42.7	24.0	10.7
1955	38.2	32.7	0.0	—	43.6	38.2	3.6	12.6
1956	40.0	36.8	0.0	—	8.0	8.9	15.2	39.2
1957	67.0	45.8	0.0	—	18.4	29.0	12.8	21.2
1958	59.8	39.0	0.0	—	14.6	20.7	0.0	—
1959	10.8	20.5	30.1	19.4	57.8	54.8	0.0	—
1960	39.2	29.9	35.1	34.0	11.3	6.2	14.4	29.9
1961	9.6	11.2	45.6	48.8	12.0	10.4	19.2	13.6
1962	12.1	18.2	51.5	43.9	0.0	—	31.8	31.8
1963	8.7	21.7	69.6	52.2	0.0	—	21.7	26.1
1964	6.7	8.3	91.6	89.1	0.0	—	1.7	2.5
1965	12.6	23.7	78.5	67.4	0.0	—	0.0	—
Total	30.8	28.0	21.7	20.0	17.4	20.2	17.2	16.9

Table 6-8 (Continued)

Year	Martin		Foreign	
	Actual	Predicted	Actual	Predicted
1947	8.6%	30.5%	0.0%	—
1948	13.0	36.5	0.0	—
1949	0.0	—	0.0	—
1950	17.6	25.5	0.0	—
1951	28.6	22.2	0.0	—
1952	52.7	38.5	0.0	—
1953	3.1	11.0	0.0	—
1954	0.0	—	0.0	—
1955	0.0	—	14.5	16.3%
1956	0.0	—	36.8	15.2
1957	0.0	—	2.8	3.9
1958	0.0	—	25.6	40.2
1959	0.0	—	1.2	5.4
1960	0.0	—	0.0	—
1961	0.0	—	13.6	16.0
1962	0.0	—	4.5	6.1
1963	0.0	—	0.0	—
1964	0.0	—	0.0	—
1965	0.0	—	8.9	8.9
Total	6.9	9.0	6.0	5.9

the rival Lockheed aircraft, on the other hand, are often above actual deliveries in the pre-1959 period. Those for the Boeing 707 after 1958 are less than the actual. Douglas, that is, seems to have achieved somewhat higher market shares up to 1958 and somewhat lower market shares after 1958 than would be expected from the variables of equation (6.1).

Underlying this consideration is the possibility that particular carriers have had preferences for the particular aircraft manufacturers such that they have not switched among manufacturers despite cost and performance differences among aircraft. Of the "Big Four" carriers, TWA is the only one to have had no DC-6s, DC-7s, or DC-8s in its fleet. Eastern had none of these until 1955, when it began acquisition of DC-7Bs. After this, it purchased DC-6, DC-7, and DC-8 aircraft.

Eastern and TWA purchased a variety of Lockheed "Constellations"; American and United purchased none. United, however, acquired 11 Boeing 377s as well as numbers of Douglas aircraft. United might have purchased considerably more of the 377s had the scheduled delivery dates been met. Thus, during the period when Douglas and Lockheed were the principal domestic producers of long-range aircraft, TWA bought only Lockheeds and American bought only Douglas. Eastern mixed Lockheed and Douglas planes and, to a smaller extent, United mixed Douglas and Boeing.[13]

[13] For clues of a possible explanation of TWA's exclusive use of "Constellations," see the New York Times (September 22, 1968), p. 1, where an award of damages to TWA was made

Although American had no "Constellations," it was, with Eastern a large purchaser of the Lockheed "Electra" in 1959 and 1960. No aversion to Lockheed is apparent in this instance. Of the earlier short-range planes, Eastern and TWA bought Martin 202s and 404s, while American bought Convair 240s and United, 340s and 440s. Eastern acquired 440s in addition to its Martins in 1958. Thus, TWA bought its twin-engined short-ranged planes from only Martin; United and American, from Convair. Eastern again bought both. Neither Douglas nor Lockheed manufactured comparable planes—a fact not conducive to assessing the strength of carriers' loyalties—though both attempted models for this market. That these attempts did not succeed indicates that carrier loyalties have definite limits.

Of the long-range jets, Boeing 707s, 720s, and Convair 990s are operated by American. Eastern has acquired Boeing 720s and DC-8s. United has DC-8s and 720s and TWA, 707s and Convair 880s. Boeing 727s had been delivered to all of the "Big Four" domestic carriers by the end of 1964. Up to the end of 1965 the one clear pattern is TWAs failure to buy any new Douglas aircraft after the DC-3.[14] The general impression, however, is that, with the exception of TWA, new aircraft have been selected by the carriers with little influence from loyalties or other ties to particular manufacturers. This seems especially so after the introduction of the jets.

Technical Change and the Market
Penetration of Particular Aircraft and
Aircraft Manufacturers

The results of the present chapter complement and reinforce those of previous chapters. While overall seat miles supplied by the trunk carriers seem largely explicable in terms of convention economic variables, neither the total demand for new aircraft nor the relative demands for particular planes can be so conventionally explained. Operating costs, themselves closely related to technology, are statistically important in the demand for particular planes, but other performance characteristics and availability are critical in both total and relative demands over the years.

Although the model ages of new and existing planes were found to be a significant factor in explaining demand, the relationship between age and demand is small as compared with an apparent availability factor. That is, maintaining a high demand for newly produced aircraft depends on the manufacturer having available new types of aircraft with performance and cost characteristics not substantially inferior to those of other manufacturers.

---

because of the influence of Hughes Tool Company in the choice of propeller type Lockheed aircraft.

[14] Appendix Table D-22 shows that TWA did purchase some used DC-4s in 1949 and 1950. Since 1965, TWA has purchased DC-9s.

On one hand, this creates pressure for continuous change which, in a scientific environment affording change in discontinuous spurts, carries with it concomitant risks of technological as well as financial failure. On the other hand, submission to the alternative of low-level scientific and research efforts carries with it the risk of losses in market shares and, from this, financial failure.

In the case of commercial aircraft, the losses in market shares from failures to produce technically competitive planes are obvious. The demise in the earlier years of the Fords, Fokkers, Stinsons, and Curtiss planes came from the Boeing, Douglas and, in smaller degree, Lockheed successes with the two-engined, low-wing, all metal monoplanes. Boeing and eventually Lockheed were subsequently forced from this market by Douglas' technically and economically superior DC-3.

Lockheed and Boeing were not, however, pushed into companywide financial failure from the market failures of their commercial aircraft. Military orders sustained them and each attempted new commercial planes prior to World War II. Lacking the military orders—that is, in a market environment more typical of most industries—Lockheed and Boeing would presumably have failed. Still, success in developing new commercial planes was not easy. Boeing missed with both the 307 and the 377, despite their being derived from successful military aircraft.[15] Douglas and Lockheed captured virtually all of the market for long-range planes until the jets appeared.

The years of the introduction of the jets illustrates again the tendency toward market concentration and changing relative market positions. The early appearance of the Boeing 707 placed Douglas in a position of acute market and financial distress. Save for military work in aircraft and missiles, Douglas could hardly have avoided bankruptcy. Convair, too, approached financial disaster with the CV-880 and CV-990.

[15] For additional detail, see the discussion of these aircraft in the next chapter.

7

Sources of the Antecedent Technological Developments

Introduction

The details of aircraft developments and sales to the domestic truck carriers fail to support the view that larger firms with entrenched market positions, because of conditions resulting from their position in the market, strive for continuous and fundamental innovations. Indeed, the weight of the evidence is much to the contrary. Aircraft firms that successfully innovate appear to press for stretched versions of their originally successful models.[1] In the course of their doing so, they seem to have ignored advances in technology that were creating opportunities for more basic innovations. Eventually, a new success appears from either established or new producers and the market structure changes. These changes in structure, it can well be argued, depend on changes in technology. There is thus substantial support for the hypothesis advanced in the first chapter.

The support is not complete, however. The hypothesis is that the tendencies toward concentration—or, in the specific instance of the militarily supported aircraft industry, toward one firm's having sudden increases in market shares—occur where there are related scientific and technological disciplines advancing for reasons independent of the goals of the firms. It is on these advances that significant new innovations are based and, hence, it is on these that technologically determined changes in market structure depend.

This chapter investigates research and development activities leading, first, to the DC-3 generation of aircraft and, second, to the development of the Boeing 707 type of subsonic jet transports. These are the biggest of the technological breakthroughs in the period covered. In addition to attention to these larger changes, aspects of the development of aircraft in the intervening period are more briefly treated.[2]

The Technology of the DC-3 Generation of Aircraft

The DC-3 can be regarded as the culmination of development efforts that yielded planes such as the Boeing 247, the DC-1 and DC-2, and the Lockheed

---

[1] J. C. Hunsaker, "Forty Years of Aeronautical Research," *The Smithsonian Report* (1955), p. 263, notes that both engine and aircraft manufacturers tend to "make small changes based on experience. . . . Every effort is made to improve a particular airplane to prolong its vogue in production. This development effort is restricted to conservative changes in a basic design acceptable to the customer."

[2] The history of aviation technology is offered with some misgiving. There is not, unfortunately, a comprehensive treatise on which to rely. There are a large number of books in the romance of aviation category and a smaller number of company, industry, and military aircraft histories. Even collectively, these are far from adequate for present purposes.

L-10. All used two radial engines which, for the times, were of high horse-power and had low weight-to-power ratios. Quite clearly, the development of planes of the weight and performance characteristics of the DC-3 required improved engines which, in turn, required improved aviation fuels.

Neither the development of the higher powered air-cooled radial engines nor that of improved aviation fuels in the period up to the mid-1930s can be attributed to research by or demands derived from commercial aircraft manufacturers. Interest in the larger air-cooled engines arose in the United States when the Army Air Service became aware of development efforts in such engines in Britain shortly after World War I.[3] From 1919 to 1926, "every cent going into the development of engines" by private companies came from the government.[4] In addition, government agencies—especially the research group at the Army's McCook Field (later Wright Field and, still later, Wright-Patterson Air Force Base) engaged directly in engine research. By 1925, the Curtiss R-1454 engine, rated at 390 horsepower and weighing 830 pounds, passed bench tests. In the next year, the newly formed Pratt and Whitney Company produced the Wasp engine. The first version weighed 650 pounds and was rated at 400 horsepower.[5] By the time of the Boeing 247, a reliable Pratt and Whitney engine of 550 horsepower was available. Indeed, it had been used on the earlier Lockheed "Vega" and on previous Boeing air-craft as well. By the time of the DC-3, engines of 1,000 horsepower could have been purchased virtually "off the shelf."

The basic developments underlying improved aviation fuels for radial gasoline-fueled engines were completed for reasons quite unrelated to avia-tion. Most of the chemical developments were from research in private indus-try, but their application to aviation and a number of testing and specifica-tion methods were the result of government research at McCook (Wright) Field, and the National Bureau of Standards.[6]

The mounting of engines in the leading edges of the wings was researched primarily by the Langley Memorial Aeronautical Laboratory of the National Advisory Committee for Aeronautics. The addition in 1927 of a propeller research tunnel at that facility yielded a 1930 design for an engine mounting faired into the leading edge. This had much improved lift-drag character-istics.[7] The design remained fundamentally unchanged through the DC-7 and "Constellation" types of aircraft.[8]

The wings of the DC-1, 2, and 3 were derived directly from a planform

[3] Reliance here is on Robert Schlaifer and S. D. Heron, *Development of Aircraft Engines and Aviation Fuels* (1950). This book is precisely of the sort said in note 2 to be lacking for aircraft.

[4] *Ibid.*, p. 160.

[5] *Ibid.*, pp. 186,190. Changes in the structure of the aircraft engine industry are not traced here but are fully consistent with the view of relations between structure and technology which is being pressed.

[6] For details, see Schlaifer and Heron, *op. cit.*, pp. 549–705.

[7] Hunsaker, "Forty Years", p. 258.

[8] P. W. Brooks, *The Modern Airliner* (1961), p. 68.

developed by John K. Northrop for the high-performance Northrup "Alpha" and "Gamma" aircraft. The multicellular, internally braced rib and spar construction also came from Northrop.[9] Less directly, however, the wings of the DC-3, as well as those of the other planes of its generation, owe their origin to NACA and other non-commercial or non-United States research. In particular, the DC-1 had a NACA 2215 wing section at the root—with fillets into the fuselage which were the results of NACA research—and a NACA 2209 section at the tip.[10] One consequence of the 15 percent thick root section was added space for retracting the landing gear and for storing fuel.

The Douglas planes, unlike the Boeing 247, used a split trailing-edge flap to reduce stall speed and to improve lift for takeoff. This also came from Northrop, but the general device was old enough to have been used on production aircraft during World War I. The first use was probably on the experimental English S.E. 4 of 1914. The Sopwith of 1916 had flaps. A number of flap forms, including area increasing types, evolved in the 1920s.[11] Indeed, the more sophisticated Handley-Page Slot lift device was patented in 1919 and was used on a number of planes in the 1920s. More recently, the same sort of slot received minor use on the DC-8.[12]

Lift and drag research, involving various airfoils and stall, landing, and takeoff speeds were among the early research topics of NACA.[13] This work included research on high lift by boundary-layer control and, among other things, produced the famous NACA long-chord cowl for radial air-cooled engines. On a Curtiss AT-5A pursuit plane, the cowl increased the maximum speed from 118 to 137 miles per hour, the equivalent of that which might have been produced by 83 additional horsepower.[14] Again, the DC-3 generation of aircraft utilized the NACA cowl.[15]

As the airfoils and other drag-reducing wing and engine configurations appeared, drag from other aspects of aircraft design became more obviously important. NACA investigated even such things as location of gasoline filler caps. Tests released at the 1928 General Conference with aircraft manufacturers showed that the drag from the landing gear on a Sperry Messenger was 40 percent of total drag.[16] Thereafter, interest in retractable gear for commer-

[9] D. J. Ingells, *The Plane That Changed the World* (1966), pp. 30, 34.

[10] Brooks, *Modern Airliner*, p. 82; Hunsaker, *op. cit.*, p. 258.

[11] J. L. Nayler and E. Ower, *Aviation: Its Technical Development* (1965), p. 259.

[12] *Ibid.*, pp. 259–260.

[13] These involved speeds up to Mach .95 as early as 1924. See M. D. Keller, *Fifty Years of Flight Research: A Chronology of the Langley Research Center*, 1917–1966, Comment Edition, NASA (1966) (mimeo), p. 26. The research by NACA was mainly through empirical experimentation with models in wind tunnels until the mid-1920s. Boundary-layer theory, however, had been set out fairly clearly by Ludwig Prandtl in 1904; Prandtl's theory of lift appeared in 1918. Practical applications of Prandtl's theories in aircraft design did not begin until the late 1920s. See Nayler and Ower, *Aviation*, pp. 255–261.

[14] Hunsaker, "Forty Years", p. 257.

[15] The first 247s used the Townend ring, developed in England in 1927. The NACA cowl was developed shortly thereafter.

[16] Keller, *Flight Research*, p. 32.

cial aircraft grew. The Lockheed "Orion" was the first transport equipped with such gear. The Boeing 247 was the first of the all-metal, low-wing, two-engined transports to utilize the device. But, as with flaps, retractable gear had appeared much earlier, especially on racing aircraft.[17] Prior to the 247, Boeing had used a retracting mechanism on the Model 200 "Monomail," the Model 221 "Monomail," and the B-9 bomber.[18]

The use of the improved airfoils and of other drag-reducing design features depended ultimately on the development of construction techniques. In particular, wing construction with no external bracing and strong, yet light, fuselage construction was needed. Here the credit for basic development goes to three Germans, Professor Hugo Junker, Dr. Adolph Rohrbach, and H. A. Wagner, and to the Dutch aircraft manufacturer, Anthony Fokker.

Junker's J.4 biplane of 1917 was the first all-metal plane with duralumin, corrugated skin. This skin, however, was laid over a metal structure which bore most of the loads.[19] Rohrbach completed a successful smooth stressed skin craft in 1919 and experimented with what, for the time, were high wing loadings. Wagner, an associate of Rohrbach, further improved the methods of stressed skin construction and with Rohrbach developed the box-spar type of wing.[20] Fokker experimented with cantilever wing construction, though the early versions were wood and plywood rather than aluminum and duralumin. Fokker's work seems to have influenced that of William B. Stout in the United States. Stout was the designer of the Stout and Ford Trimotors, planes that bore a striking resemblance to the Fokker Trimotors.[21] Rohrbach's work also had an influence on John K. Northrop's design of the "Alpha" and, from there, the path leads quite directly to Douglas aircraft.[22]

The development of monocoque fuselages paralleled that of stressed skin cantilever wings. The Frenchman, Becherean, originated the term with his "Monocoque Deperdussion" racing plane of 1912.[23] This was not a common method of construction for some time, however. The Short "Silver Streak" of the mid-1920's had a light alloy monocoque fuselage. Lockheed developed a method of producing plywood monocoque structures which appeared first in the "Vega" of 1927.[24]

Boeing used a semi-monocoque duralumin construction on part of the fuse-

[17] Brooks, *Modern Airliner*, p. 74; Nayler and Ower, *op. cit.*, p. 255.

[18] Brooks, *Modern Airliner*, p. 75; P. M. Bowers, *Boeing Aircraft Since 1916* (1966), pp. 175–181. Boeing also experimented with a streamlined, nonretracting gear for the 221, indicating its lack of commitment to the retracting concept as late as 1930.

[19] Brooks, *Modern Airliner*, pp. 70–71; C. H. Gibbs-Smith, *The Aeroplane: An Historical Survey* (1960), pp. 93, 96.

[20] Nayler and Ower, *Aviation*, p. 272; Gibbs-Smith, *op. cit.*, p. 96; Brooks, *op. cit.*, pp. 71–72.

[21] Brooks, *Modern Airlines*, pp. 57–59.

[22] *Ibid.*, pp. 73–74.

[23] Gibbs-Smith, *op. cit.*, p. 83. The term monocoque means single shell and pure monocoque aircraft had no longitudinal stringers to stiffen them.

[24] Brooks, *Modern Airliner*, p. 57.

lage of its XP-9 fighter, developed between 1928 and 1930.[25] It is probable that this course by Boeing was stimulated by a 1927 paper of Rohrbach's and the attendance of Boeing managers at an air race in Los Angeles in 1928 at which the advantages of stressed-skin construction were made obvious.[26] In any event, the Model 200 and Model 221 "Monomails" and the Boeing 247 were aircraft with thick-rooted, cantilever wings and monocoque fuselages. Douglas subsequently studied the 247 design in the initial phases of work on the DC-1.[27]

During the period of development of the DC-3 generation of commercial aircraft, a new generation of bombers was being developed. Some commercial planes were outgrowths of military development efforts—but some military planes were also outgrowths of efforts at the commercial aircraft market. Thus, unlike the post-World War II period to be discussed below, it cannot with generality be contended that military aircraft were antecedent to commercial planes of the same general performance and technical characteristics. Up to the DC-3, both military and commercial planes adopted the technologies outlined above. It is true, nonetheless, that the underlying rationale for public support of aviation research and development was related to military rather than commercial needs.[28]

The conjunction of military and commercial developments is illustrated by Boeing projects of the period. The Model 200 "Monomails" provided aerodynamic and structural advances which aided in the development of Models 214 and 215. These models became the B-9 bomber. Models 220 and 221, variants of the Model 200, led to Model 246, the improved B-9A bomber. From this, the Boeing 247 emerged, incorporating the structural and aerodynamic features of the immediately preceding Boeing planes and, of course, additional improvements.

In other companies, the mix of production of new types tended to be predominantly military or predominantly commercial through the mid-1930s. A particularly outstanding early military development was the Martin 123, which later led to the B-10, B-12, and B-14 bomber designations. The Martin 123, was developed in advance of the Boeing 247 but, contrary to the history of the developments at Boeing, appeared as a radical departure from previous Martin models. Martin had not had a family of land-type commercial or bomber models prior to the Martin 123. The plane was, nonetheless, very sophisticated in its use of new technologies.

[25] Bowers, *Boeing Aircraft Since 1916*, pp. 173–174.

[26] Brooks, *Modern Airliner*, p. 73.

[27] Ingells, *Plane That Changed The World*, p. 30.

[28] The research at installations such as McCook Field and the Naval Aircraft Factory seems obviously in the military category. That at NACA, the Bureau of Standards and universities is less obviously so. Surveys of NACA's activities, including research sponsored by NACA at universities and other non-military government facilities, fail to show a significant, direct influence by the commercial industry until at least the late 1930's. See Hunsaker, "Forty Years", and Keller, *Flight Research*.

The Martin 123 was delivered to the Army in March 1932. It was an all-metal, twin-engined ship with a single, cantilever wing rooted at mid-fuselage level. It had retractable landing gear and, with the 675 horsepower engines (in contrast to the 550 horsepower units of the 247), was capable of flying more weight a longer distance at higher speeds than could other bombers or commercial planes available in the next year or two.[29] Yet no commercial variant appeared.

Throughout the period under consideration, Douglas had little military work directly related to the DC-1, 2, and 3 developments. The "Dolphin" amphibian, which was ordered as a military plane, provided experience with radial engines, low-drag Townend ring cowls, cantilever wings, and sheet metal fuselage structures, but the "Dolphin" was hardly the direct antecedent of the DC-1. Neither was the Douglas O-35, though it yielded some experience with retractable gear. Instead, Douglas went to the DC-1 project much as Martin went to the 123. Each adopted a variety of the developments of the past decade without themselves having attempted planes of similar types in the immediately preceding years.

Douglas did develop military planes from the early "DC" series. Aside from cargo and military transport versions of the DC-2 and DC-3, there was the Douglas DB-1, or B-18 bomber, which was based closely on the DC-2 and was procured through 1938 by the Army Air Corps.[30] Douglas, in fact, was hesitant to begin work on the DC-3 because of the heavy orders for the B-18s and a fear that the commercial market was saturated.[31]

A number of other instances of the new technology being attempted can be mentioned. The string of Lockheeds, from the "Vega" through the L-10 "Electra," have been treated in various places above. Consolidated Aircraft used the Lockheed "Altair" design to produce the PB-2 planes. Curtiss used an all-metal, monocoque fuselage in its P-23 and, after 1930, in the A-8, A-10, and A-12 series of attack monoplanes. The Northrop A-17 was a development of the "Gamma" and "Delta" which, as noted above, also affected the Douglas commercial planes. The histories of these and of other planes are obscured, however, by the shift in military research during the mid-1930s and

[29] The comparisons are as follows:

Aircraft	Gross Weight	Total Horsepower	Wing Area	Maximum Speed	Range
Model 123	12,560 lbs	1,350 hp	640 ft^2	207 mph	600 miles
B-10B	16,400	1,550	678	213	1,240
247	12,650	1,100	836	182	485
247A	12,405	1,250	836	198	650
DC-2	18,080	1,420	942	213	500

Note the relatively high wing-loads of the Model 123 and the B-10. Data on the military planes are from F. G. Swanborough, *United States Military Aircraft Since 1909* (1963).

[30] For additional detail, see F. G. Swanborough, *op. cit.*, pp. 218–220.

[31] On Douglas' reluctance, see Ingells, *Plane That Changed The World*, pp. 85, 93–95.

the role of that research and of military aircraft procurement on commercial aircraft development.

Commercial and Military Aviation Research and Development after the Mid-1930s

The National Advisory Committee on Aeronautics was formed in 1915 "to investigate the scientific problems involved in flight and to give advice to the military air services and other aviation services of the government." [32] It seems fairly clear, however, that its activities tended to shift through its lifetime from research that lacked a specific military or commercial purpose to that relating to specific military missions and even to specific military aircraft.

The Committee began annual conferences with military and industrial representatives in 1926. While research at Langley centered on the projects regarded by Langley personnel as being of value to the civil industry during the early 1930s,[33] the industry was dissatisfied with NACA's program. One result was an action by President Hoover—on December 9, 1932—transferring NACA to the Department of Commerce. This action was subsequently nullified.[34] The military had more influence on the Committee and as a consequence NACA research became more intensively a program of applied military research.[35] The industry view by 1936 was that "Much of the work . . . is secret. . . . It involves the national defense." [36] The industry did gain increased access to NACA in 1938 by obtaining CAA representation on the Committee. But by then, defense work was a dominant activity.

This changed the nature of the industry's reliance on exogenous science and technology. Prior to this time, developments in both military and commercial aircraft occurred from technical developments achieved with neither a specific military nor commercial purpose. After this, technical developments more often had a defined military purpose and new types of commercial planes more often had visible antecedents in military aircraft.

The story of the Douglas DC-4E is indicative of the problems inherent in attempts at commercial planes which are in advance of well-established technology. In timing, the DC-4E development followed closely that of the Boeing Model 299—or B-17 bomber—but the latter did not provide Douglas with adequate knowledge to press forward with the DC-4E as he had with the DC-2 and DC-3. With $500,000 of development funds supplied by TWA, American, Eastern, United, and Pan American Airlines, and with virtually

[32] Statement of Dr. Joseph S. Ames, *Hearings of the President's Aircraft Board* (1925), p. 340.
[33] Keller, *Flight Research*, p. 34.
[34] *Ibid.*, p. 35.
[35] *Ibid.*, pp. 47, 49.
[36] *Aircraft Year Book* (1935), p. 100.

assured orders, the DC-4E simply failed to materialize as a potentially successful commercial plane.[37]

The DC-4E was attempted at a time when aerodynamic design was essentially static. Professor E. P. Warner noted in early 1937 that ". . . external form no longer owes itself to designer inspiration. . . . Point by point, the aerodynamic laboratories [at Langley Field and abroad] have covered the aerodynamic features of design, and proved that one way is best and others not so good . . . [Military and transport aircraft] which do not adhere faithfully to that formula would be better planes if they did." [38] The DC-4E, which attempted innovation in its size, three-rudder tail, tricycle landing gear, and, initially, cabin pressurization, was not the aircraft that was to prove Warner wrong.[39]

Consolidated and, probably, Martin made preliminary attempts at four-engined commercial planes before the end of 1937.[40] Lockheed, at the instigation of Howard Hughes and TWA, began work on a four-engined design with transcontinental range capabilities in 1939.[41] But the first aircraft of the general type of the eventually dominant DC-4 and "Constellation" generations was the Boeing 307. It came directly from the B-17 bomber. After the war, Boeing's 377 arose from the B-29 and the C-97 developments. The 707 grew somewhat less directly from the B-47 and B-52. The lineage between military aircraft and most other commercial planes is less obvious. Table 7-1 provides a number of characteristics for U.S. bomber aircraft, however, to show that, while progress in piston-engined commercial planes continued through the mid-1950s, military developments were a number of years ahead.

The final Douglas piston-engined plane, the DC-7C, went into service in 1956.[42] The last Lockheed piston-engined plane was the L-1649, of 1957. Lockheed also produced the L-188 "Electra" turboprop, introduced in 1959. Yet the Boeing B-50A, a stretch of the 1942 B-29, was a larger, longer-ranged and, save for the L-188, faster (at maximum speeds) aircraft than any of these.[43] The B-19, a very slow and lightly loaded craft of 1941, was nearly as heavy and, in wing span, much larger than any of the later Douglas or Lockheed piston-engined commercial planes. The B-36 of 1946 was heavier, larger and nearly as fast as any of the commercial planes of the following decade. Thus, in these few bombers alone, technology was advanced in ways that permitted commercial developments.

---

[37] For comment at the time, see *Aviation* (April 1936), p. 45; (July 1936), p. 47; (March 1937), p. 49; (May 1937), p. 37.

[38] E. P. Warner, "Airplane Design in 1936," *Aviation* (January 1937), p. 67.

[39] Plans to pressurize were dropped very early in the development.

[40] *Aviation* (August 1937), p. 42.

[41] Brooks, *Modern Airliner*, pp. 100–104.

[42] The last to be designed, that is. The DC-6B was the last in production.

[43] The B-50A cruised at only 235 mph. A final version, the TB-50H, was lighter, but cruised at 410 mph.

Table 7-1

Characteristics of Selected Piston Engined and Turboprop Bomber Aircraft.

Aircraft	Manufacturer	Years of First Flight	Gross Weight	Wing Load	Maximum Speed
B-19	Douglas	1941	140,000 lbs	33 lbs/ft²	224 mph
Y1B-20	Boeing	1938	87,600	30	258
XB-24	Consolidated *a*	1939	38,360	37	310
B-25H	North American	1940	33,500	61	275
B-26	Martin	1940	27,200	45	315
XB-28	North American	1942	35,740	53	372
B-29	Boeing *b*	1942	110,000	63	358
YB-32	Consolidated	1942	101,662	71	376
B-36	Consolidated	1946	265,000	55	346
B-50A	Boeing	1947	168,708	98	385

a Also produced by Douglas, Ford, and North American.
b Also produced by Bell and Martin.
Sources: L. S. Jones, *U.S. Bombers: B-1—B-70* (1966); F. G. Swanborough, *United States Military Aircraft Since 1909* (1963).

The L-188 is not directly descended from a military plane. But Lockheed had produced two prototypes of the turboprop C-130 transport under a 1952 contract. The first flew in 1954.[44] By the time the L-188 prototypes flew in late 1957, Lockheed had some five years of experience with military turboprops of roughly the same size. In addition, Lockheed had learned a great deal from the British experience with the Viscount and the British Britannia series.[45] Although this technology was available to Douglas and Boeing, they both chose to forgo it in favor of turbojet commercial planes.

The 707 Generation of Commercial Aircraft

The development of jet aircraft—commercial as well as military—overlaps the period of piston engined planes very considerably. The design of Boeing's B-47 began in late 1943. Douglas began design of the XB-43, essentially a modification of the XB-42, in 1944. Convair's XB-46 design was initiated in 1944 also. There had been interest in jets well before this, but no commercial firms in the United States had sufficient interest and resources to take the lead in engine development. Thus, it is quite clear that so far as United States manufacture of either military or commercial planes is concerned, jet development waited until an exogenous technology had overcome the early obstacles.[46]

It is not clear when research on specific commercial transports by United

[44] Swanborough, *U.S. Military Aircraft*, pp. 317–319.
[45] Cf. R. E. G. Davies, *A History of the World's Airlines* (1963), pp. 438–450.
[46] For more details and an analysis of why the United States lagged behind England and Germany in turboject development, see Schlaifer and Heron, *Development of Aircraft Engines*, pp. 440–508.

States manufacturers began. Boeing, quite certainly, was studying alternative models with configurations akin to the C-97 in late 1949 or early 1950.[47] By the middle of 1952, Douglas had a full scale mock-up of a jet transport with a 35 degree swept-back wing. This erroneously convinced some that Douglas had a clear lead in the jet transport field at that time.[48]

By the end of the same year, Boeing had started work on a flying prototype of its jet transport—eventually to be known as the 707. That Boeing was significantly ahead of Douglas and Lockheed was acknowledged by early 1953.[49] The 707 prototype flew in December 1957; the DC-8, in May 1958, after an accelerated development program that began in 1955 and eventually cost $215 million.[50] Lockheed dropped its L-193 design prior to the prototype stage. Convair's 880 was announced in 1956 and had first flight in January 1959. Both the 880 and 990 suffered time-consuming and costly modifications in the course of development.

The 707, DC-8, 880, and 990 were, of course, developments of profound importance. They involved major R and D expenditures by the responsible companies. Yet it remains clear that their basic technologies came from other sources and for other reasons. An immediate impetus to the United States manufacturers was the de Havilland "Comet." Indicative of the existence of the basic technology well prior to United States commercial efforts, its development began in 1946 and its first flight occurred in 1949. The plane entered service with BOAC in 1952—more than six years before the 707 entered Pan American service—and orders by international carriers were heavy.[51] In a sense, the subsequent role of Boeing as well as Douglas in this market was saved only by the structural fatigue which the first "Comet" suffered.

The "Comet" was, nonetheless, a small plane with only 40 passenger seats and the relatively slow cruising speed of 465 miles per hour. In military developments, both larger and faster aircraft were in production in the United States. For example, as shown in Table 7-2, the Boeing B-47 flew in an experimental version in 1947. Its top speed was 578 miles per hour; its gross weight, 162,500 pounds. Deliveries of the B-47B, which with later modifications had a top speed in excess of 600 miles per hour and a gross weight of 180,000 pounds, began in 1951. The wing load was 105 pounds per square foot. These characteristics are much in the order of those of the 707 and the DC-8.

The B-52 flew in an experimental configuration in the same year that the "Comet" entered commercial service. The XB-52, however, weighed 390,000 pounds loaded. While design work on the plane dates back to 1945, the final configuration was largely set in 1948.[52] There is, moreover, a traceable relation-

[47] *Aviation Week* (July 24, 1950), p. 16.
[48] *Aviation Week* (August 11, 1952), p. 13.
[49] J. McDonald, "Jet Airliners: Year of Decision," *Fortune* (April, May 1953).
[50] Brooks, *Modern Airliner*, pp. 132–133; *Wall Street Journal* (September 11, 1959), p. 23.
[51] Davies, *World's Airlines*, pp. 451–455.
[52] Swanborough, *U.S. Military Aircraft*, p. 107.

Table 7-2

Characteristics of Selected Jet Bomber Aircraft.

Aircraft	Manufacturer	Year of First Flight	Gross Weight	Wing Load	Maximum Speed
XB-43	Douglas	1946	40,000 lbs	71 lbs/ft^2	507 mph
XB-45	North American	1947	81,418	70	580
XB-46	Convair	1947	91,000	71	545
XB-47	Boeing [a]	1947	162,500	105	578
XB-48	Martin	1947	102,600	77	495
XB-51	Martin	1949	55,932	102	645
XB-52	Boeing	1952	390,000	98	600+
B-58A	Convair	1956	160,000	104	1300+
YB-60	Convair	1952	300,000	—	520
RB-66	Douglas	1954	78,000	100	620
B-70	North American	1962	—	—	Mach 3

[a] 274 B-47s were built by Douglas; 385 by Lockheed.

Source: L. S. Jones, *U.S. Bombers: B-1—B-70* (1966); F. S. Swanborough, *United States Military Aircraft Since 1909* (1963).

ship between the Boeing 707 and KC-135 transports and the B-29, C-97, 377 "Stratocruiser," B-47, and B-52. The C-97, Boeing Model 367, was developed during World War II. It was a transport version of the B-29. After the war, the 377 was just a commercial transport adaptation of the 367 series. During the same period, work was begun on a Model 424 bomber, which was a proposed jet version of the B-29. The latter had already contributed substantially to the C-97 and 377, which were piston engined transports. Model 424 yielded to the Model 432, which was to have unswept wings and four jet engines encased in the fuselage. Then, in 1945, the German investigations of the sweep wing were discovered by Boeing engineers.[53] This led to Model 448, with swept wings and encased engines and, finally, in October 1945, to Model 450. This is the B-47 design, with engines hung on pods beneath the wings.[54]

Work on the 367 type of transport was continuing and at some indefinite point it was recognized by Boeing that the B-29 wing and piston engines promised little additional improvement in transport performance. From this line of development—indeed, the first commercial aircraft prototype was designated Model 367–80 internal to Boeing—came the 707 and KC-135 transports.[55] These aircraft were "a logical combination of the proven aerodynamic and structural features of the B-47 and B-52 combined with the cabin capacity of the Model 367 and other conventional transports." [56]

[53] See R. Perry, *Innovation and Military Requirements: A Comparative Study*, RM-5182-PR, The RAND Corporation (August 1967).

[54] See Bowers, *Boeing Aircraft Since 1916*, pp. 323–330.

[55] *Ibid.*, pp. 348–350.

[56] *Ibid.*, p. 352.

The marked similarity between the 707 and the DC-8 suggests that both planes depended on much the same prior developments. Unless one recognizes the slightly longer landing gear, the 30 degree rather than 35 degree sweep on the wings, or the nostrils on the nose of the standard DC-8, it is difficult to distinguish it from the 707. Douglas did manufacture 274 B-47s during the Korean War period, and Douglas did precede Boeing in mocking-up a jet with 35 degree swept wings. These facts, however, seem inadequate to explain the stricking resemblance of the DC-8 and the 707.

Any one of Boeing, Douglas, Lockheed, or Convair might have been first among U.S. commercial manufacturers of jet transports. The technology was there to adapt to—not risklessly or costlessly, to be sure, but it was there. Perhaps the biggest risk by 1953 was not technological in character. Instead, it was risk with respect to what sort of jet to build and when to build it. Consolidated elected to delay its start. The situation between Boeing, Lockheed, and Douglas was well described at the time. "It is pretty clear," John McDonald wrote prophetically in 1953, "that all three builders cannot stay in this market; perhaps not even two can make money on jets in the next ten years. The first question is which of the three, Douglas, Lockheed, or Boeing, is going to drop out. This will be settled by victorious timing." [57]

The risks of alternative strategies were spelled out. "Boeing, smarting under the defeat of the Stratocruiser (loss, \$15,400,000) but flushed with the success of its all-jet high performance long-range bomber, the B-52 (and the B-47), has made a move in the jet-transport field that is at once daring and cautious. The move is daring in its aim of getting to market first . . . and cautious in being embodied in a dual civil-military basic transport design, which can be developed in either or both directions. . . .

"Douglas and Lockheed are in the opposite position. Occupants of the old market, they intend to be 'late' and better in the new one, the later the better if the customers will hold. Their sales strategy is to make a paper jet and make no investment until they have enough orders to justify the cost of tooling. . . .

"But, while Douglas and Lockheed are pursuing similar strategies, they will be mortally opposed to each other if Boeing gets in; for in that event there will be little opportunity for compromise between them. . . . The first one to get enough orders to risk tooling will freeze design and make a first run to market, leaving the other to pull out a full arsenal of price and product offerings, or leave the market." [58]

How better to say it? In an environment of radical technological change there is great market risk related to when to dip into the technology and create a new product. Too soon or too late, too radically or too conservatively—each may be a source of failure in the market. The proper balance is so difficult to achieve that the market, by rewarding the successful and punishing the failures, tends to become concentrated.

[57] J. McDonald, *loc cit.*, p. 217.
[58] *Ibid.*, pp. 217–218.

8 Epilogue

Summary

The central task of this book is now completed. A number of advances in science and technology relating to aircraft manufacture have been traced in substantial detail. It has been shown that many of these occurred for reasons quite unrelated and, often, quite antecedent to their use in the production of commercial aircraft. The advances, nonetheless, provided opportunities and incentives for manufacturers of commercial aircraft to develop new types of planes.

The stream of innovations from the late 1920s through the mid-1960s has had the effects suggested by the hypothesis presented in Chapter 1. The number of manufacturers of commercial planes has decreased radically and there have been large shifts in the market shares of the remaining ones. Indeed, the decrease in numbers would likely have been greater and the possibility of entry by new producers would likely have been much less had there not been huge procurement of military aircraft and related R and D through much of the period.

The risks that firms face in a rapidly changing technological environment have been illustrated. Some of the manufacturers erred by failing to develop new aircraft types which technological changes were making possible. Others erred by attempting types which, except with enormous development costs, were not technically feasible. A few—and only a few—succeeded in avoiding these mistakes and, thus, in maintaining a position in the market.

Little more can be said in the way of conclusions. The evidence that has been gathered generally supports the hypothesis, but neither the nature of the hypothesis nor the method of analysis is such that more definitive conclusions are warranted. Still, some additional words relating to the results of other empirical studies can be offered.

Other Empirical Studies

There are apparently no other studies that have attempted directly to test the effects of exogeneous science and changing bases of technology on industry structure. There are, of course, numerous and, in smaller number, excellent studies of relations between industry structure and various measures of technology change.[1] These, however, hardly get to the point being argued here be-

---

[1] Among the latter, and in addition to references provided below, are E. Mansfield, "Size of Firm, Market Structure and Innovation," *Journal of Political Economy* (December 1963); O. E. Williamson, "Market Structure and Innovation," *Journal of Political Economy* (February 1965); J. Schmookler, "Bigness, Fewness, and Research," *Journal of Political Economy*

cause they were generally performed to test different hypotheses and because the statistical relationships between technology and structure are themselves silent with respect to cause and effect.

There are, nonetheless, a few cases in which researchers have suggested a relationship between exogeneous science and differences in the technological aspects of market performance of various industries. These have not pressed to the point of an analysis of industry structure but, by noting the correlation between an outside science on, say, industrial R and D or another measure of technological change, they do yield a measure of support for the views developed here. It is hard to dispute that industries with heavy R and D spending do tend to be concentrated. If, however, interindustry differences in levels of R and D spending are associated with differences in the extent to which a science is proximate to the activities of industries and if differences in R and D spending are not associated with differences in concentration alone, the essential ingredients of the market process which I suggest exists are at least demonstrated to occur in appropriate industrial patterns.

An early expression along these lines was provided by Yale Brozen. "The invention of synthetic fibers," Brozen noted, "not only provided new materials and new aspirations for what might be done with old materials but also stimulated the development of a body of knowledge approaching a science of textile fibers. *With at least a semi-scientific base the cost of discovering and developing new technology could be reduced and research become an economically worthwhile outlet for investment.*" [2]

Still, the synthetic fiber case is one in which industry played a large part in the development of the science. While dacron may be the product of the individual research of Whinfield and Dickson, nylon and, indeed, polymerization are much the products of du Pont and the chemical industry. Brozen did not stop with this illustration, however. "This experience, and others, provides a clue to the future direction of inventive activity in the form of research and development programs. Where a scientific base which can replace empirical methods has been developed fairly recently, or where basic advances are made which add to an old scientific base, research spending may be expected to begin growing. The more basic research in any given field, the greater the prospect for the development of a scientific base. . . ." [3] This is more to the point, but no possible effect on market structure is suggested.

Richard Nelson, Merton Peck, and Edward Kalachek argue even more directly that differences in scientific bases are important in determining industrial technological advances. "By providing a context of knowledge for trans-

_____

(December 1959); W. S. Comanor, "Market Structure, Product Differentiation and Industrial Research," *Quarterly Journal of Economics* (November 1967); W. R. MacLaurin, "Technical Progress in Some American Industries," *American Economic Review* (May 1954); G. W. Nutter, "Monopoly, Bigness and Progress," *Journal of Political Economy* (June 1959).

[2] Yale Brozen, "Trends in Industrial Research and Development," *Journal of Business* (July 1960), p. 209. (Emphasis added)

[3] *Ibid.*

cending the details of existing technology, advances in science have led to a succession of radical technological advances. This is not to say that major advances in technology follow recent advances in science closely and directly. . . . Lack of close proximity in time, however, should not obscure the point that the earlier advances were pivotal. Indeed, science-based inventions have been the major factor differentiating the products and processes of the twentieth from the nineteenth centuries. . . ." [4]

Continuing, these authors observe that, "Establishing a science base is not the same thing as exploring the feasibility of a particular design concept before deciding to initiate a development effort. . . . The objectives generally are far broader. Often the type of research involved is the sort that scientists would undertake simply to advance their own disciplines. . . ." Then, after noting the impact of large profit and non-profit organizations in adding scientific knowledge and creating scientific bases for industry, they add, "The electronics and chemical industries are particularly fortunate in the existence of a closely related scientific discipline. But even here much research and hardware experimentation are undertaken which probably would not be done by academics. In the case of aviation, an entire new discipline was developed [by government support for research in aerodynamics in the 1920s and 1930s]. Some industries were, in a sense born close to science; others formed their own science base, but in any case it takes considerable effort to remain close to science." [5]

It is not clear that Nelson, Peck, and Kalachek intended to infer that the considerable effort required to keep close to science might have differential effects on the abilities of firms to survive in such an environment. With such an inference, however, their description is much in line with my theme—a science progressing for reasons not directly related to market variables, a relatedness between this science and an industry's products and processes, search in the science by firms of the industry, possible contributions by the firms to the science, and varying degrees of commercial success among the firms.

That this is not far from the interpretation intended seems clear from their mild criticism of Schumpeter's *Capitalism, Socialism and Democracy.* "[W]hile he recognized that major advances come more easily in the science-based industries, Schumpeter failed to see that the reason is not the resources of the large corporation, or the organized R and D laboratory, but rather the large and continuing effort toward basic and exploratory research." [6]

F. M. Scherer has provided perhaps the most interesting statistical tests covering a number of industries. Scherer investigated differences in inventive activities of industries, measured by the number of patents issued to 448 of the largest firms in the United States, in terms of "technological opportunity,

[4] R. R. Nelson, M. J. Peck, and E. A. Kalachek, *Technology, Economic Growth and Public Policy* (1967), p. 40.
[5] Ibid., pp. 41–42.
[6] Ibid., p. 43.

firm size, product-line diversification, and monopoly power." With firm sizes held constant, Scherer found that the most important explanation of inter-industry differences in patenting "is a set of influences best described under the heading 'technological opportunity.' Technological opportunity in this context could relate partly to industry traditions or to demand conditions not manifested in mere sales volume, but it seems most likely to be associated with dynamic supply conditions dependent in turn upon the broad advance of technological knowledge. . . . In effect, science and technology exert a push on inventive output [in industries such as electrical equipment and chemicals much greater than that for industries such as paper, food products and clothing]." [7]

After a variety of statistical approaches, Scherer concludes that, "(1) Inventive output increases with firm sales, but generally at a less than proportionate rate. (2) Differences in technical opportunity—e.g., differences in technical investment possibilities unrelated to mere volume of sales and typically opened by the broad advance of knowledge—are a major factor responsible for interindustry differences in inventive output. (3) Inventive output does not appear to be systematically related to variations in market power, prior profitability, liquidity or (when participation in fields with high technological opportunity is accounted for) degree of product line diversification. . . . Perhaps a bevy of fact-mechanics can still preserve the Schumpeter engine [of *Capitalism, Socialism and Democracy*] from disgrace, but at present the outlook seems pessimistic." [8]

These additional words by others are, of course, more comforting than conclusive. There may be no fully conclusive test possible for isolating the specific causal nexus between science, inventive activity, innovation and market structure. For my part, I find the evidence convincing that science has played a greater role in determining industry structure than has industry structure played in determining patterns of technological change.

[7] F. M. Scherer, "Firm Size, Market Structure, Opportunity and the Output of Patented Inventions," *American Economic Review* (December 1965), p. 1100.
[8] *Ibid.*, pp. 1121–1122.

Appendixes

Appendix A

**Domestic Airlines Entering Scheduled
Service, 1914–1938**

This appendix gives the names and initial routes of United States domestic
airlines, arranged by the year the lines entered scheduled operation. The listing
was developed to define a group of carriers analogous to the domestic trunk
lines and to determine the importance of the omitted airlines in the fleet composition data for years prior to 1938.

Table A-1

Airlines Entering United States Scheduled Domestic Service [a], 1914–1938.

Airline	Initial Routes
Prior to 1926	
St. Petersburg—Tampa Airboat Line (1914)	St. Petersburg—Tampa
Aero Limited (1919)	New York—Atlantic City—Miami—Nassau
Aeromarine West Indies Co. (1919)	Key West—Havana; New York—Atlantic City (1921); Detroit—Cleveland (1921); Miami—Nassau (1922)
Sid Champlain Aircraft Co. (1919)	Los Angeles—Catalina
Pacific Marine Airways (1922)	San Pedro—Catalina
Ryan Airlines (1925)	Los Angeles—San Diego
1926	
Ford Motor Co.	Detroit—Chicago—Cleveland
Varney Air Lines	Elko—Pasco
Robertson Aircraft Corp.	Chicago—St. Louis
Western Air Express	Salt Lake City—Los Angeles
National Air Transport	Chicago—Dallas
Colorado Airways	Cheyenne—Pueblo
Florida Airways Corp.	Atlanta—Miami
Stout Air Services	New York—Boston
Philadelphia Rapid Transit Service	Philadelphia—Washington
Colonial Air Transport	New York—Boston
Pacific Air Transport	Seattle—San Francisco—Los Angeles
Northwest Airways	Chicago—St. Paul
1927	
Clifford Ball [b]	Cleveland—Pittsburgh
Boeing Air Transport [c]	Chicago—San Francisco
National Air Transport	Chicago—New York
St. Tamany—Gulf Coast Airway	Atlanta—New Orleans
Standard Airlines	Los Angeles—El Paso
Embry-Riddle	Cincinnati—Chicago
Colonial-Western Airways	Cleveland—Albany

Table A-1 (Continued)

Airline	Initial Routes
1928	
Texas Air Transport	Galveston—Dallas—San Antonio
West Coast Air Transport	San Francisco—Portland—Seattle
Maddox Air lines	Los Angeles—San Francisco
Pitcairn Aviation [d]	New York—Atlanta
Gulf Air Lines (Southern Air Transport)	New Orleans—Atlanta—Houston
Mutual	Los Angeles—Oakland
Wichita	Kansas City—Wichita
United States Air Transport	Washington—New York
Braniff Airlines	Tulsa—Oklahoma City
Thompson Aeronautical Corp.	Chicago—Bay City—Pontiac
National Parks Airways	Salt Lake City—Great Falls
Continental Air Lines [e]	Louisville—Cleveland
Universal Aviation Corp. [f]	Chicago—Cleveland
Canadian Colonial Airway	Montreal—New York
Capitol Airway	Chicago—Indianapolis
Midwest	Waterloo—Des Moines
Interstate Airlines	Atlanta—Chicago
Jefferson	Rochester—Minneapolis
Rankin	Portland—Yakima
Spokane	n.a.
Commercial	Seattle—Vancouver
Central Airlines	Tulsa—Wichita
Northern Airlines	n.a.
1929	
Atlantic Coast Airways	New York—Atlantic City
Browers Air Service	Wichita—Omaha
Continental Air Express [g]	Los Angeles—Alameda
Curtiss Wright Flying Service	Chicago Airport—Grant Park
Delta Air Service	Dallas—Shreveport—Monroe—Jackson— Meridian—Birmingham
Eastern Air Transport	New York—Atlanta
Southwest Air Fast Express	Dallas—Tulsa—St. Louis—Sweetwater— Kansas City
Gorst Air Transport	Seattle—Bremerton
Kohler Aviation Corp.	Grand Rapids—Milwaukee
Mamer Air Transport	Portland—Spokane
Mason and Dixon Air Lines	Cincinnati—Detroit
Mid-Continent Air Express [h]	Denver—El Paso—Kansas City
Middle States Air Lines	Akron—Detroit—Pittsburgh
Nevada Airlines	Los Angeles—Reno—Las Vegas
New Orleans Air Line	New Orleans—Pilottown
Pickwick	San Diego—Los Angeles
Pittsburgh Airways	Pittsburgh—Newark
Rapid Air Lines	Rapid City—Huron
Seagull Airlines	Salt Lake City—Ely
Transcontinental Air Transport [i]	Los Angeles—Columbus
Wedell-Williams Air Service	New Orleans—Shreveport—St. Louis— Grand Isle
Yellow Cab Airways	Kansas City—Twin Cities
United States Airways	Kansas City—Denver

Table A-1 (Continued)

Airline	Initial Routes
1930	
Air Ferries	San Francisco—Alameda—Vallejo
Bowen	Houston—Fort Worth—Tulsa; Oklahoma City—Dallas
Clarksburg Airways	Charleston—Pittsburgh
Dixie Flying Service	Greensboro—Washington
Eagle Air Lines	Kansas City—Des Moines
Kalispell Airways	Kalispell—Butte
Michigan Air Express	Grand Rapids—Harbor Springs
Main Flying Service	Cincinnati—Pittsburgh
Frank Martz Coach Co.	Wilkes Barre—New York
New England and Western Air Transport Co.	Albany—Boston
New York Airways	Atlantic City—New York
New York, Philadelphia and Washington Airways *i*	New York—Washington
Sky View Flying Service	Pittsburgh—Niagara Falls
Cromwell Airlines	San Angelo—Dallas—San Antonio
Transcontinental and Western Airlines	Los Angeles—Kansas City—Columbus
United States Airways	Kansas City—Denver
Western Air Service Corp.	Oklahoma City—Omaha
Trans-American Air Lines	Pontiac—Muskegon
United Air Lines *k*	(various routes of combined lines)
1931	
American Airways *l*	(various routes of combined lines)
Border Air Lines	Sheridan—Great Falls
Century Air Lines	St. Louis—Chicago—Toledo—Cleveland—Detroit
Century-Pacific Airlines	Los Angeles—San Francisco—San Diego—Phoenix
Metropolitan Air Ferry Service	North Beach—Newark—Brooklyn
Oklahoma-Texas Airline	Wichita Falls—Ponca City
Richmond Air Transport	Richmond—Washington
Chicago Detroit Airways	Chicago—Detroit
Trump Airways	Little Rock—Tulsa
Tuxhorn Flying School	Springfield—Kansas City
Reed Airlines	Wichita Falls—Oklahoma City—Ponca City
Varney Air Service *m*	Los Angeles—San Francisco
Wilmington-Catalina Air Lines	Wilmington—Avalon
Wyoming-Montana Air Lines *n*	Denver—Sheridan—Casper—Billings
1932	
Champlain Air Transport	Plattsburg—Burlington
Coast Airways	Los Angeles—Santa Barbara
Commuters Air Service	Hartford—Springfield
Gilpin Air Lines	San Diego—Los Angeles
Hanfords Tri-State Air Lines *o*	Sioux City—St. Paul
Hunter Airways	Memphis—Tulsa
Inter-City Air Lines	Springfield—Boston

Table A-1 (Continued)

1932 (Continued)

Maine Air Transport	Rockland—Stonington
Portland Airways	Portland—Walla Walla

1933

Cardiff and Peacock Airlines	Los Angeles—San Francisco
G & G Airlines Co., Ltd.	San Diego—Los Angeles
Licon Airways	Islip—New Haven
National Airways, Inc. *p*	Boston—Bangor
Pacific Seaboard Air Lines *q*	Los Angeles—San Francisco
Ozark Airways	Springfield—Kansas City

1934

Central Airlines	Washington—Detroit
Chesapeake Air Ferries	Baltimore—Ocean City
Delta Air Lines *r*	Charleston—Dallas
Island Airlines	New Bedford—Nantucket
Long ad Harmon	Amarillo—Fort Worth
National Airline System	Daytona Beach—St. Petersburg
Robertson Airplane Service Co.	Houston—New Orleans

1935

Columbia Airlines	Detroit—Louisville
Consolidated Airlines	Alameda—Sacramento
Land O'Lakes Airline	Detroit—St. Ignace
Watertown Airways	St. Paul—Spearfish

1936

Capital Airlines	Boise—Pocatello
Condor Air Lines	San Francisco—Salinas
Grand Canyon Airlines	Boulder City—Grand Canyon
Palm Springs Airlines	Los Angeles—Palm Springs

1937

Airline Feeder System, Inc.	New York—Westfield
Atlantic and Gulf Coast Airlines	Savannah—Mobile—Jacksonville
Miami-Key West Airways	Miami—Key West

1938

Marquette Airlines	St. Louis—Detroit
Mayflower Airlines	Boston—Nantucket

a Appearance of new lines which represent only name changes are, unless noted, eliminated as far as possible. For example, Alfred Frank Air Line, operating in 1934, is the same line as National Parks, which entered in 1928. Boston and Maine Airways, of 1937, is National Airways, formed in 1934. This subsequently became Northeast Airlines. General Airlines, 1934, is a renaming of Western Air Express, which maintained a separate existence after a 1930 merger with T.A.T.-Maddux. Mid-Continent Airlines, 1938, is the old Hanford's Tri-States Air Line of 1932.

b This became Pennsylvania Air Lines in 1930 and, after merger with Central Air Lines, eventually was renamed Capital Airlines.

c The predecessor company to United Air Lines, which is listed separately in 1930.

[d] The predecessor company to Eastern Air Lines, or Eastern Air Transport, which is listed separately as a 1929 entry.

[e] Not the same as the present Continental Air Lines. The latter grew from Varney Air Service, a 1931 entry.

[f] Original operating company of the Aviation Corporation, which subsequently developed American Airways.

[g] Not the same as the present Continental Air Lines.

[h] Not the same as the Mid-Continent Air Lines of 1938. The latter was formed as Hanford's Tri-States Air Line in 1932.

[i] This company, after mergers with Maddux and Western Air Express in 1930, became Transcontinental and Western Air, later Trans World Airlines.

[j] Also known as Ludington Air Lines in 1931 and 1932. The line disappeared in a merger with Eastern.

[k] Formerly known as Boeing Air Transport, a 1927 entry.

[l] American Airlines after 1934.

[m] A reentry by Varney after the Varney Air Lines, of 1926, was absorbed by United.

[n] Subsequently Wyoming and, later, Inland Air Lines.

[o] Subsequently Mid-Continent Air Lines.

[p] Subsequently Boston and Maine and, later, Northeast Air Lines.

[q] Subsequently Chicago and Southern Air Lines.

[r] A reentry of Delta after suspension of Delta Air Service of 1929.

Sources: *Air Commerce Bulletin* (1929–1938); R. E. G. Davis, *A History of the World's Airlines* (1964).

Appendix B

Characteristics of Commercial Aircraft

This appendix consists of two tables. Table B-1 gives selected characteristics for aircraft in the fleets of the domestic trunk carriers between 1932 and 1965. Table B-2 gives the same characteristics for other aircraft which were intended for commercial service but which were not operated by the trunk carriers.

The data in Table B-1 were used in the operating cost regressions in Chapter 3. Data from both Table B-1 and Table B-2 were used to make the cost comparisons in Chapters 4, 5, and 6.

Table B-1

Selected Characteristics of Landtype Passenger Aircraft with Four or More Passenger Capacity Used by U.S. Domestic Trunk Carriers, 1932–1965

| Manufacturer | Type | Specific Models | Year Entered Domestic Service | Engines [a] | | | Typical Passenger Capacity |
				Number	Type	Total Power	
Fokker	Single-Engine	"Universal"	1926	1	P	220	6
		"Super-Universal"	1928	1	P	425	6
		F-14	1929	1	P	525	7
Hamilton	Hamilton	H-45	1928	1	P	400	7
		H-47	1928	1	P	500	7
Ford	Tri-Motor	—	1926	3	P	—	—
		4-AT	1928	3	P	660	12
		4-AT-E	1929	3	P	900	12
		5-AT-B	1929	3	P	1,350	15
		5-AT-C	1929	3	P	1,350	15
		6-AT	1929	3	P	900	13
		7-AT	1929	3	P	1,050	13
		5-AT-D	1931	3	P	1,260	14
		4-AT-F	1931	3	P	900	12
Fairchild	Fairchild	71	1928	1	P	425	6
		71A	1930	1	P	450	6
	"Pilgrim"	100	1930	1	P	475	8
Fokker	Tri-Motor	F-10A	1928	3	P	1,275	10
Bellanca	"Pacemaker"	—	1929	1	P	300	5
		—	1930	1	P	300	5
Travel Air	Travel Air	A-6000A	1929	1	P	420	6
		6000-B	1929	1	P	300	5
Stinson	Single-Engine	"Detroiter"	1926	1	P	—	—
		SM-1DA	1928	1	P	220	5
		SM-1DB	1928	1	P	220	5
		SM-1F	1929	1	P	300	5
		SM-6B	1929	1	P	450	7
Lockheed	"Vega"	—	1928	1	P	220	4
		—	1929	1	P	450	5
		"Wasp"	1929	1	P	450	6
		—	1929	1	P	300	6
		5-C	1930	1	P	420	6
		DL-1	1930	1	P	450	6
Ryan	Brougham	B-5	1929	1	P	300	5
		B-7	1929	1	P	420	5
Boeing	B-40	40-C	1928	1	P	400	4
		40-B4	1929	1	P	525	4
Curtiss	"Condor"	—	1929	2	P	1,200	19
Boeing	B-80A	—	1929	3	P	1,575	16
Metal Aircraft Corp.	"Flamingo"	G-2H	1929	1	P	510	7
Fokker	F-32	—	1930	4	P	2,100	30
Consolidated	"Fleetster"	17	1930	1	P	575	7
		17–20	1930	1	P	575	7
		20	1930	1	P	575	5

Gross Take-Off Weight	Empty Weight	Loading b		Cruise Speed		Normal Full Load Cruise Range	Service Ceiling	Initial Climb Rate
		Wing	Power	Typical In Use	Listed			
4,000	—	12.1	18.2	—	—	—	—	—
4,750	3,230	12.5	11.2	—	118	735	18,000	1,000
7,200	4,038	13.1	13.7	—	95	425	14,000	700
5,750	3,300	14.3	14.4	—	115	600	16,000	950
5,750	3,450	14.9	11.0	—	120	600	18,000	1,000
—	—	—	—	—	—	—	—	—
10,130	6,169	12.9	15.3	—	—	—	—	—
10,130	6,696	12.9	11.3	—	110	560	14,500	950
13,250	7,576	16.0	9.8	—	—	—	—	—
13,500	7,500	16.1	10.0	—	113	525	16,000	900
12,144	7,048	—	13.5	—	—	—	—	—
12,910	7,280	—	12.3	—	—	—	—	—
14,000	8,320	16.8	12.1	—	120	550	17,500	975
11,000	6,929	—	12.2	—	—	—	—	—
5,500	2,930	—	12.9	—	—	—	—	—
5,500	3,156	16.6	12.2	—	110	650	15,000	675
6,500	3,700	15.6	13.7	—	122	450	18,000	900
13,100	7,780	15.4	10.3	—	118	765	18,000	1,400
4,300	2,275	15.7	14.3	—	110	900	18,000	1,250
4,300	2,465	—	14.3	—	125	850	17,000	900
5,250	3,250	16.2	12.5	—	120	680	18,000	1,000
4,230	2,550	15.8	14.1	—	110	500	16,000	800
—	—	—	—	—	—	—	—	—
4,500	2,432	—	20.5	—	—	—	—	—
4,500	2,522	—	20.5	—	—	—	—	—
4,300	2,614	14.7	14.3	—	115	700	17,000	1,000
5,350	3,496	16.0	11.9	—	125	625	18,000	1,200
—	—	—	—	—	—	—	—	—
4,033	2,465	—	9.0	—	—	—	—	—
4,265	2,490	—	9.5	—	—	—	—	—
4,220	2,305	14.7	14.1	—	125	800	16,000	1,200
4,500	2,565	16.4	10.7	—	150	700	19,750	1,345
4,750	2,850	17.0	10.6	—	180	660	18,500	1,300
4,000	2,250	14.3	13.3	—	110	800	18,000	1,000
4,283	2,500	15.3	10.2	—	120	500	20,000	1,350
6,075	3,522	11.1	15.2	—	102	600	12,000	600
6,510	3,822	11.9	14.5	—	110	535	16,100	750
17,378	11,352	11.5	7.3	—	116	—	17,000	870
17,500	10,413	14.0	11.1	—	125	460	15,500	900
6,000	3,460	16.8	11.8	—	115	580	14,000	900
22,500	14,200	16.7	10.7	—	120	—	18,000	1,200
5,600	3,326	17.9	9.8	—	150	500	19,000	1,050
5,600	3,443	17.8	9.8	—	153	700	19,000	1,050
5,900	3,439	18.8	10.3	—	140	500	17,500	1,100

Table B-1 (continued)

Manufacturer	Type	Specific Models	Year Entered Domestic Service	Engines [a]		Total Power	Typical Passenger Capacity
				Number	Type		
Stinson	Tri-Motor	SM-6000	1930	3	P	645	9
		SM-6000A	1930	3	P	645	8
		SM-6000B1	1931	3	P	645	9
		SM-6000B2	1931	3	P	645	8
		U	1932	3	P	720	9
		A	1934	3	P	780	8
Curtiss	"Kingbird"	D-1	1930	2	P	480	6
		D-2	1930	2	P	600	6
Boeing	221	—	1930	1	P	575	6
Northrop	"Alpha"	—	1930	1	P	420	6
		—	1931	1	P	450	6
Lockheed	"Orion"	Model 9	1931	1	P	450	6
		9B	1932	1	P	575	4
		9E	1933	1	P	450	5
		9F	1933	1	P	645	4
		9D	1933	1	P	550	4
Boeing	247	247	1933	2	P	1,050	10
		247D	1933	2	P	1,100	10
Curtiss-Wright	"Condor II"	T-32	1933	2	P	1,400	16
		—	1933	2	P	1,430	16
Douglas	DC-2	—	1934	2	P	1,420	14
Airplane Dev't	"Vultee"	V-1-A	1934	1	P	735	9
Lockheed	"Electra"	10A	1934	2	P	800	10
		10C	1934	2	P	900	10
		10B	1935	2	P	880	10
		10E	1935	2	P	1,100	10
Douglas	DC-3	DST	1936	2	P	2,400	14
		DC-3	1936	2	P	2,400	21
Lockheed	L-12	L-12A	1936	2	P	800	6
		L-12B	1936	2	P	840	6
Beech	18	18-A	1937	2	P	640	6
		18-B	1937	2	P	570	6
Lockheed	L-14	L-14H	1937	2	P	1,600	12
Lockheed	L-18	L-18-10	1940	2	P	1,800	14
		L-18-14	1940	2	P	2,100	14
		L-18-40	—	2	P	—	—
		L-18-50	—	2	P	—	—
		L-18-56	—	2	P	2,400	14
Boeing	307	—	1940	4	P	4,400	33
Lockheed	L-049/749	L-049	1946	4	P	8,800	51
		L-649	1947	4	P	10,000	55
		L-749	1947	4	P	10,000	55
Douglas	DC-4	—	1946	4	P	5,800	54
Douglas	DC-6	DC-6	1947	4	P	9,600	60
		DC-6B	1951	4	P	10,000	66
Martin	202	—	1947	2	P	4,800	40

| Gross Take-Off Weight | Empty Weight | Loading [b] | | Cruise Speed | | Normal Full Load Cruise Range | Service Ceiling | Initial Climb Rate |
		Wing	Power	Typical In Use	Listed			
8,500	5,475	17.3	13.5	—	—	—	—	—
—	—	—	—	—	—	—	—	—
—	—	—	—	—	—	—	—	—
—	—	—	—	—	—	—	—	—
9,300	6,055	16.2	12.9	—	119	400	13,000	825
10,200	7,200	20.4	13.1	—	165	640	17,000	1,000
6,115	3,754	15.1	12.7	—	120	454	14,700	820
6,115	3,887	15.1	10.2	—	120	415	18,000	1,000
8,000	4,990	15.0	13.9	—	137	500	14,000	850
4,500	2,678	15.3	10.7	—	140	420	19,300	1,400
4,850	2,979	—	—	—	—	—	—	—
5,200	3,250	18.7	11.6	—	180	600	21,600	1,430
5,400	3,570	19.4	9.4	—	—	—	—	—
5,400	3,664	—	12.0	—	—	—	—	—
5,401	3,708	—	8.4	—	—	—	—	—
5,800	3,640	19.7	10.5	—	205	720	22,000	1,400
12,650	8,400	15.1	11.5	—	189	500	25,400	—
13,650	8,950	16.3	12.4	—	189	500	25,400	—
16,800	11,235	13.2	12.5	—	150	600	17,500	1,000
17,500	11,465	14.5	12.2	—	167	650	23,000	1,200
18,200	12,000	19.2	12.8	170	170	500	23,200	1,090
8,500	5,307	22.1	11.6	—	205	1,000	20,000	1,000
9,400	5,855	20.3	11.7	—	190	500	20,000	900
10,100	6,325	22.0	11.2	—	195	500	21,150	1,100
10,000	6,300	21.8	11.4	180	186	500	18,200	1,230
10,500	7,100	22.9	9.5	—	205	500	25,800	1,200
24,000	16,000	24.3	10.0	175	188	850	21,800	1,200
24,000	15,300	24.3	10.0	175	190	850	21,500	1,200
8,400	—	—	10.5	—	205	—	—	—
8,400	5,765	23.8	10.0	—	213	715	23,350	1,470
6,700	4,270	19.3	10.5	184	196	850	24,000	1,500
6,500	4,130	19.3	11.4	180	190	850	20,000	1,350
15,000	9,650	27.2	9.4	180	224	1,000	24,300	1,640
18,500	12,208	30.2	10.3	—	—	—	—	—
18,500	11,626	30.2	8.8	220	229	850	27,000	1,850
—	—	—	—	—	—	—	—	—
—	—	—	—	—	—	—	—	—
18,600	—	33.5	7.8	—	230	—	—	—
42,000	30,000	28.3	9.5	200	220	2,700	26,200	1,200
98,000	63,900	59.3	11.1	285	310	2,300	24,700	1,370
—	—	—	—	—	—	—	—	—
107,000	65,700	64.8	10.7	285	323	2,600	23,800	1,234
73,000	40,500	50.1	12.6	205	234	1,900	24,000	880
97,200	58,216	66.4	10.1	310	310	3,000	28,500	1,100
100,000	56,491	68.4	10.0	300	316	2,800	27,000	1,130
39,900	25,795	46.2	8.3	255	255	800	22,800	1,450

Table B-1 (continued)

Manufacturer	Type	Specific Models	Year Entered Domestic Service	Engines [a] Number	Type	Total Power	Typical Passenger Capacity
Consolidated	CV-240	—	1948	2	P	4,800	40
Boeing	377	—	1949	4	P	14,000	70
Martin	404	—	1951	2	P	4,800	44
Lockheed	1049	L-1049B	1951	4	P	11,200	83
		L-1049C	1953	4	P	13,000	83
		L-1049D	1953	4	P	13,000	83
		L-1049E	1953	4	P	13,000	83
		L-1049G	1955	4	P	13,600	80
Consolidated	340/440	340	1952	2	P	4,800	44
		440	1956	2	P	5,000	52
Douglas	DC-7	DC-7A	1953	4	P	13,000	76
		DC-7B	1955	4	P	13,000	76
		DC-7C	1956	4	P	13,600	70
Vickers-Armstrong	700/800	V-745	1955	4	TP	6,680	48
		V-812	1958	4	TP	7,200	52
Lockheed	1649	1649A	1957	4	P	13,600	75
Boeing	707	707–120	1958	4	TJ	54,000	132
		707–220	1959	4	TJ	63,200	132
		707-120B	1961	4	TF	68,000	132
Lockheed	L-188	—	1959	4	TP	15,000	85
Douglas	DC-8	DC-8-10	1959	4	TJ	54,000	132
		DC-8-20	1960	4	TJ	67,200	132
		DC-8-50	1961	4	TF	72,000	142
Convair	880	Model 22	1960	4	TJ	42,400	110
Boeing	720	720	1960	4	TJ	48,000	110
		720B	1961	4	TF	72,000	120
SUD	"Caravelle"	6R	1961	2	TJ	25,200	64
Convair	990	990	1962	4	TF	—	—
		990-30A-6	1963	4	TF	64,000	110
Boeing	727	727-100	1964	3	TF	42,000	110
BAC	111	111–200	1965	2	TF	20,800	79
Douglas	DC-9	DC-9-10(11)	1965	2	TF	24,000	90

[a] Types are: P = piston, TP = turbo-prop, TJ = turbo-jet, TF = turbo-fan. Total power is maximum take-off horsepower for piston and turbo-prop engines; pounds of thrust for turbo-jet and turbo-fan engines.

[b] Wing loading is in gross weight pounds per square foot of wing area. Engine loading is in gross weight pounds per horsepower.

Sources: Aviation (Statistical Issues); *Automotive Industries* (Specification Issues); *Air Commerce Bulletin* (ATC records); *Flight* (Commercial Aircraft Survey Issues); *Aviation Week and Space Technology* (Inventory Issues); R.E.G. Davies, *History of the Worlds Airlines*, Table 51.

Gross Take-Off Weight	Empty Weight	Loading [b]		Cruise Speed		Normal Full Load Cruise Range	Service Ceiling	Initial Climb Rate
		Wing	Power	Typical in Use	Listed			
41,790	27,682	49.6	8.4	270	272	500	26,200	1,520
145,800	83,500	81.4	10.4	300	300	3,000	33,000+	1,030
42,750	27,799	49.5	8.9	260	280	860	27,300	1,400
120,000	—	72.7	10.7	300	320	2,900	24,000	1,100
133,000	69,700	80.6	10.2	305	330	3,000	24,100	1,125
133,000	69,700	80.6	10.2	305	330	3,000	24,100	1,125
133,000	69,700	80.6	10.2	305	330	3,000	24,100	1,125
137,500	73,016	82.2	10.1	310	335	4,000	30,100	1,600
47,000	29,486	51.1	9.8	280	284	700	25,000	1,220
49,100	31,305	53.4	9.8	280	289	550	25,000	1,230
122,200	65,900	83.5	9.4	350	370	3,600	28,200	1,150
126,000	68,073	86.1	9.7	350	361	3,700	23,900	1,135
143,000	72,643	87.4	10.5	310	355	4,350	22,800	1,050
64,500	37,070	70.0	—	315	320	1,500	30,000	1,500
72,500	41,565	75.3	—	314	356	1,890	30,000	1,900
156,000	85,553	84.3	11.5	340	350	5,000	29,700	1,660
258,000	118,000	106.0	—	550	590	3,000	41,000	—
247,000	122,000	101.5	—	550	600	3,300	41,000	—
258,000	118,000	106.0	—	560	610	4,200	41,000	—
113,000	55,993	86.9	—	405	405	1,600	32,000	2,150
273,000	120,999	100.2	—	544	570	4,000	40,000	—
276,000	123,757	101.3	—	544	570	4,200	40,000	
315,000	126,525	115.6	—	550	580	6,000	40,000	—
184,500	84,300	92.0	—	556	600	3,500	40,000	—
230,000	110,800	94.5	—	560	605	3,600	41,000	—
235,000	115,000	96.6	—	560	610	4,200	41,000	—
110,230	63,206	63.5	—	505	522	2,300	40,000	2,460
—	—	—	—	—	—	—	—	—
255,000	—	113.3	—	605	621	4,600	40,000	—
152,000	85,500	92.1	—	570	596	1,600	41,000	—
78,500	46,405	80.1	—	550	550	1,600	40,000	—
77,700	50,300	83.2	—	550	560	1,470	40,000	—

Table B-2

Selected Characteristics of Landtype Passenger Aircraft Developed for Transport Service but Not Used by U.S. Domestic Trunk Carriers.

Manufacturer	Type	Year Available for Order	Engines		Total Power	Typical Passenger Capacity
			Num-ber	Type		
Douglas	Cl	1927	1	P	400	9
Bellanca	CH	1928	1	P	200	5
General	101-A	1929	2	P	440	8
International	F-18	1929	1	P	200	5
Pittsburgh	Thaden, T-1	1929	1	P	425	7
Keystone	K-47-D	1929	3	P	1,275	10
Keystone	Patrician	1929	3	P	1,575	18
Buhl	GA-8A(& B)	1929	1	P	525	7
Buhl	CA-6	1929	1	P	300	5
Cunningham-Hall	PT-6	1929	1	P	300	5
Cessna	CW-6	1929	1	P	300	5
Cessna	CPW-6	1929	1	P	400	5
Air Transport	T-6 [a]	1929	3	P	300	5
Curtiss-Robertson	Thrush-J	1929	1	P	225	5
Bach	3-CT-9	1929	3	P	875	9
Bellanca	Skyrocket	1930	1	P	420	5
Ogden	Osprey	1930	3	P	270	5
Curtiss-Wright	6B	1930	1	P	300	5
Bellanca	Airbus	1930	1	P	600	10
Bellanca	Aircruiser	1931	1	P	575	10
Emsco	B-3A	1931	1	P	420	8
Simplex	W-6	1931	1	P	450	5
Shamrock	3-6PW-300	1931	1	P	300	5
Curtiss-Wright	CW-A6-A	1931	1	P	420	7
Curtiss-Wright	Kingbird D-3	1931	2	P	600	7
Bellanca	Skyrocket F-2	1932	1	P	450	5
Scout	Senior	1933	1	P	(optional)	6
Chamberlin	C-81, C-82	1933	1	P	300	6
Solar	M-S-2	1933	1	P	420	8
General	GA-43A	1934	1	P	715	10
Northrop	Delta 1-A	1934	1	P	715	8
Bellanca	Aircruiser	1934	1	P	715	13
Bellanca	Sr. Skyrocket	1935	1	P	550	5
Bellanca	Sr. Pacemaker	1935	1	P	420	7
Allan H. Lockheed	Alcor Duo-6	1935	2	P	420	6
Bellanca	Air Transport	1935	2	P	1,430	13
Burnelli	UB-14	1935	2	P	1,500	12
Fairchild	C-31	1936	1	P	750	14
Stinson	B	1936	2	P	520	5
Kinner	Invader	1936	2	P	720	5
Crusader	AG-7	1936	2	P	500	6
Air Transport	B-6	1937	2	P	500	6
Air Transport	B-8	1938	2	P	640	8
Barkley-Grow	T8P-1	1938	2	P	800	10
Burnelli	CB-34	1940	3	P	2,700	34
Douglas	DC-5	1940	2	P	2,200	16
Curtiss-Wright	Transport	1940	2	P	3,000	40

Gross Take-Off Weight	Empty Weight	Loading		Cruise Speed	Cruise Range	Service Ceiling	Initial Climb Rate
		Wing	Power				
7,400	3,800	—	18.5	—	—	—	—
4,050	2,190	14.8	20.3	105	—	—	850
6,300	—	12.6	14.3	105	—	—	1,000
3,750	2,200	10.4	18.8	110	500	14,000	850
5,600	—	13.7	13.2	110		—	800
12,300	—	10.8	9.6	120	—	—	1,200
16,000	9,555	16.3	10.2	120	500	12,000	850
6,300	3,542	13.6	12.0	120	775	18,000	1,000
4,500	2,478	14.8	15.0	115	720	15,000	900
4,350	2,680	11.7	14.5	115	700	17,500	1,050
3,950	2,175	13.7	13.2	120	610	17,500	900
4,250	2,425	14.3	10.6	130	660	19,000	1,300
4,500	2,752	14.3	15.0	125	450	18,000	1,100
3,800	2,260	12.4	16.9	102	—	13,200	650
8,000	4,800	14.9	9.1	135	525	19,000	1,200
4,600	2,610	16.8	11.0	130	650	20,000	1,450
4,500	2,850	14.4	16.7	105	500	14,100	880
4,452	2,739	15.9	14.8	115	560	16,000	900
9,500	5,490	14.8	15.9	125	750	14,500	750
9,590	5,155	14.8	16.7	123	—	—	—
6,600	4,199	—	15.7	—	—	—	—
3,753	1,983	12.4	8.3	—	—	—	—
3,055	1,935	13.2	10.2	117	—	—	—
5,600	3,332	14.6	13.3	114	725	18,000	950
6,600	4,466	15.6	11.0	120	585	17,600	1,120
5,600	3,240	18.0	12.4	148	1,450	19,000	1,000
7,840	4,440	16.3	—	—	—	—	—
4,440	2,400	17.1	14.8	105	—	—	—
7,000	3,650	14.1	16.7	115	—	—	—
8,750	5,430	19.0	12.2	190	680	14,000	700
7,000	4,100	19.2	9.8	201	1,700	24,800	1,000
11,400	6,115	17.2	15.9	155	610	16,000	700
5,600	3,440	15.2	10.2	180	600	25,000	1,240
5,600	3,250	15.5	13.3	145	860	12,000	700
5,090	2,885	18.2	12.1	160	660	20,000	1,400
14,422	8,402	21.7	10.1	170	750	27,000	1,500
14,000	8,000	20.4	9.3	185	600	22,000	1,250
12,400	7,322	15.5	16.5	140	665	17,000	—
6,600	4,500	18.5	12.7	160	900	16,000	1,150
10,100	6,325	22.0	13.6	190	900	20,000	1,225
6,000	3,597	—	—	180	720	20,000	1,000
5,500	3,102	14.6	11.0	180	500	21,000	1,230
6,500	3,730	18.1	10.2	180	500	22,000	1,400
8,750	5,649	24.8	10.9	192	750	19,000	1,300
33,500	19,360	23.4	12.4	206	1,440	22,000	1,092
20,000	13,674	24.2	9.1	202	1,500	23,700	1,585
40,000	24,750	29.4	13.3	220	1,500	26,900	1,440

Table B-2 (continued)

| Manufacturer | Type | Year Available for Order | Engines | | Typical Passenger Capacity |
			Number	Type	Total Power	
Lockheed	L-144	1940	4	P	4,400	40
Consolidated	32 Landplane	1941	4	P	—	21
Lockheed	75-77 Saturn	1946	2	P	1,200	16
Hughes	Feederliner	1946	2	P	1,650	18
Douglas	DC-8 *b*	1946	2	P	2,480	48
Consolidated	CV-37	1946	6	P	30,000	216
Republic	RC-2 Rainbow	1946	4	P	14,000	46
Hughes	H-4	1947	8	P	28,000	—
Lockheed	Constitution	1947	4	P	12,000	180
Beech	Twin-Quad	1948	4	P	15,000	23
Douglas	DC-9 *c*	1948	2	P	3,300	28
Chase	YC-122	1951	2	P	2,850	30
Chase	C-123B	1952	2	P	5,000	60
Douglas	R4D-8	1953	2	P	2,950	35
Stroukoff	YC-134A	1958	2	P	7,800	73

Sources: See Table 5.

a Also known as Kruetzer K-5.

b Not to be confused with subsequent DC-8 turbojet transport with same designation.

c Not to be confused with subsequent DC-9 turbofan transport with same designation.

Gross Take-Off Weight	Empty Weight	Loading		Cruise Speed	Cruise Range	Service Ceiling	Initial Climb Rate
		Wing	Power				
43,000	26,960	43.0	9.8	258	1,570	24,300	1,695
47,000	—	—	—	—	—	—	—
14,000	9,634	37.9	11.7	200	1,600	26,000	1,460
18,500	11,000	—	11.2	186	—	28,500	1,290
39,500	23,915	35.9	15.9	270	1,560	30,000	1,150
320,000	164,100	67.2	10.7	340	4,200	30,000	—
114,200	68,024	69.1	8.2	400+	4,100	41,000	1,680
400,000	—	35.0	14.3	175	3,000	17,000	675
184,000	114,575	—	15.3	286	6,300	—	—
19,500	—	—	13.0	180	1,450	—	1,000
30,000	19,600	—	9.1	242	2,125	—	—
32,000	19,000	39.4	11.2	200	2,900	—	1,250
54,000	30,000	44.2	10.8	205	2,050	—	1,350
31,000	19,500	32.1	10.5	238	4,700	—	1,350
81,700	37,380	—	10.5	—	—	—	—

Appendix C

Aircraft in Aggregate Fleet of Domestic Trunk Air Lines

This appendix gives the composition of aggregate fleet of the trunk line carriers for the years 1932 to 1965. The aircraft listed comprise the full fleets, whether acquired new or used and whether owned or leased by the carriers. The data in Table C-1 provide the basis for the estimates of concentration made in Chapter 2.

Table C-1

Fleets of Landtype Aircraft Operated by U.S. Domestic Passenger Trunk Air Carriers, by Type of Aircraft, 1932–1965.

Year (Dec. 31)	DC-2	DC-3	DC-4	DC-6 DC-6A DC-6B	DC-7 DC-7B DC-7C	DC-8	DC-9	Douglas Total
1932	—	—	—	—	—	—	—	—
1933	1 [a]	—	—	—	—	—	—	1
1934	21 [a]	—	—	—	—	—	—	21
1935	57 [a]	—	—	—	—	—	—	57
1936	55	29	—	—	—	—	—	84
1937	50	76	—	—	—	—	—	126
1938	46	97	—	—	—	—	—	143
1939	44	137	—	—	—	—	—	181
1940	31	232	—	—	—	—	—	263
1941	13	267	—	—	—	—	—	280
1942	—	154	—	—	—	—	—	154
1943	—	174	—	—	—	—	—	174
1944	—	253	—	—	—	—	—	253
1945	—	374	—	—	—	—	—	374
1946	—	443	162	—	—	—	—	605
1947	—	420	169	78	—	—	—	667
1948	—	368	145	103	—	—	—	616
1949	—	316	160	104	—	—	—	580
1950	—	289	146	109	—	—	—	544
1951	—	285	137	139	—	—	—	561
1952	—	246	124	161	—	—	—	531
1953	—	164	123	180	16	—	—	483
1954	—	125	109	185	61	—	—	480
1955	—	128	100	190	77	—	—	495
1956	—	118	76	218	99	—	—	511
1957	—	92	39	266	169	—	—	566
1958	—	82	31	270	214	—	—	597
1959	—	50	25	269	189	18	—	551
1960	—	35	18	257	179	56	—	545
1961	—	30	—	223	172	68	—	493
1962	—	11	—	192	164	76	—	443
1963	—	9	—	180	138	78	—	405
1964	—	7	—	171	103	86	—	367
1965	—	7	—	147	44	99	4	301

[a] Includes one DC-1.

(continued)

Table C-1 (continued)

Year (Dec. 31)	B-40	B-80	B-221	B-247	B-307	B-377	B-707	B-720 B-720B	B-727	Boeing Total
1932	57	12	2	—	—	—	—	—	—	71
1933	33	11	2	54	—	—	—	—	—	100
1934	30	10	2	57	—	—	—	—	—	99
1935	27	8	—	57	—	—	—	—	—	92
1936	1	7	—	54	—	—	—	—	—	62
1937	—	—	—	48	—	—	—	—	—	48
1938	—	—	—	39	—	—	—	—	—	39
1939	—	—	—	39	—	—	—	—	—	39
1940	—	—	—	30	5	—	—	—	—	35
1941	—	—	—	28	5	—	—	—	—	33
1942	—	—	—	—	—	—	—	—	—	0
1943	—	—	—	1	—	—	—	—	—	1
1944	—	—	—	1	—	—	—	—	—	1
1945	—	—	—	—	5	—	—	—	—	5
1946	—	—	—	—	5	—	—	—	—	5
1947	—	—	—	—	5	—	—	—	—	5
1948	—	—	—	—	5	—	—	—	—	5
1949	—	—	—	—	5	10	—	—	—	15
1950	—	—	—	—	5	10	—	—	—	15
1951	—	—	—	—	—	16	—	—	—	16
1952	—	—	—	—	—	16	—	—	—	16
1953	—	—	—	—	—	16	—	—	—	16
1954	—	—	—	—	—	11	—	—	—	11
1955	—	—	—	—	—	10	—	—	—	10
1956	—	—	—	—	—	9	—	—	—	9
1957	—	—	—	—	—	9	—	—	—	9
1958	—	—	—	—	—	9	—	—	—	9
1959	—	—	—	—	—	6	50	—	—	56
1960	—	—	—	—	—	—	62	22	—	84
1961	—	—	—	—	—	—	62	79	—	141
1962	—	—	—	—	—	—	78	97	—	175
1963	—	—	—	—	—	—	92	99	—	191
1964	—	—	—	—	—	—	106	106	88	300
1965	—	—	—	—	—	—	125	114	167	406

Table C-1 (continued)

Year (Dec. 31)	L-Vega	L-Orion	L-10 Electra	L-12	L-14	L-18	L-049 L-649 L-749	L-1049	L-1649	L-188	Lockheed Total
1932	18	12	—	—	—	—	—	—	—	—	30
1933	18	21	—	—	—	—	—	—	—	—	39
1934	12	20	11	—	—	—	—	—	—	—	43
1935	12	15	31	—	—	—	—	—	—	—	58
1936	8	—	41	3	—	—	—	—	—	—	52
1937	5	—	37	3	6	—	—	—	—	—	51
1938	—	—	33	3	9	—	—	—	—	—	45
1939	—	—	34	3	2	—	—	—	—	—	39
1940	—	—	24	—	2	12	—	—	—	—	38
1941	—	—	16	—	—	13	—	—	—	—	29
1942	—	—	—	—	—	10	—	—	—	—	10
1943	—	—	—	—	—	14	—	—	—	—	14
1944	—	—	—	—	—	16	—	—	—	—	16
1945	—	—	—	—	—	18	—	—	—	—	18
1946	—	—	—	—	—	12	12	—	—	—	24
1947	—	—	—	—	—	12	30	—	—	—	42
1948	—	—	—	—	—	12	36	—	—	—	48
1949	—	—	—	—	—	11	55	—	—	—	66
1950	—	—	—	—	—	11	86	—	—	—	97
1951	—	—	—	—	—	11	96	5	—	—	112
1952	—	—	—	—	—	11	101	24	—	—	136
1953	—	—	—	—	—	11	105	32	—	—	148
1954	—	—	—	—	—	12	102	39	—	—	153
1955	—	—	—	—	—	9	108	63	—	—	180
1956	—	—	—	—	—	10	108	73	—	—	191
1957	—	—	—	—	—	10	107	81	25	—	223
1958	—	—	—	—	—	7	104	89	29	—	229
1959	—	—	—	—	—	—	98	86	28	96	308
1960	—	—	—	—	—	—	69	82	25	107	283
1961	—	—	—	—	—	—	62	69	24	122	277
1962	—	—	—	—	—	—	36	65	27	117	245
1963	—	—	—	—	—	—	34	65	24	117	240
1964	—	—	—	—	—	—	34	54	22	117	227
1965	—	—	—	—	—	—	29	46	5	117	197

Table C-1 (continued)

Year (Dec. 31)	Fleet-ster	CV-240	CV-340 CV-440	CV-880	CV-990	Consoli-dated Total	M-202	M-404	Martin Total
1932	3	—	—	—	—	3	—	—	—
1933	7	—	—	—	—	7	—	—	—
1934	7	—	—	—	—	7	—	—	—
1935	6	—	—	—	—	6	—	—	—
1936	5	—	—	—	—	5	—	—	—
1937	—	—	—	—	—	—	—	—	—
1938	—	—	—	—	—	—	—	—	—
1939	—	—	—	—	—	—	—	—	—
1940	—	—	—	—	—	—	—	—	—
1941	—	—	—	—	—	—	—	—	—
1942	—	—	—	—	—	—	—	—	—
1943	—	—	—	—	—	—	—	—	—
1944	—	—	—	—	—	—	—	—	—
1945	—	—	—	—	—	—	—	—	—
1946	—	—	—	—	—	—	—	—	—
1947	—	—	—	—	—	—	9	—	9
1948	—	69	—	—	—	69	24	—	24
1949	—	97	—	—	—	97	24	—	24
1950	—	103	—	—	—	103	33	—	33
1951	—	102	—	—	—	102	12	18	30
1952	—	99	24	—	—	123	12	96	108
1953	—	93	98	—	—	191	12	100	112
1954	—	92	116	—	—	208	12	100	112
1955	—	89	118	—	—	207	11	99	110
1956	—	88	137	—	—	225	11	97	108
1957	—	88	160	—	—	248	11	95	106
1958	—	65	159	—	—	224	10	95	105
1959	—	39	137	—	—	176	—	85	85
1960	—	41	113	14	—	168	—	72	72
1961	—	21	104	38	—	163	—	36	36
1962	—	13	86	44	15	158	—	16	16
1963	—	10	77	45	19	151	—	—	—
1964	—	—	69	47	19	135	—	—	—
1965	—	—	67	46	18	131	—	—	—

Table C-1 (continued)

Year (Dec. 31)	Stinson Single Engine	Stinson Trimotor	Stinson Total	Fokker Single Engine	F-10	F-32	Fokker Total
1932	32	26	58	19	28	9	56
1933	17	23	40	14	16	—	30
1934	11	37	48	4	2	—	6
1935	6	42	48	1	—	—	1
1936	1	27	28	—	—	—	—
1937	—	9	9	—	—	—	—
1938	—	4	4	—	—	—	—
1939	—	2	2	—	—	—	—
1940	—	2	2	—	—	—	—
1941	—	—	—	—	—	—	—
1942	—	—	—	—	—	—	—
1943	—	—	—	—	—	—	—
1944	—	—	—	—	—	—	—
1945	—	—	—	—	—	—	—
1946	—	—	—	—	—	—	—
1947	—	—	—	—	—	—	—
1948	—	—	—	—	—	—	—
1949	—	—	—	—	—	—	—
1950	—	—	—	—	—	—	—
1951	—	—	—	—	—	—	—
1952	—	—	—	—	—	—	—
1953	—	—	—	—	—	—	—
1954	—	—	—	—	—	—	—
1955	—	—	—	—	—	—	—
1956	—	—	—	—	—	—	—
1957	—	—	—	—	—	—	—
1958	—	—	—	—	—	—	—
1959	—	—	—	—	—	—	—
1960	—	—	—	—	—	—	—
1961	—	—	—	—	—	—	—
1962	—	—	—	—	—	—	—
1963	—	—	—	—	—	—	—
1964	—	—	—	—	—	—	—
1965	—	—	—	—	—	—	—

Table C-1 (continued)

Year (Dec. 31)	Condor CO Transport	T-32 Condor II Transport	CIR Kingbird	Travel Air	Hamilton Silver Streak	Fairchild Pilgrim 100
1932	5	—	9	12	9	20
1933	5	17	9	3	8	10
1934	4	23	5	1	8	—
1935	—	17	5	—	1	—
1936	—	8	—	—	—	—
1937	—	—	—	—	—	—
1938	—	—	—	—	—	—
1939	—	—	—	—	—	—
1940	—	—	—	—	—	—
1941	—	—	—	—	—	—
1942	—	—	—	—	—	—
1943	—	—	—	—	—	—
1944	—	—	—	—	—	—
1945	—	—	—	—	—	—
1946	—	—	—	—	—	—
1947	—	—	—	—	—	—
1948	—	—	—	—	—	—
1949	—	—	—	—	—	—
1950	—	—	—	—	—	—
1951	—	—	—	—	—	—
1952	—	—	—	—	—	—
1953	—	—	—	—	—	—
1954	—	—	—	—	—	—
1955	—	—	—	—	—	—
1956	—	—	—	—	—	—
1957	—	—	—	—	—	—
1958	—	—	—	—	—	—
1959	—	—	—	—	—	—
1960	—	—	—	—	—	—
1961	—	—	—	—	—	—
1962	—	—	—	—	—	—
1963	—	—	—	—	—	—
1964	—	—	—	—	—	—
1965	—	—	—	—	—	—

Table C-1 (continued)

Year (Dec. 31)	Fairchild 71	Bellanca Pacemaker	Flamingo	Ford Trimotor	Ryan Brougham	Northrop Alpha
1932	20	2	9	63	1	6
1933	—	7	9	44	1	6
1934	—	6	—	47	—	6
1935	—	—	—	26	—	—
1936	—	—	—	8	—	—
1937	—	—	—	—	—	—
1938	—	—	—	—	—	—
1939	—	—	—	—	—	—
1940	—	—	—	—	—	—
1941	—	—	—	—	—	—
1942	—	—	—	—	—	—
1943	—	—	—	—	—	—
1944	—	—	—	—	—	—
1945	—	—	—	—	—	—
1946	—	—	—	—	—	—
1947	—	—	—	—	—	—
1948	—	—	—	—	—	—
1949	—	—	—	—	—	—
1950	—	—	—	—	—	—
1951	—	—	—	—	—	—
1952	—	—	—	—	—	—
1953	—	—	—	—	—	—
1954	—	—	—	—	—	—
1955	—	—	—	—	—	—
1956	—	—	—	—	—	—
1957	—	—	—	—	—	—
1958	—	—	—	—	—	—
1959	—	—	—	—	—	—
1960	—	—	—	—	—	—
1961	—	—	—	—	—	—
1962	—	—	—	—	—	—
1963	—	—	—	—	—	—
1964	—	—	—	—	—	—
1965	—	—	—	—	—	—

Table C-1 (continued)

Year (Dec. 31)	Beechcraft 18	Vultee V-1-A	Viscount V-745	Viscount V-812	S-210 Caravelle	BAC-111	GRAND TOTAL
1932	—	—	—	—	—	—	374
1933	—	—	—	—	—	—	336
1934	—	10	—	—	—	—	334
1935	—	10	—	—	—	—	321
1936	—	10	—	—	—	—	257
1937	1	—	—	—	—	—	235
1938	—	—	—	—	—	—	231
1939	—	—	—	—	—	—	261
1940	—	—	—	—	—	—	338
1941	—	—	—	—	—	—	342
1942	—	—	—	—	—	—	164
1943	2	—	—	—	—	—	191
1944	1	—	—	—	—	—	271
1945	—	—	—	—	—	—	397
1946	—	—	—	—	—	—	634
1947	—	—	—	—	—	—	723
1948	—	—	—	—	—	—	762
1949	—	—	—	—	—	—	782
1950	—	—	—	—	—	—	792
1951	—	—	—	—	—	—	821
1952	—	—	—	—	—	—	914
1953	—	—	—	—	—	—	950
1954	—	—	—	—	—	—	964
1955	—	—	8	—	—	—	1010
1956	—	—	54	—	—	—	1098
1957	—	—	59	—	—	—	1211
1958	—	—	66	14	—	—	1244
1959	—	—	67	15	—	—	1258
1960	—	—	61	13	—	—	1226
1961	—	—	56	13	17	—	1196
1962	—	—	55	12	20	—	1124
1963	—	—	46	11	20	—	1064
1964	—	—	45	11	20	—	1105
1965	—	—	44	11	20	12	1122

Sources: 1932–1937—See notes to Table 2–2, p. 22; 1938–1948—*Annual Airline Statistics,* Civil Aeronautics Board; 1949—*Aviation Week* (February 27, 1950), p. 121; *World Airline Record* (1950); 1950—*Aviation Week* (February 26, 1951), p. 110. *Statistical Study of U.S. Civil Aircraft,* Civil Aeronautics Administration (as of July 1, 1950); 1951—*Statistical Study of U.S. Civil Aircraft* (as of January 1, 1952). *Aviation Week* (February 25, 1952), p. 113; 1952—*Statistical Study of U.S. Civil Aircraft* (as of January 1, 1953); 1953—*Statistical Study of U.S. Civil Aircraft* (as of January 1, 1954). *World Airline Record* (1955); *The Aeroplane* (November 27, 1953), pp. 741–742; 1954—*Statistical Study of U.S. Civil Aircraft* (as of January 1, 1955); 1955—*Statistical Study of U.S. Civil Aircraft* (as of January 1, 1956); *The Aeroplane* (November 25, 1955), pp. 835–836; (November 23, 1956), pp. 758–759; 1956–1960—*Statistical Study of U.S. Civil Aircraft;* 1961—*Annual Airline Statistics;* 1962–1963—*FAA Statistical Handbook of Aviation;* 1964—*Handbook of Airline Statistics;* 1965—*FAA Statistical Handbook of Aviatio.n*

Appendix D

**Aircraft in Fleets of Individual Carriers,
by Carriers**

This appendix consists of 26 tables giving the composition of the fleets of individual airlines for the years of their operation between 1932 and 1965. That is, these tables contain the data given in Table C-1 disaggregated by airline.

Table D-1

Aircraft in Fleet of American Airlines, 1932–1965.

Aircraft

Year	DC-2	DC-3	DC-4	DC-6 DC-6A DC-6B	DC-7 DC-7B	B-707	B-720 B-720B	B-727	Lockheed "Orion"	L-188	Convair 240
1932	—	—	—	—	—	—	—	—	—	—	—
1933	—	—	—	—	—	—	—	—	5	—	—
1934	—	—	—	—	—	—	—	—	5	—	—
1935	16	—	—	—	—	—	—	—	5	—	—
1936	15	20	—	—	—	—	—	—	—	—	—
1937	15	29	—	—	—	—	—	—	—	—	—
1938	15	30	—	—	—	—	—	—	—	—	—
1939	13	44	—	—	—	—	—	—	—	—	—
1940	5	76	—	—	—	—	—	—	—	—	—
1941	—	79	—	—	—	—	—	—	—	—	—
1942	—	43	—	—	—	—	—	—	—	—	—
1943	—	47	—	—	—	—	—	—	—	—	—
1944	—	66	—	—	—	—	—	—	—	—	—
1945	—	87	—	—	—	—	—	—	—	—	—
1946	—	86	46	—	—	—	—	—	—	—	—
1947	—	60	46	37	—	—	—	—	—	—	—
1948	—	24	19	50	—	—	—	—	—	—	56
1949	—	—	18	49	—	—	—	—	—	—	73
1950	—	—	7	49	—	—	—	—	—	—	79
1951	—	—	8	65	—	—	—	—	—	—	78
1952	—	—	8	66	—	—	—	—	—	—	77
1953	—	—	14 ᵃ	78	12	—	—	—	—	—	76
1954	—	—	9 ᵃ	78	25	—	—	—	—	—	76
1955	—	—	9 ᵃ	78	25	—	—	—	—	—	74
1956	—	—	2 ᵃ	82	35	—	—	—	—	—	73
1957	—	—	2 ᵃ	95	55	—	—	—	—	—	73
1958	—	—	—	83	58	—	—	—	—	—	54
1959	—	—	—	82	31	24	—	—	—	23	34
1960	—	—	—	60	33	24	9	—	—	33	37
1961	—	—	—	50	33	24	25	—	—	33	21
1962	—	—	—	44	32	23	25	—	—	24	13
1963	—	—	—	42	23	27	22	—	—	24	10
1964	—	—	—	37	21	27	22	16	—	24	—
1965	—	—	—	33	9	34	22	29	—	24	—

ᵃ Freight service only.

Type

Convair 990	Stinson Single Engined	Stinson Trimotors	Fokker F-10	Fokker F-32	Curtiss T-32	"Travel Air"	Fairchild 100	Fairchild 71	Ford Trimotor	Vultee V-1-A	Total
—	16	10	14	7	—	8	20	17	16	—	108
—	8	10	7	—	9	—	10	—	15	—	64
—	—	17	—	—	15	—	—	—	14	8	59
—	—	11	—	—	10	—	—	—	4	8	54
—	—	15	—	—	3	—	—	—	—	10	63
—	—	3	—	—	—	—	—	—	—	—	47
—	—	—	—	—	—	—	—	—	—	—	45
—	—	—	—	—	—	—	—	—	—	—	57
—	—	—	—	—	—	—	—	—	—	—	81
—	—	—	—	—	—	—	—	—	—	—	79
—	—	—	—	—	—	—	—	—	—	—	43
—	—	—	—	—	—	—	—	—	—	—	47
—	—	—	—	—	—	—	—	—	—	—	66
—	—	—	—	—	—	—	—	—	—	—	87
—	—	—	—	—	—	—	—	—	—	—	132
—	—	—	—	—	—	—	—	—	—	—	143
—	—	—	—	—	—	—	—	—	—	—	149
—	—	—	—	—	—	—	—	—	—	—	140
—	—	—	—	—	—	—	—	—	—	—	135
—	—	—	—	—	—	—	—	—	—	—	151
—	—	—	—	—	—	—	—	—	—	—	151
—	—	—	—	—	—	—	—	—	—	—	180
—	—	—	—	—	—	—	—	—	—	—	188
—	—	—	—	—	—	—	—	—	—	—	186
—	—	—	—	—	—	—	—	—	—	—	192
—	—	—	—	—	—	—	—	—	—	—	225
—	—	—	—	—	—	—	—	—	—	—	195
—	—	—	—	—	—	—	—	—	—	—	194
—	—	—	—	—	—	—	—	—	—	—	196
—	—	—	—	—	—	—	—	—	—	—	186
15	—	—	—	—	—	—	—	—	—	—	176
19	—	—	—	—	—	—	—	—	—	—	167
19	—	—	—	—	—	—	—	—	—	—	166
18	—	—	—	—	—	—	—	—	—	—	169

Table D-2

Aircraft in Fleet of Bowen Air Lines,[a] 1932–1935.

| | Aircraft Type | | | | |
Year	Lockheed "Vega"	Lockheed "Orion"	Stinson Single Engined	Vultee V-1-A	Total
1932	4	2	1	—	7
1933	4	2	—	—	6
1934	—	2	—	2	4
1935	—	2	—	—	2

[a] Absorbed by Braniff Air Lines, 1935.

Table D-3

Aircraft in Fleet of Braniff Air Lines, 1932–1965.

Year	DC-2	DC-3	DC-4	DC-6 DC-6A DC-6B	DC-7C	B-707	B-720 B-720B	Aircraft Lockheed "Vega"
1932	—	—	—	—	—	—	—	8
1933	—	—	—	—	—	—	—	8
1934	—	—	—	—	—	—	—	6
1935	—	—	—	—	—	—	—	6
1936	—	—	—	—	—	—	—	3
1937	7	—	—	—	—	—	—	—
1938	7	—	—	—	—	—	—	—
1939	6	3	—	—	—	—	—	—
1940	6	8	—	—	—	—	—	—
1941	5	11	—	—	—	—	—	—
1942	—	7	—	—	—	—	—	—
1943	—	7	—	—	—	—	—	—
1944	—	11	—	—	—	—	—	—
1945	—	16	—	—	—	—	—	—
1946	—	20	8	—	—	—	—	—
1947	—	17	10	5	—	—	—	—
1948	—	16	9	6	—	—	—	—
1949	—	16	9	6	—	—	—	—
1950	—	13	9	6	—	—	—	—
1951	—	13	9	9	—	—	—	—
1952	—	33	8	9	—	—	—	—
1953	—	24	7	9	—	—	—	—
1954	—	24	2	9	—	—	—	—
1955	—	23	—	9	—	—	—	—
1956	—	23	—	9	4	—	—	—
1957	—	23	—	9	7	—	—	—
1958	—	20	—	10	6	—	—	—
1959	—	8	—	10	6	1	—	—
1960	—	1	—	11	5	4	—	—
1961	—	—	—	11	5	4	3	—
1962	—	—	—	11	5	4	4	—
1963	—	—	—	11	5	4	5	—
1964	—	—	—	11	5	4	6	—
1965	—	—	—	4	5	4	8	—

Type

L-10	L-049 L-649 L-749	188	Convair 240	Convair 340/ 440	Ford Tri-motor	Vultee V-1-A	BAC-111	Total
—	—	—	—	—	—	—	—	8
—	—	—	—	—	—	—	—	8
—	—	—	—	—	—	—	—	6
7	—	—	—	—	2	2	—	17
7	—	—	—	—	2	—	—	12
6	—	—	—	—	—	—	—	13
6	—	—	—	—	—	—	—	13
5	—	—	—	—	—	—	—	14
—	—	—	—	—	—	—	—	14
—	—	—	—	—	—	—	—	16
—	—	—	—	—	—	—	—	7
—	—	—	—	—	—	—	—	7
—	—	—	—	—	—	—	—	11
—	—	—	—	—	—	—	—	16
—	—	—	—	—	—	—	—	28
—	—	—	—	—	—	—	—	32
—	—	—	—	—	—	—	—	31
—	—	—	—	—	—	—	—	31
—	—	—	—	—	—	—	—	28
—	—	—	—	—	—	—	—	31
—	—	—	3	7	—	—	—	60
—	—	—	—	23	—	—	—	63
—	—	—	—	23	—	—	—	58
—	—	—	—	25	—	—	—	57
—	2	—	—	30	—	—	—	68
—	2	—	—	30	—	—	—	71
—	—	—	—	30	—	—	—	66
—	—	7	—	31	—	—	—	63
—	—	8	—	31	—	—	—	60
—	—	8	—	29	—	—	—	60
—	—	9	—	19	—	—	—	52
—	—	9	—	19	—	—	—	53
—	—	9	—	17	—	—	—	52
—	—	9	—	15	—	—	12	57

Table D-4

Aircraft in Fleet of Capital Airlines,[a] 1932–1960.

							Stin-				
			DC-6				L-049	son	Fair-	Ford	Vis-
			DC-6A				L-649	Tri-	child	Tri-	count
Year	DC-3	DC-4	DC-6B	B-247	L-10	L-749	motor	71	motor	745	Total
1932	—	—	—	—	—	—	3	3	—	—	6
1933	—	—	—	—	—	—	—	—	5	—	5
1934	—	—	—	—	3	—	—	—	5	—	8
1935	—	—	—	5	—	—	—	—	5	—	10
1936	—	—	—	5	—	—	5	—	—	—	10
1937	—	—	—	12	—	—	—	—	—	—	12
1938	—	—	—	12	—	—	—	—	—	—	12
1939	6	—	—	14	—	—	—	—	—	—	20
1940	13	—	—	6	—	—	—	—	—	—	19
1941	18	—	—	4	—	—	—	—	—	—	22
1942	6	—	—	—	—	—	—	—	—	—	6
1943	7	—	—	—	—	—	—	—	—	—	7
1944	16	—	—	—	—	—	—	—	—	—	16
1945	25	—	—	—	—	—	—	—	—	—	25
1946	29	22	—	—	—	—	—	—	—	—	51
1947	25	23	—	—	—	—	—	—	—	—	48
1948	24	23	—	—	—	—	—	—	—	—	47
1949	24	25	—	—	—	—	—	—	—	—	49
1950	28	25	—	—	—	5	—	—	—	—	58
1951	28	24	—	—	—	5	—	—	—	—	57
1952	25	24	—	—	—	7	—	—	—	—	56
1953	25	25	—	—	—	12	—	—	—	—	62
1954	21	25	—	—	—	12	—	—	—	—	58
1955	21	24	—	—	—	12	—	—	—	8	65
1956	19	13	—	—	—	12	—	—	—	54	98
1957	18	12	—	—	—	12	—	—	—	59	101
1958	19	12	—	—	—	11	—	—	—	59	101
1959	11	12	—	—	—	11	—	—	—	57	91
1960	10	10	11	—	—	—	—	—	—	51	82

[a] Pennsylvania Airlines through 1935; Pennsylvania-Central Airlines through 1947; Capital Airlines, 1948 to merger with United in 1961.

Table D-5

Aircraft in Fleet of Central Airlines,[a]
1934–1935.

Aircraft Type

Year	Lockheed "Vega"	Stinson Trimotor	Total
1934	2	5	7
1935	—	5	5

[a] Merged with Pennsylvania Air Lines, 1936.

Table D-6

Aircraft in Fleet of Chicago and Southern Air Lines,[a] 1933–1952.

Aircraft Type

Year	DC-3	DC-4	L-10	L-049 L-649 L-749	Stinson Tri-motor	Bellanca "Pace-maker"	Total
1933	—	—	—	—	—	5	5
1934	—	—	—	—	—	6	6
1935	—	—	—	—	6	—	6
1936	—	—	4	—	—	—	4
1937	—	—	5	—	—	—	5
1938	—	—	5	—	—	—	5
1939	—	—	5	—	—	—	5
1940	5		1	—	—	—	6
1941	6	—	—	—	—	—	6
1942	4	—	—	—	—	—	4
1943	4	—	—	—	—	—	4
1944	6	—	—	—	—	—	6
1945	12	—	—	—	—	—	12
1946	14	4	—	—	—	—	18
1947	12	4	—	—	—	—	16
1948	12	5	—	—	—	—	17
1949	13	6	—	—	—	—	19
1950	12	2	—	3	—	—	17
1951	12	—	—	6	—	—	18
1952	12	—	—	6	—	—	18

[a] Pacific Seaboard Air Lines in 1933; merged with Delta in 1953.

169

Table D-7

Aircraft in Fleet of Colonial Airlines,[a] 1939–1955.

Year	DC-2	DC-3	DC-4	Total
1939	1	2	—	3
1940	—	4	—	4
1941	—	4	—	4
1942	—	2	—	2
1943	—	2	—	2
1944	—	4	—	4
1945	—	5	—	5
1946	—	14	—	14
1947	—	10	—	10
1948	—	10	—	10
1949	—	12	2	14
1950	—	8	4	12
1951	—	8	4	12
1952	—	8	4	12
1953	—	8	5	13
1954	—	8	5	13
1955	—	8	5	13
1956	—	8	5	13

Aircraft Type is the spanning header over DC-2, DC-3, DC-4.

[a] Absorbed by Eastern Air Lines, June 1, 1956; fleet recorded separately through January 1, 1957.

Table D-8

Aircraft in Fleet of Columbia Airlines,[a] 1935.

Year	Stinson Trimotor
1935	5

[a] Operated Detroit, St. Louis, Cincinnati routes, 1935 only.

Table D-9

Aircraft in Fleet of Continental Air Lines,[a] 1932–1965.

		DC-6 DC-6A	DC-7			Lockheed	Lockheed	Lockheed
Year	DC-3	DC-6B	DC-7B	B-707	B-720B	"Vega"	"Orion"	L-12
1932	—	—	—	—	—	—	6	—
1933	—	—	—	—	—	—	5	—
1934	—	—	—	—	—	—	5	—
1935	—	—	—	—	—	—	4	—
1936	—	—	—	—	—	1	—	3
1937	—	—	—	—	—	1	—	3
1938	—	—	—	—	—	—	—	3
1939	—	—	—	—	—	—	—	3
1940	—	—	—	—	—	—	—	—
1941	—	—	—	—	—	—	—	—
1942	—	—	—	—	—	—	—	—
1943	—	—	—	—	—	—	—	—
1944	1	—	—	—	—	—	—	—
1945	6	—	—	—	—	—	—	—
1946	12	—	—	—	—	—	—	—
1947	12	—	—	—	—	—	—	—
1948	12	—	—	—	—	—	—	—
1949	9	—	—	—	—	—	—	—
1950	10	—	—	—	—	—	—	—
1951	10	—	—	—	—	—	—	—
1952	10	—	—	—	—	—	—	—
1953	10	2	—	—	—	—	—	—
1954	9	2	—	—	—	—	—	—
1955	21	3	—	—	—	—	—	—
1956	15	3	—	—	—	—	—	—
1957	15	—	4	—	—	—	—	—
1958	13	3	5	—	—	—	—	—
1959	10	—	5	4	—	—	—	—
1960	8	—	5	5	—	—	—	—
1961	5	1	5	5	—	—	—	—
1962	5	—	5	4	4	—	—	—
1963	4	—	5	4	5	—	—	—
1964	1	1	2	6	6	—	—	—
1965	1	—	—	7	6	—	—	—

[a] Varney Air Transport to 1937.

Type

Lockheed L-14	L-18	Convair 240	Convair 340/440	Viscount 812	Total
—	—	—	—	—	6
—	—	—	—	—	5
—	—	—	—	—	5
—	—	—	—	—	4
—	—	—	—	—	4
—	—	—	—	—	4
—	—	—	—	—	3
2	—	—	—	—	5
2	3	—	—	—	5
—	6	—	—	—	6
—	3	—	—	—	3
—	4	—	—	—	4
—	4	—	—	—	5
—	1	—	—	—	7
—	—	—	—	—	12
—	—	—	—	—	12
—	—	5	—	—	17
—	—	5	—	—	14
—	—	5	—	—	15
—	—	5	—	—	15
—	—	5	—	—	15
—	—	—	7	—	19
—	—	—	6	—	17
—	—	—	6	—	30
—	—	—	9	—	27
—	—	—	9	—	28
—	—	—	9	14	44
—	—	—	—	15	34
—	—	—	—	13	31
—	—	—	—	13	29
—	—	—	—	12	30
—	—	—	—	11	29
—	—	—	—	11	27
—	—	—	—	11	25

Table D-10

Aircraft in Fleet of Delta Airlines, 1934–1965.

Year	DC-2	DC-3	DC-4	DC-6 DC-6A DC-6B	DC-7 DC-7B	DC-8	DC-9	Aircraft Lockheed "Vega"
1934	—	—	—	—	—	—	—	—
1935	—	—	—	—	—	—	—	2
1936	—	—	—	—	—	—	—	—
1937	—	—	—	—	—	—	—	—
1938	—	—	—	—	—	—	—	—
1939	—	—	—	—	—	—	—	—
1940	4	1	—	—	—	—	—	—
1941	—	5	—	—	—	—	—	—
1942	—	4	—	—	—	—	—	—
1943	—	5	—	—	—	—	—	—
1944	—	7	—	—	—	—	—	—
1945	—	12	—	—	—	—	—	—
1946	—	17	7	—	—	—	—	—
1947	—	19	7	—	—	—	—	—
1948	—	19	7	4	—	—	—	—
1949	—	20	6	6	—	—	—	—
1950	—	20	6	6	—	—	—	—
1951	—	20	6	7	—	—	—	—
1952	—	20	5	7	—	—	—	—
1953	—	21	—	7	—	—	—	—
1954	—	16	—	7	7	—	—	—
1955	—	16	—	7	11	—	—	—
1956	—	16	—	7	11	—	—	—
1957	—	15	—	7	19	—	—	—
1958	—	12	—	7	21	—	—	—
1959	—	10	—	12	21	6	—	—
1960	—	10	—	11	20	6	—	—
1961	—	10	—	11	20	6	—	—
1962	—	—	—	11	19	10	—	—
1963	—	—	—	11	19	12	—	—
1964	—	—	—	11	19	15	—	—
1965	—	—	—	11	19	19	4	—

Type

L-10	L-049 L-649 L-749	Convair 340/ 440	Convair 880	Stinson Trimotor	Total
—	—	—	—	5	5
2	—	—	—	7	11
3	—	—	—	1	4
5	—	—	—	—	5
5	—	—	—	—	5
5	—	—	—	—	5
5	—	—	—	—	10
4	—	—	—	—	9
—	—	—	—	—	4
—	—	—	—	—	5
—	—	—	—	—	7
—	—	—	—	—	12
—	—	—	—	—	24
—	—	—	—	—	26
—	—	—	—	—	30
—	—	—	—	—	32
—	—	—	—	—	32
—	—	—	—	—	33
—	—	—	—	—	32
—	6	20	—	—	54
—	3	20	—	—	53
—	6	20	—	—	60
—	4	25	—	—	63
—	4	28	—	—	73
—	4	28	—	—	72
—	—	28	—	—	77
—	—	26	9	—	82
—	—	24	12	—	83
—	—	21	16	—	77
—	—	21	16	—	79
—	—	19	16	—	80
—	—	19	16	—	88

Table D-11

Aircraft in Fleet of Eastern Airlines, 1932–1965.

Aircraft

Year	DC-2	DC-3	DC-4	DC-6 DC-6A DC-6B	DC-7 DC-7B	DC-8	B-720 B-720B	B-727	L-10	L-049 L-649 L-749
1932	—	—	—	—	—	—	—	—	—	—
1933	—	—	—	—	—	—	—	—	—	—
1934	—	—	—	—	—	—	—	—	—	—
1935	14	—	—	—	—	—	—	—	5	—
1936	13	2	—	—	—	—	—	—	5	—
1937	11	5	—	—	—	—	—	—	—	—
1938	10	10	—	—	—	—	—	—	—	—
1939	10	15	—	—	—	—	—	—	—	—
1940	3	34	—	—	—	—	—	—	—	—
1941	—	40	—	—	—	—	—	—	—	—
1942	—	20	—	—	—	—	—	—	—	—
1943	—	22	—	—	—	—	—	—	—	—
1944	—	31	—	—	—	—	—	—	—	—
1945	—	48	—	—	—	—	—	—	—	—
1946	—	53	19	—	—	—	—	—	—	—
1947	—	53	19	—	—	—	—	—	—	14
1948	—	52	19	—	—	—	—	—	—	13
1949	—	51	18	—	—	—	—	—	—	20
1950	—	49	25	—	—	—	—	—	—	20
1951	—	48	15	—	—	—	—	—	—	20
1952	—	16	11	—	—	—	—	—	—	20
1953	—	—	12	—	—	—	—	—	—	19
1954	—	—	11	—	—	—	—	—	—	19
1955	—	—	9	2	12	—	—	—	—	19
1956	—	—	9	2	19	—	—	—	—	19
1957	—	—	—	—	24	—	—	—	—	18 [a]
1958	—	—	1	9	48	—	—	—	—	18 [a]
1959	—	—	1	7	48	—	—	—	—	18
1960	—	—	—	7	48	11	—	—	—	1
1961	—	—	—	7	48	15	13	—	—	—
1962	—	—	—	—	47	15	15	—	—	—
1963	—	—	—	—	46	15	15	—	—	—
1964	—	—	—	—	40	17	15	24	—	—
1965	—	—	—	—	7	18	15	42	—	—

[a] Twenty-four aircraft attributed to Eastern in 1957; 23 in 1958, in *Statistical Study of U.S. Civil Aircraft* (January 1, 1958; January 1, 1959). Davies, *History of the World's Airlines*, Table 24, indicates 18 for Autumn, 1958. This seems to be the better figure.

Type

L-1049	L-188	Con-vair 340/440	M-404	Stinson Tri-motor	Fokker F-10	Con-dor "CO" Trans-port	Con-dor II Trans-port	C-R "King-bird"	Ford Tri-motor	Total
—	—	—	—	—	3	5	—	9	5	22
—	—	—	—	8	—	5	8	9	—	30
—	—	—	—	5	—	4	8	5	—	22
—	—	—	—	—	—	—	7	5	—	31
—	—	—	—	—	—	—	5	—	—	25
—	—	—	—	—	—	—	—	—	—	16
—	—	—	—	—	—	—	—	—	—	20
—	—	—	—	—	—	—	—	—	—	25
—	—	—	—	—	—	—	—	—	—	37
—	—	—	—	—	—	—	—	—	—	40
—	—	—	—	—	—	—	—	—	—	20
—	—	—	—	—	—	—	—	—	—	22
—	—	—	—	—	—	—	—	—	—	31
—	—	—	—	—	—	—	—	—	—	48
—	—	—	—	—	—	—	—	—	—	72
—	—	—	—	—	—	—	—	—	—	86
—	—	—	—	—	—	—	—	—	—	84
—	—	—	—	—	—	—	—	—	—	89
—	—	—	—	—	—	—	—	—	—	94
5	—	—	9	—	—	—	—	—	—	97
14	—	—	56	—	—	—	—	—	—	117
22	—	—	60	—	—	—	—	—	—	113
29	—	—	60	—	—	—	—	—	—	119
29	—	—	60	—	—	—	—	—	—	131
32	—	—	59	—	—	—	—	—	—	140
38	—	20	58	—	—	—	—	—	—	158
38	—	20	58	—	—	—	—	—	—	192
38	40	20	56	—	—	—	—	—	—	228
38	39	20	52	—	—	—	—	—	—	216
37	39	20	36	—	—	—	—	—	—	215
37	39	20	16	—	—	—	—	—	—	189
37	39	20	—	—	—	—	—	—	—	172
37	39	20	—	—	—	—	—	—	—	192
37	39	20	—	—	—	—	—	—	—	178

Table D-12

Aircraft in Fleet of Inland Airlines,[a] 1932–1951.

| | Aircraft Type | | | | | | | |
Year	DC-3	DC-4	B-247	L-10	L-18	Stinson Single Engined	Beech-craft 18	Total
1932	—	—	—	—	—	5	—	5
1933	—	—	—	—	—	4	—	4
1934	—	—	—	—	—	6	—	6
1935	—	—	1	2	—	6	—	9
1936	—	—	2	2	—	1	—	5
1937	—	—	6	—	—	—	—	6
1938	—	—	6	—	—	—	—	6
1939	—	—	6	—	—	—	—	6
1940	—	—	5	—	—	—	—	5
1941	—	—	5	—	—	—	—	5
1942	—	—	—	—	1	—	—	1
1943	—	—	—	—	1	—	2	3
1944	1	—	—	—	1	—	1	3
1945	1	—	—	—	1	—	—	2
1946	1	—	—	—	—	—	—	1
1947	1	—	—	—	—	—	—	1
1948	1	—	—	—	—	—	—	1
1949	1	—	—	—	—	—	—	1
1950	6	1	—	—	—	—	—	7
1951	4	—	—	—	—	—	—	4

[a] Wyoming Air Service to 1938; merged with Western Air Lines, 1952.

Table D-13

Aircraft in Fleet of Long and Harmon,[a] 1933–1934.

| | Aircraft Type | | |
Year	Stinson Single Engined	"Travel Air"	Total
1933	5	1	6
1934	5	1	6

[a] Merged with Braniff, 1935.

Table D-14

Aircraft in Fleet of Ludington Lines,[a] 1932.

	Aircraft Type				
Year	Lockheed "Orion"	"Fleetster"	Stinson Single Engined	Stinson Tri-motor	Total
1932	2	3	1	9	15

[a] Merged with Eastern Air Lines, 1933.

Table D-15

Aircraft in Fleet of Mid-Continent Airlines,[a] 1932–1951.

	Aircraft Type						
Year	DC-3	Lockheed "Vega"	L-10	L-18	Convair 240	Ford Trimotor	Total
1932	—	4	—	—	—	—	4
1933	—	4	—	—	—	2	6
1934	—	4	—	—	—	2	6
1935	—	4	—	—	—	3	7
1936	—	4	2	—	—	2	8
1937	—	4	3	—	—	—	7
1938	—	—	4	—	—	—	4
1939	—	—	5	—	—	—	5
1940	—	—	5	3	—	—	8
1941	—	—	5	4	—	—	9
1942	—	—	—	2	—	—	2
1943	—	—	—	4	—	—	4
1944	—	—	—	4	—	—	4
1945	6	—	—	3	—	—	9
1946	11	—	—	—	—	—	11
1947	15	—	—	—	—	—	15
1948	18	—	—	—	—	—	18
1949	20	—	—	—	4	—	24
1950	20	—	—	—	4	—	24
1951	23	—	—	—	4	—	27

[a] Hanford's Tri-State Air Lines to 1938; merged with Braniff Air Lines in 1952.

Table D-16

Aircraft in Fleet of National Airlines, 1934–1965.

Aircraft

Year	DC-4	DC-6 DC-6A DC-6B	DC-7 DC-7B	DC-8	B-707	B-727	Lockheed "Orion"
1934	—	—	—	—	—	—	3
1935	—	—	—	—	—	—	—
1936	—	—	—	—	—	—	—
1937	—	—	—	—	—	—	—
1938	—	—	—	—	—	—	—
1939	—	—	—	—	—	—	—
1940	—	—	—	—	—	—	—
1941	—	—	—	—	—	—	—
1942	—	—	—	—	—	—	—
1943	—	—	—	—	—	—	—
1944	—	—	—	—	—	—	—
1945	—	—	—	—	—	—	—
1946	6	—	—	—	—	—	—
1947	7	4	—	—	—	—	—
1948	7	4	—	—	—	—	—
1949	9	4	—	—	—	—	—
1950	7	4	—	—	—	—	—
1951	6	8	—	—	—	—	—
1952	3	14	—	—	—	—	—
1953	—	12	4	—	—	—	—
1954	—	12	4	—	—	—	—
1955	—	12	4	—	—	—	—
1956	—	14	4	—	—	—	—
1957	—	12	7	—	—	—	—
1958	—	12	4	—	—	—	—
1959	—	12	8	—	2	—	—
1960	—	12	8	3	—	—	—
1961	—	11	8	4	—	—	—
1962	—	11	8	9	—	—	—
1963	—	—	8	12	—	—	—
1964	—	—	—	13	—	4	—
1965	—	—	—	13	—	10	—

Type

L-10	L-18	L-1049G	L-188	Convair 340/440	Stinson Trimotor	Ford Trimotor	Total
3	—	—	—	—	—	3	9
3	—	—	—	—	3	—	6
3	—	—	—	—	3	—	6
3	—	—	—	—	3	—	6
3	—	—	—	—	2	—	5
4	—	—	—	—	—	—	4
4	2	—	—	—	—	—	6
2	3	—	—	—	—	—	5
—	3	—	—	—	—	—	3
—	4	—	—	—	—	—	4
—	6	—	—	—	—	—	6
—	12	—	—	—	—	—	12
—	12	—	—	—	—	—	18
—	12	—	—	—	—	—	23
—	12	—	—	—	—	—	23
—	11	—	—	—	—	—	24
—	11	—	—	—	—	—	22
—	11	—	—	—	—	—	25
—	11	—	—	—	—	—	28
—	11	—	—	8	—	—	35
—	12	—	—	12	—	—	40
—	9	4	—	12	—	—	41
—	10	4	—	18	—	—	50
—	10	4	—	18	—	—	51
—	7	7	—	18	—	—	48
—	—	4	12	15	—	—	53
—	—	4	12	6	—	—	45
—	—	4	14	6	—	—	47
—	—	4	17	5	—	—	54
—	—	4	17	—	—	—	41
—	—	—	17	—	—	—	34
—	—	—	17	—	—	—	40

Table D-17

Aircraft in Fleet of National Parks Airways,[a] 1932–1936.

				Aircraft Type		
Year	B-40	B-80	B-247	Fokker Single Engined	Ford Trimotor	Total
1932	2	—	—	5	—	7
1933	2	—	—	4	1	7
1934	2	—	—	4	—	6
1935	2	—	2	1	—	5
1936	1	1	3	—	—	5

[a] Also known as Alfred Frank Air Line. Merged with Western Air Lines in 1937.

Table D-18

Aircraft in Fleet of Northeast Airlines,[a] 1933–1965.

										Aircraft Type
Year	DC-3	DC-4	DC-6 DC-6A DC-6B	B-727	L-10	Convair 240	Convair 880	Stinson Tri-motor	Viscount 745	Total
1933	—	—	—	—	—	—	—	5	—	5
1934	—	—	—	—	—	—	—	5	—	5
1935	—	—	—	—	—	—	—	5	—	5
1936	—	—	—	—	3	—	—	3	—	6
1937	—	—	—	—	3	—	—	3	—	6
1938	—	—	—	—	3	—	—	2	—	5
1939	—	—	—	—	3	—	—	2	—	5
1940	—	—	—	—	5	—	—	2	—	7
1941	3	—	—	—	1	—	—	—	—	4
1942	2	—	—	—	—	—	—	—	—	2
1943	2	—	—	—	—	—	—	—	—	2
1944	3	—	—	—	—	—	—	—	—	3
1945	6	—	—	—	—	—	—	—	—	6
1946	11	3	—	—	—	—	—	—	—	14
1947	11	3	—	—	—	—	—	—	—	14
1948	8	3	—	—	—	—	—	—	—	11
1949	8	1	—	—	—	5	—	—	—	14
1950	8	—	—	—	—	5	—	—	—	13
1951	7	—	—	—	—	5	—	—	—	12
1952	9	—	—	—	—	4	—	—	—	13
1953	12	—	—	—	—	7	—	—	—	19
1954	12	—	—	—	—	7	—	—	—	19
1955	11	—	—	—	—	6	—	—	—	17
1956	11	—	—	—	—	6	—	—	—	17
1957	11	—	10	—	—	6	—	—	—	27
1958	11	—	10	—	—	5	—	—	7	33
1959	11	—	10	—	—	—	—	—	10	31
1960	6	—	10	—	—	—	4	—	10	30
1961	6	—	10	—	—	—	6	—	9	31
1962	6	—	9	—	—	—	8	—	9	32
1963	5	—	15	—	—	—	3	—	—	23
1964	6	—	16	—	—	—	4	—	—	26
1965	6	—	17	2	—	—	4	—	—	29

[a] National Airways, 1933 to 1936; Boston and Maine Airways, 1937; Northeast Airlines thereafter.

Table D-19

Aircraft in Fleet of Northwest Airlines, 1932–1965.

Aircraft

Year	DC-3	DC-4	DC-6 DC-6A DC-6B	DC-7C	DC-8	B-377	B-707	B-720B	B-727
1932	—	—	—	—	—	—	—	—	—
1933	—	—	—	—	—	—	—	—	—
1934	—	—	—	—	—	—	—	—	—
1935	—	—	—	—	—	—	—	—	—
1936	—	—	—	—	—	—	—	—	—
1937	—	—	—	—	—	—	—	—	—
1938	—	—	—	—	—	—	—	—	—
1939	7	—	—	—	—	—	—	—	—
1940	13	—	—	—	—	—	—	—	—
1941	11	—	—	—	—	—	—	—	—
1942	7	—	—	—	—	—	—	—	—
1943	8	—	—	—	—	—	—	—	—
1944	13	—	—	—	—	—	—	—	—
1945	21	—	—	—	—	—	—	—	—
1946	23	12	—	—	—	—	—	—	—
1947	22	18	—	—	—	—	—	—	—
1948	13	17	—	—	—	—	—	—	—
1949	2	18	—	—	—	10	—	—	—
1950	2	18	—	—	—	10	—	—	—
1951	5	23	—	—	—	10	—	—	—
1952	8	24	—	—	—	10	—	—	—
1953	8	19	4	—	—	10	—	—	—
1954	8	19	5	—	—	10	—	—	—
1955	7	17	9	—	—	10	—	—	—
1956	6	18	10	—	—	9	—	—	—
1957	5	15	17	8	—	9	—	—	—
1958	4	12	21	17	—	9	—	—	—
1959	—	12	23	17	—	6	—	—	—
1960	—	8	22	15	4	—	—	—	—
1961	—	—	14	8	5	—	—	9	—
1962	—	—	11	7	4	—	—	13	—
1963	—	—	9	6	1	—	5	13	—
1964	—	—	4	6	—	—	8	16	3
1965	—	—	5	4	—	—	13	16	14

Type

Lockheed "Orion"	L-10	L-14	L-188	M-202	"Travel Air"	Hamilton Silver Streak	Ford Trimotor	Total
—	—	—	—	—	3	9	3	15
3	—	—	—	—	2	8	3	16
3	—	—	—	—	—	8	3	14
—	12	—	—	—	—	1	1	14
—	12	—	—	—	—	—	—	12
—	12	6	—	—	—	—	—	18
—	7	9	—	—	—	—	—	16
—	7	—	—	—	—	—	—	14
—	4	—	—	—	—	—	—	17
—	4	—	—	—	—	—	—	15
—	—	—	—	—	—	—	—	7
—	—	—	—	—	—	—	—	8
—	—	—	—	—	—	—	—	13
—	—	—	—	—	—	—	—	21
—	—	—	—	—	—	—	—	35
—	—	—	—	9	—	—	—	49
—	—	—	—	24	—	—	—	54
—	—	—	—	24	—	—	—	54
—	—	—	—	21	—	—	—	51
—	—	—	—	—	—	—	—	38
—	—	—	—	—	—	—	—	42
—	—	—	—	—	—	—	—	41
—	—	—	—	—	—	—	—	42
—	—	—	—	—	—	—	—	43
—	—	—	—	—	—	—	—	43
—	—	—	—	—	—	—	—	54
—	—	—	—	—	—	—	—	63
—	—	—	9	—	—	—	—	67
—	—	—	9	—	—	—	—	58
—	—	—	16	—	—	—	—	52
—	—	—	16	—	—	—	—	51
—	—	—	16	—	—	—	—	50
—	—	—	16	—	—	—	—	53
—	—	—	16	—	—	—	—	68

Table D-20

Aircraft in Fleet of Rapid Air Transport,[a] 1932–1933.

	Aircraft Type		
Year	Bellanca "Pacemaker"	Ryan "Brougham"	Total
1932	2	1	3
1933	2	1	3

[a] Operated Kansas City–Omaha route, 1932–1933.

Table D-21

Aircraft in Fleet of Trans-American Airlines Corp,[a] 1932.

	Aircraft Type					
Year	Stinson Single Engined	Stinson Trimotor	Fokker F-10	"Travel Air"	Ford Trimotor	Total
1932	8	4	2	1	1	16

[a] Corporate existence terminated after control assumed by Aviation Corporation, 1932.

Table D-22

Aircraft in Fleet of Trans World Airlines, 1932–1965.

Aircraft

Year	DC-2	DC-3	DC-4	B-307	B-707	B-720B	B-727	Lockheed "Vega"	Lockheed "Orion"	L-049 L-649 L-749	L-1049
1932	—	—	—	—	—	—	—	2	2	—	—
1933	1 ᵃ	—	—	—	—	—	—	2	2	—	—
1934	21 ᵃ	—	—	—	—	—	—	—	2	—	—
1935	27 ᵃ	—	—	—	—	—	—	—	—	—	—
1936	27	—	—	—	—	—	—	—	—	—	—
1937	17	13	—	—	—	—	—	—	—	—	—
1938	14	19	—	—	—	—	—	—	—	—	—
1939	14	22	—	—	—	—	—	—	—	—	—
1940	13	24	—	5	—	—	—	—	—	—	—
1941	8	29	—	5	—	—	—	—	—	—	—
1942	—	24	—	—	—	—	—	—	—	—	—
1943	—	28	—	—	—	—	—	—	—	—	—
1944	—	37	—	—	—	—	—	—	—	—	—
1945	—	49	—	5	—	—	—	—	—	—	—
1946	—	70	—	5	—	—	—	—	—	12	—
1947	—	76	—	5	—	—	—	—	—	16	—
1948	—	72	—	5	—	—	—	—	—	23	—
1949	—	62	13	5	—	—	—	—	—	35	—
1950	—	51	14	5	—	—	—	—	—	58	—
1951	—	46	14	—	—	—	—	—	—	65	—
1952	—	42	13	—	—	—	—	—	—	68	10
1953	—	13	13	—	—	—	—	—	—	68	10
1954	—	—	12	—	—	—	—	—	—	68	10
1955	—	—	11	—	—	—	—	—	—	71	30
1956	—	4	10	—	—	—	—	—	—	71	37
1957	—	—	8	—	—	—	—	—	—	71 ᵇ	39
1958	—	—	6	—	—	—	—	—	—	71	44
1959	—	—	—	—	19	—	—	—	—	69	44
1960	—	—	—	—	27	—	—	—	—	68	40
1961	—	—	—	—	27	4	—	—	—	62	28
1962	—	—	—	—	47	—	—	—	—	36	24
1963	—	—	—	—	52	—	—	—	—	34	24
1964	—	—	—	—	61	—	16	—	—	34	17
1965	—	—	—	—	67	—	21	—	—	29	9

ᵃ Includes one DC-1.

ᵇ 74 aircraft attributed to TWA in *Statistical Study of U.S. Civil Aircraft* (January 1, 1958). Davies, *History of the World's Airlines*, Table 24, indicates 71 for Autumn, 1958. This seems to be the better figure.

ᶜ 27 aircraft attributed to TWA in *Statistical Study of U.S. Civil Aircraft* (January 1, 1958). Davies, Table 24, indicates a total of 48 M-202s and M-404s for Autumn, 1958. A total of 37 M-404s seems to be the better figure.

Type

L-1649	Consolidated "Fleetster"	Convair 880	M-202	M-404	Fokker Single Engined	Fokker F-10	Fokker F-32	Ford Tri-motor	Northrup "Alpha"	Beechcraft 18	Total
—	—	—	—	—	6	4	2	19	6	—	41
—	7	—	—	—	2	4	—	16	6	—	40
—	7	—	—	—	—	2	—	15	6	—	53
—	6	—	—	—	—	—	—	10	—	—	43
—	5	—	—	—	—	—	—	4	—	—	36
—	—	—	—	—	—	—	—	—	—	1	31
—	—	—	—	—	—	—	—	—	—	—	33
—	—	—	—	—	—	—	—	—	—	—	36
—	—	—	—	—	—	—	—	—	—	—	42
—	—	—	—	—	—	—	—	—	—	—	42
—	—	—	—	—	—	—	—	—	—	—	24
—	—	—	—	—	—	—	—	—	—	—	28
—	—	—	—	—	—	—	—	—	—	—	37
—	—	—	—	—	—	—	—	—	—	—	54
—	—	—	—	—	—	—	—	—	—	—	87
—	—	—	—	—	—	—	—	—	—	—	97
—	—	—	—	—	—	—	—	—	—	—	100
—	—	—	—	—	—	—	—	—	—	—	115
—	—	—	12	—	—	—	—	—	—	—	140
—	—	—	12	9	—	—	—	—	—	—	146
—	—	—	12	40	—	—	—	—	—	—	185
—	—	—	12	40	—	—	—	—	—	—	156
—	—	—	12	40	—	—	—	—	—	—	142
—	—	—	11	39	—	—	—	—	—	—	162
—	—	—	11	38	—	—	—	—	—	—	171
25	—	—	11	37 [c]	—	—	—	—	—	—	191
29	—	—	10	37	—	—	—	—	—	—	197
28	—	—	—	29	—	—	—	—	—	—	189
25	—	1	—	20	—	—	—	—	—	—	181
24	—	20	—	—	—	—	—	—	—	—	165
27	—	20	—	—	—	—	—	—	—	—	154
24	—	26	—	—	—	—	—	—	—	—	160
22	—	27	—	—	—	—	—	—	—	—	177
5	—	26	—	—	—	—	—	—	—	—	157

Table D-23

Aircraft in Fleet of United Air Lines, 1932–1965.

Aircraft

Year	DC-3	DC-4	DC-6 DC-6A DC-6B	DC-7 DC-7B	DC-8	B-40	B-80	B-221	B-247
1932	—	—	—	—	—	53	12	2	—
1933	—	—	—	—	—	30	11	2	54
1934	—	—	—	—	—	28	10	2	55
1935	—	—	—	—	—	25	8	—	44
1936	7	—	—	—	—	—	6	—	33
1937	29	—	—	—	—	—	—	—	24
1938	35	—	—	—	—	—	—	—	17
1939	35	—	—	—	—	—	—	—	15
1940	50	—	—	—	—	—	—	—	15
1941	54	—	—	—	—	—	—	—	14
1942	33	—	—	—	—	—	—	—	—
1943	38	—	—	—	—	—	—	—	1
1944	50	—	—	—	—	—	—	—	1
1945	67	—	—	—	—	—	—	—	—
1946	70	24	—	—	—	—	—	—	—
1947	75	26	32	—	—	—	—	—	—
1948	78	30	39	—	—	—	—	—	—
1949	69	29	39	—	—	—	—	—	—
1950	58	23	44	—	—	—	—	—	—
1951	55	23	50	—	—	—	—	—	—
1952	53	19	62	—	—	—	—	—	—
1953	34	23	64	—	—	—	—	—	—
1954	18	20	64	25	—	—	—	—	—
1955	13	19	62	25	—	—	—	—	—
1956	11	16	77	26	—	—	—	—	—
1957	—	2	95	45	—	—	—	—	—
1958	1	—	91	55	—	—	—	—	—
1959	—	—	86	53	12	—	—	—	—
1960	—	—	86	45	32	—	—	—	—
1961	9	—	84	45	38	—	—	—	—
1962	—	—	79	41	38	—	—	—	—
1963	—	—	78	26	38	—	—	—	—
1964	—	—	77	10	41	—	—	—	—
1965	—	—	77	—	49	—	—	—	—

Type

B-377	B-720 B-720B	B-727	L-18	Convair 340/ 440	Stinson Single Engine	Ford Tri- motor	Viscount 745	Cara- velle 210	Total
—	—	—	—	—	1	19	—	—	87
—	—	—	—	—	—	2	—	—	99
—	—	—	—	—	—	5	—	—	100
—	—	—	—	—	—	1	—	—	78
—	—	—	—	—	—	—	—	—	46
—	—	—	—	—	—	—	—	—	53
—	—	—	—	—	—	—	—	—	52
—	—	—	—	—	—	—	—	—	50
—	—	—	4	—	—	—	—	—	69
—	—	—	—	—	—	—	—	—	68
—	—	—	—	—	—	—	—	—	33
—	—	—	—	—	—	—	—	—	39
—	—	—	—	—	—	—	—	—	51
—	—	—	—	—	—	—	—	—	67
—	—	—	—	—	—	—	—	—	94
—	—	—	—	—	—	—	—	—	133
—	—	—	—	—	—	—	—	—	147
—	—	—	—	—	—	—	—	—	137
—	—	—	—	—	—	—	—	—	125
6	—	—	—	—	—	—	—	—	134
6	—	—	—	17	—	—	—	—	157
6	—	—	—	40	—	—	—	—	167
1	—	—	—	55	—	—	—	—	183
—	—	—	—	55	—	—	—	—	174
—	—	—	—	55	—	—	—	—	185
—	—	—	—	55	—	—	—	—	197
—	—	—	—	54	—	—	—	—	201
—	—	—	—	43	—	—	—	—	194
—	13	—	—	30	—	—	—	—	206
—	21	—	—	25	—	—	47	17	286
—	29	—	—	21	—	—	46	20	274
—	29	—	—	17	—	—	46	20	254
—	29	25	—	13	—	—	45	20	260
—	29	49	—	13	—	—	44	20	281

Table D-24

Aircraft in Fleet of United States Airways,[a]
1932–1933.

Year	Aircraft Type "Flamingo"
1932	9
1933	9

[a] Operated Kansas City–
Denver route, 1932–1933.

Table D-25

Aircraft in Fleet of Wedell-Williams Air
Service,[a] 1933, 1935.

Year	Aircraft Type Lockheed "Orion"
1933	4
1935	4

[a] Discontinuous opera-
tions to 1936; merged with
Eastern Air Lines, 1937.

Table D-26

Aircraft in Fleet of Western Air Lines, 1932–1965.

Aircraft

Year	DC-3	DC-4	DC-6 DC-6A DC-6B	B-40	B-247	B-707	B-720B
1932	—	—	—	2	—	—	—
1933	—	—	—	1	—	—	—
1934	—	—	—	—	2	—	—
1935	—	—	—	—	5	—	—
1936	—	—	—	—	11	—	—
1937	—	—	—	—	6	—	—
1938	3	—	—	—	4	—	—
1939	3	—	—	—	4	—	—
1940	4	—	—	—	4	—	—
1941	7	—	—	—	5	—	—
1942	2	—	—	—	—	—	—
1943	4	—	—	—	—	—	—
1944	7	—	—	—	—	—	—
1945	13	—	—	—	—	—	—
1946	12	11	—	—	—	—	—
1947	12	6	—	—	—	—	—
1948	9	6	—	—	—	—	—
1949	9	6	—	—	—	—	—
1950	4	5	—	—	—	—	—
1951	6	5	—	—	—	—	—
1952	10	5	3	—	—	—	—
1953	9	5	4	—	—	—	—
1954	9	6	8	—	—	—	—
1955	8	6	8	—	—	—	—
1956	5	3	14	—	—	—	—
1957	5	—	21	—	—	—	—
1958	2	—	24	—	—	—	—
1959	—	—	27	—	—	—	—
1960	—	—	27	—	—	2	—
1961	—	—	24	—	—	2	4
1962	—	—	16	—	—	—	7
1963	—	—	14	—	—	—	10
1964	—	—	14	—	—	—	12
1965	—	—	—	—	—	—	18

Type

L-10	L-18	L-188	Convair 240	Fokker Single Engined	Fokker F-10	Total
—	—	—	—	8	5	15
—	—	—	—	8	5	14
5	—	—	—	—	—	7
—	—	—	—	—	—	5
—	—	—	—	—	—	11
—	—	—	—	—	—	6
—	—	—	—	—	—	7
—	—	—	—	—	—	7
—	—	—	—	—	—	8
—	—	—	—	—	—	12
—	1	—	—	—	—	3
—	1	—	—	—	—	5
—	1	—	—	—	—	8
—	1	—	—	—	—	14
—	—	—	—	—	—	23
—	—	—	—	—	—	18
—	—	—	8	—	—	23
—	—	—	10	—	—	25
—	—	—	10	—	—	19
—	—	—	10	—	—	21
—	—	—	10	—	—	28
—	—	—	10	—	—	28
—	—	—	9	—	—	32
—	—	—	9	—	—	31
—	—	—	9	—	—	31
—	—	—	9	—	—	35
—	—	—	6	—	—	32
—	—	5	5	—	—	37
—	—	6	4	—	—	39
—	—	12	—	—	—	42
—	—	12	—	—	—	35
—	—	12	—	—	—	36
—	—	12	—	—	—	38
—	—	12	—	—	—	30

Appendix E

Aircraft in Fleets of Individual Carriers, by Aircraft Type

The appendix consists of 58 tables giving the number of aircraft of particular types in the fleets of domestic trunk airlines. The tables contain the data given in Table C-1 disaggregated by aircraft type.

Table E-1

DC-2 Aircraft in Fleets of U.S. Domestic Trunk Airlines, 1932–1965.

Year (Dec. 31)	Carrier						Total
	TWA	American	Eastern	Braniff	Colonial	Delta	
1933	1 [a]	—	—	—	—	—	1
1934	21 [a]	—	—	—	—	—	21
1935	27 [a]	16	14	—	—	—	57
1936	27	15	13	—	—	—	55
1937	17	15	11	7	—	—	50
1938	14	15	10	7	—	—	46
1939	14	13	10	6	1	—	44
1940	13	5	3	6	—	4	31
1941	8	—	—	5	—	—	13

[a] Includes one DC-1 delivered to TWA in 1933.

Table E-2

DC-3 Aircraft in Fleets of U.S. Domestic Trunk Airlines,[a] 1932–1965.

							Carrier
Year (Dec. 31)	American	Eastern	United	TWA	Western	Braniff	Penna-Central [b]
1936	20	2	7	—	—	—	—
1937	29	5	29	13	—	—	—
1938	30	10	35	19	3	—	—
1939	44	15	35	22	3	3	6
1940	76	34	50	24	4	8	13
1941	79	40	54	29	7	11	18
1942	43	20	33	24	2	7	6
1943	47	22	38	28	4	7	7
1944	66	31	50	37	7	11	16
1945	87	48	67	49	13	16	25
1946	86	53	70	70	12	20	29
1947	60	53	75	76	12	17	25
1948	24	52	78	72	9	16	24
1949	—	51	69	62	9	16	24
1950	—	49	58	51	4	13	28
1951	—	48	55	46	6	13	28
1952	—	16	53	42	10	33	25
1953	—	—	34	13	9	24	25
1954	—	—	18	—	9	24	21
1955	—	—	13	—	8	23	21
1956	—	—	11	4	5	23	19
1957	—	—	—	—	5	23	18
1958	—	—	1	—	2	20	19
1959	—	—	—	—	—	8	11
1960	—	—	—	—	—	1	10
1961	—	—	9	—	—	—	—
1962	—	—	—	—	—	—	—
1963	—	—	—	—	—	—	—
1964	—	—	—	—	—	—	—
1965	—	—	—	—	—	—	—

Notes:
  [a] Includes DSTs, 1936 to 1941, and 3 Super DC-3s operated by Capital Airlines, 1950–1951.
  [b] Capital Airlines from 1948 to 1961; merged with United, 1961.
  [c] Merged with Eastern, 1956.

Colo-nial [c]	North-west	Delta	Chicago & South-ern [d]	North-east	Conti-nental	Inland [e]	Mid-Conti-nent [f]	Total
—	—	—	—	—	—	—	—	29
—	—	—	—	—	—	—	—	76
—	—	—	—	—	—	—	—	97
2	7	—	—	—	—	—	—	137
4	13	1	5	—	—	—	—	232
4	11	5	6	3	—	—	—	267
2	7	4	4	2	—	—	—	154
2	8	5	4	2	—	—	—	174
4	13	7	6	3	1	1	—	253
5	21	12	12	6	6	1	6	374
14	23	17	14	11	12	1	11	443
10	22	19	12	11	12	1	15	420
10	13	19	12	8	12	1	18	368
12	2	20	13	8	9	1	20	316
8	2	20	12	8	10	6	20	289
8	5	20	12	7	10	4	23	285
8	8	20	12	9	10	—	—	246
8	8	21	—	12	10	—	—	164
8	8	16	—	12	9	—	—	125
8	7	16	—	11	21 [g]	—	—	128
8	6	16	—	11	15	—	—	118
—	5	15	—	11	15	—	—	92
—	4	12	—	11	13	—	—	82
—	—	10	—	11	10	—	—	50
—	—	10	—	6	8	—	—	35
—	—	10	—	6	5	—	—	30
—	—	—	—	6	5	—	—	11
—	—	—	—	5	4	—	—	9
—	—	—	—	6	1	—	—	7
—	—	—	—	6	1	—	—	7

[d] Merged with Delta, 1953.
[e] Merged with Western, 1952.
[f] Merged with Braniff, 1952.
[g] Increase over 1954 due to merger of Continental and Pioneer Airlines in April 1955.

Table E-3

DC-4 Aircraft in Fleets of U.S. Domestic Trunk Airlines, 1932–1965.

Carrier

Year (Dec. 31)	American	Eastern	United	Braniff	Penna-Central [a]	Chicago Southern [b]	Delta
1946	46	19	24	8	22	4	7
1947	46	19	26	10	23	4	7
1948	19	19	30	9	23	5	7
1949	18	18	29	9	25	6	6
1950	7	25	23	9	25	2	6
1951	8	15	23	9	24	—	6
1952	8	11	19	8	24	—	5
1953	14 [e]	12	23	7	25	—	—
1954	9	11	20	2	25	—	—
1955	9	9	19	—	24	—	—
1956	2	9	16	—	13	—	—
1957	2	—	2	—	12	—	—
1958	—	1	—	—	12	—	—
1959	—	1	—	—	12	—	—
1960	—	—	—	—	10	—	—

[a] Capital Airlines from 1948.
[b] Merged with Delta, 1953.
[c] Merged with Eastern, 1956.
[d] Merged with Western, 1952.
[e] American used DC-4s exclusively for freight service in 1953 and thereafter.

National	Northeast	Northwest	Western	TWA	Colonial [c]	Inland [d]	Total
6	3	12	11	—	—	—	162
7	3	18	6	—	—	—	169
7	3	17	6	—	—	—	145
9	1	18	6	13	2	—	160
7	—	18	5	14	4	1	146
6	—	23	5	14	4	—	137
3	—	24	5	13	4	—	124
—	—	19	5	13	5	—	123
—	—	19	6	12	5	—	109
—	—	17	6	11	5	—	100
—	—	18	3	10	5	—	76
—	—	15	—	8	—	—	39
—	—	12	—	6	—	—	31
—	—	12	—	—	—	—	25
—	—	8	—	—	—	—	18

Table E-4

DC-6, DC-6A, and DC-6B Aircraft in Fleets of U.S. Domestic Trunk Airlines,[a] 1932–1965.

Year (Dec. 31)	American	United	Braniff	National	Delta	Western	Carrier Continental
1947	37	32	5	4	—	—	—
1948	50	39	6	4	4	—	—
1949	49	39	6	4	6	—	—
1950	49	44	6	4	6	—	—
1951	65	50	9	8	7	—	—
1952	66	62	9	14	7	3	—
1953	78	64	9	12	7	4	2
1954	78	64	9	12	7	8	2
1955	78	62	9	12	7	8	3
1956	82	77	9	14	7	14	3
1957	95	95	9	12	7	21	—
1958	83	91	10	12	7	24	3
1959	82	86	10	12	12	27	—
1960	60	86	11	12	11	27	—
1961	50	84	11	11	11	24	1
1962	44	79	11	11	11	16	—
1963	42	78	11	—	11	14	—
1964	37	77	11	—	11	14	1
1965	33	77	4	—	11	—	—

[a] The 78 aircraft shown for 1947 were grounded on November 12, 1947; return to service began on March 21, 1948.

Northwest	Eastern	Northeast	Capital	Total
—	—	—	—	78
—	—	—	—	103
—	—	—	—	104
—	—	—	—	109
—	—	—	—	139
—	—	—	—	161
4	—	—	—	180
5	—	—	—	185
9	2	—	—	190
10	2	—	—	218
17	—	10	—	266
21	9	10	—	270
23	7	10	—	269
22	7	10	11	257
14	7	10	—	223
11	—	9	—	192
9	—	15	—	180
4	—	16	—	171
5	—	17	—	147

Table E-4a

DC-6 Aircraft in Fleets of U.S. Domestic Trunk Airlines,[a] 1932–1965.

Year (Dec. 31)	American	United	Braniff	National	Delta	Total
1947	37	32	5	4	—	78
1948	50	39	6	4	4	103
1949	49	39	6	4	6	104
1950	49	44	6	4	6	109
1951	48	43	9	4	7	111
1952	49	43	9	7	7	115
1953	50	43	9	4	7	113
1954	50	43	9	4	7	113
1955	50	42	9	4	7	112
1956	50	42	9	4	7	112
1957	50	42	9	4	7	112
1958	50	42	9	4	7	112
1959	50	37	9	4	12	112
1960	43	37	9	4	11	104
1961	36	37	9	4	11	97
1962	32	32	9	4	11	88
1963	30	31	9	—	11	81
1964	30	30	9	—	11	80
1965	n.a.	30	n.a.	—	11	n.a.

[a] The number of DC-6A and DC-6B aircraft in fleets can be found as differences between entries in Appendix Tables 4 and 4a.

Table E-5

DC-7 Aircraft in Fleets of U.S. Domestic Trunk Airlines,[a] 1932–1965.

Year (Dec. 31)	American	National	United	Delta	Eastern	Braniff	Continental	Northwest	Total
1953	12	4	—	—	—	—	—	—	16
1954	25	4	25	7	—	—	—	—	61
1955	25	4	25	11	12	—	—	—	77
1956	35	4	26	11	19	4 [b]	—	—	99
1957	55	7	45	19	24	7 [b]	4	8 [b]	169
1958	58	4	55	21	48	6 [b]	5	17 [b]	214
1959	31	8	53	21	48	6 [b]	5	17 [b]	189
1960	33	8	45	20	48	5 [b]	·5	15 [b]	179
1961	33	8	45	20	48	5 [b]	5	8 [b]	172
1962	32	8	41	19	47	5 [b]	5	7 [b]	164
1963	23	8	26	19	46	5 [b]	5	6 [b]	138
1964	21	—	10	19	40	5 [b]	2	6 [b]	103
1965	9	—	—	19	7	5 [b]	—	4 [b]	44

[a] Includes DC-7, DC-7B and DC-7C aircraft.
[b] DC-7C aircraft.

Table E-6

DC-8 Aircraft in Fleets of U.S. Domestic Trunk Airlines, 1932–1965.

Year	Carrier					
(Dec. 31)	United	Delta	Eastern	National	Northwest	Total
1959	12	6	—	—	—	18
1960	32	6	11	3	4	56
1961	38	6	15	4	5	68
1962	38	10	15	9	4	76
1963	38	12	15	12	1	78
1964	41	15	17	13	—	86
1965	49	19	18	13	—	99

Table E-7

DC-9 Aircraft in Fleets of U.S. Domestic Trunk Airlines, 1932–1965.

Year	Carrier
(Dec. 31)	Delta
1965	4

Table E-8

Boeing B-40 Aircraft in Fleets of U.S. Domestic Trunk Airlines,[a] 1932–1965.

Year	Carrier			
(Dec. 31)	United	National Parks	Western Air Express	Total
1932	53	2	2	57
1933	30	2	1	33
1934	28	2	—	30
1935	25	2	—	27
1936	—	1	—	1

[a] B-40B-4 and B-40C aircraft only.

Table E-9

Boeing B-80 Aircraft in Fleets of U.S. Domestic Trunk Airlines,[a] 1932–1965.

Year	Carrier		
(Dec. 31)	United	National Parks	Total
1932	12	—	12
1933	11	—	11
1934	10	—	10
1935	8	—	8
1936	6	1	7

[a] Includes B-80 and B-80A aircraft.

Table E-10

Boeing B-221 Aircraft in Fleets of U.S. Domestic Trunk Airlines,[a] 1932–1965.

Year (Dec. 31)	Carrier United
1932	2
1933	2
1934	2

[a] Includes B-200 and B-221 aircraft.

Table E-11

Boeing B-247 Aircraft in Fleets of U.S. Domestic Trunk Airlines,[a] 1932–1965.

Year (Dec. 31)	Carrier					
	United	Western	National Parks[b]	Penn Central	Wyoming[c]	Total
1933	54	—	—	—	—	54
1934	55	2	—	—	—	57
1935	44	5	2	5	1	57
1936	33	11	3	5	2	54
1937	24	6	—	12	6	48
1938	17	4	—	12	6	39
1939	15	4	—	14	6	39
1940	15	4	—	6	5	30
1941	14	5	—	4	5	28
1942	—	—	—	—	—	—
1943	1	—	—	—	—	1
1944	1	—	—	—	—	1

[a] Includes B-247 and B-247D aircraft.
[b] Merged with Western in 1937.
[c] Inland Airlines after 1938.

Table E-12

Boeing B-307 Aircraft in Fleets of U.S
Domestic Trunk Airlines, 1932–1965.

| | Carrier |
(*Dec. 31*)	*TWA*
1940	5
1941	5
1942	—
1943	—
1944	—
1945	5
1946	5
1947	5
1948	5
1949	5
1950	5

Table E-13

Boeing B-377 Aircraft in Fleets of U.S.
Domestic Trunk Airlines, 1932–1965.

| *Year* | Carrier | | |
(*Dec. 31*)	*Northwest*	*United* [a]	*Total*
1949	10	—	10
1950	10	—	10
1951	10	6	16
1952	10	6	16
1953	10	6	16
1954	10	1	11
1955	10	—	10
1956	9	—	9
1957	9	—	9
1958	9	—	9
1959	6	—	6

[a] United used B-377's exclusively for its West Coast-to-Hawaii routes.

Table E-14

Boeing 707 Aircraft in Fleets of U.S. Domestic Trunk Airlines, 1932–1965.

Year (Dec. 31)	Carrier							Total
	Ameri-can	TWA	Braniff	Conti-nental	National	Western	North-west	
1959	24	19	1	4	2	—	—	50
1960	24	27	4	5	—	2	—	62
1961	24	27	4	5	—	2	—	62
1962	23	47	4	4	—	—	—	78
1963	27	52	4	4	—	—	5	92
1964	27	61	4	6	—	—	8	106
1965	34	67	4	7	—	—	13	125

Table E-15

Boeing 720 and 720B Aircraft in Fleets of U.S. Domestic Trunk Airlines, 1932–1965.

Year (Dec. 31)	Carrier								Total
	United	Ameri-can	Eastern	TWA	Braniff	North-west	Western	Conti-nental	
1960	13	9	—	—	—	—	—	—	22
1961	21	25 [a]	13	4 [a]	3	9 [a]	4 [a]	—	79
1962	29	25 [a]	15	—	4	13 [a]	7 [a]	4 [a]	97
1963	29	22 [a]	15	—	5	13 [a]	10 [a]	5 [a]	99
1964	29	22 [a]	15	—	6	16 [a]	12 [a]	6 [a]	106
1965	29	22 [a]	15	—	8	16 [a]	18 [a]	6 [a]	114

[a] 720B aircraft.

Table E-16

Boeing 727 Aircraft in Fleets of U.S. Domestic Trunk Airlines, 1932–1965.

Year (Dec. 31)	Carrier							
	Eastern	United	Ameri-can	TWA	Na-tional	North-west	North-east	Total
1964	24	25	16	16	4	3	—	88
1965	42	49	29	21	10	14	2	167

Table E-17

Lockheed "Vega" Aircraft in Fleets of U.S. Domestic Trunk Airlines, 1932–1965.

Year (Dec. 31)	Carrier							
	TWA	Bowen	Braniff	Han-fords [a]	Central [b]	Delta	Varney [c]	Total
1932	2	4	8	4	—	—	—	18
1933	2	4	8	4	—	—	—	18
1934	—	—	6	4	2	—	—	12
1935	—	—	6	4	—	2	—	12
1936	—	—	3	4	—	—	1	8
1937	—	—	—	4	—	—	1	5

[a] Mid-Continent after 1938.
[b] Merged with Pennsylvania, 1936.
[c] Continental after 1937.

Table E-18

Lockheed "Orion" Aircraft in Fleets of U.S. Domestic Trunk Airlines, 1932–1965.

Year (Dec. 31)	Carrier								
	TWA	Bowen [a]	Luding-ton [b]	Varney [c]	Ameri-can	North-west	Wedell-Wil-liams [d]	Na-tional	Total
1932	2	2	2	6	—	—	—	—	12
1933	2	2	—	5	5	3	4	—	21
1934	2	2	—	5	5	3	—	3	20
1935	—	2	—	4	5	—	4	—	15

[a] Merged with Braniff, 1935.
[b] Merged with Eastern, 1933.
[c] Continental after 1937.
[d] Discontinuous operations to 1936; merged with Eastern, 1937.

Table E-19

Lockheed L-10 Aircraft in Fleets of U.S. Domestic Trunk Airlines, 1932–1965.

Year (Dec. 31)	Carrier					
	National	Pennsylvania	Western	Eastern	Braniff	Delta
1934	3	3	5	—	—	—
1935	3	—	—	5	7	2
1936	3	—	—	5	7	3
1937	3	—	—	—	6	5
1938	3	—	—	—	6	5
1939	4	—	—	—	5	5
1940	4	—	—	—	—	5
1941	2	—	—	—	—	4

	Carrier				
	Northwest	Wyoming [a]	Chicago & Southern	Hanfords [b]	National Airways [c]	Total
1934	—	—	—	—	—	11
1935	12	2	—	—	—	31
1936	12	2	4	2	3	41
1937	12	—	5	3	3	37
1938	7	—	5	4	3	33
1939	7	—	5	5	3	34
1940	4	—	1	5	5	24
1941	4	—	—	5	1	16

[a] Inland after 1938.
[b] Mid-Continent Air Lines.
[c] Northeast Air Lines after 1940; Boston and Maine, 1937–1940.

Table E-20

Lockheed L-12 Aircraft in Fleets of U.S.
Domestic Trunk Airlines, 1932–1965.

Year (Dec. 31)	Carrier Varney [a]
1936	3
1937	3
1938	3
1939	3

[a] Continental after 1937.

Table E-21

Lockheed L-14 Aircraft in Fleets of U.S.
Domestic Trunk Airlines, 1932–1965.

(Dec. 31)	Carrier Northwest	Continental	Total
1937	6	—	6
1938	9	—	9
1939	—	2	2
1940	—	2	2

Table E-22

Lockheed L-18 Aircraft in Fleets of U.S. Domestic Trunk Airlines, 1932–1965.

Year (Dec. 31)	Carrier United	Continental	Mid-Continent	National	Inland	Western	Total
1940	4	3	3	2	—	—	12
1941	—	6	4	3	—	—	13
1942	—	3	2	3	1	1	10
1943	—	4	4	4	1	1	14
1944	—	4	4	6	1	1	16
1945	—	1	3	12	1	1	18
1946	—	—	—	12	—	—	12
1947	—	—	—	12	—	—	12
1948	—	—	—	12	—	—	12
1949	—	—	—	11	—	—	11
1950	—	—	—	11	—	—	11
1951	—	—	—	11	—	—	11
1952	—	—	—	11	—	—	11
1953	—	—	—	11	—	—	11
1954	—	—	—	12	—	—	12
1955	—	—	—	9	—	—	9
1956	—	—	—	10	—	—	10
1957	—	—	—	10	—	—	10
1958	—	—	—	7	—	—	7

Table E-23

Lockheed L-049, 649, and 749 Aircraft in Fleets of U.S. Domestic Trunk Airlines, 1932–1965.

				Carrier			
Year (Dec. 31)	TWA	Eastern	Capital [a]	Chicago & Southern [b]	Delta	Braniff	Total
1946	12	—	—	—	—	—	12
1947	16	14	—	—	—	—	30
1948	23	13	—	—	—	—	36
1949	35	20	—	—	—	—	55
1950	58	20	5	3	—	—	86
1951	65	20	5	6	—	—	96
1952	68	20	7	6	—	—	101
1953	68	19	12	—	6	—	105
1954	68	19	12	—	3	—	102
1955	71	19	12	—	6	—	108
1956	71	19	12	—	4	2	108
1957	71 [c]	18 [c]	12	—	4	2	107
1958	71	18 [d]	11	—	4	—	104
1959	69	18	11	—	—	—	98
1960	68	1	—	—	—	—	69
1961	62	—	—	—	—	—	62
1962	36	—	—	—	—	—	36
1963	34	—	—	—	—	—	34
1964	34	—	—	—	—	—	34
1965	29	—	—	—	—	—	29

[a] Merged with United, 1961.

[b] Merged with Delta, 1953.

[c] 74 aircraft attributed to TWA and 24 to Eastern, *Statistical Study of U.S. Civil Aircraft* (as of Jan. 1, 1958), pp 8–9. See note *a*, Table D-11, p. 174, and note *b*, Table D-22, p. 186.

[d] 23 aircraft attributed to Eastern, *Statistical Study of U.S. Civil Aircraft* (as of Jan. 1, 1959), p. 4. See note *a*, Table D-11, p. 174.

Table E-24

Lockheed L-1049 Aircraft in Fleets of U.S. Domestic Trunk Airlines,[a] 1932–1965.

Year (Dec. 31)	Carrier			
	Eastern	TWA	National	Total
1951	5	—	—	5
1952	14	10	—	24
1953	22	10	—	32
1954	29	10	—	39
1955	29	30	4	63
1956	32	37	4	73
1957	38	39	4	81
1958	38	44	7	89
1959	38	44	4	86
1960	38	40	4	82
1961	37	28	4	69
1962	37	24	4	65
1963	37	24	4	65
1964	37	17	—	54
1965	37	9	—	46

[a] Includes all L-1049 series aircraft

Table E-25

Lockheed L-1649 Aircraft in Fleets of U.S. Domestic Trunk Airlines, 1932–1965.

Year (Dec. 31)	Carrier
	TWA
1957	25
1958	29
1959	28
1960	25
1961	24
1962	27
1963	24
1964	22
1965	5

Table E-26

Lockheed L-188 Aircraft in Fleets of U.S. Domestic Trunk Airlines, 1932–1965.

Year (Dec. 31)	Carrier						
	Eastern	American	Braniff	National	Northwest	Western	Total
1959	40	23	7	12	9	5	96
1960	39	33	8	12	9	6	107
1961	39	33	8	14	16	12	122
1962	39	24	9	17	16	12	117
1963	39	24	9	17	16	12	117
1964	39	24	9	17	16	12	117
1965	39	24	9	17	16	12	117

Table E-27

Consolidated "Fleetster" Aircraft in Fleets
of U.S. Domestic Trunk Airlines, 1932–1965.

| Year | Carrier | | |
(Dec. 31)	Ludington [a]	TWA [b]	Total
1932	3	—	3
1933	—	7	7
1934	—	7	7
1935	—	6	6
1936	—	5	5

[a] Merged with Eastern, 1933.
[b] "Fleetster" 21A aircraft.

Table E-28

Convair 240 Aircraft in Fleets of U.S. Domestic Trunk Airlines, 1932–1965.

Year (Dec. 31)	Carrier						
	American	Continental	Western	Mid-Continent [a]	Northeast	Braniff	Total
1948	56	5	8	—	—	—	69
1949	73	5	10	4	5	—	97
1950	79	5	10	4	5	—	103
1951	78	5	10	4	5	—	102
1952	77	5	10	—	4	3	99
1953	76	—	10	—	7	—	93
1954	76	—	9	—	7	—	92
1955	74	—	9	—	6	—	89
1956	73	—	9	—	6	—	88
1957	73	—	9	—	6	—	88
1958	54	—	6	—	5	—	65
1959	34	—	5	—	—	—	39
1960	37	—	4	—	—	—	41
1961	21	—	—	—	—	—	21
1962	13	—	—	—	—	—	13
1963	10	—	—	—	—	—	10

[a] Merged with Braniff, 1952.

Table E-29

Convair 340 and 440 Aircraft in Fleets of U.S. Domestic Trunk Airlines,[a] 1932–1965.

	Carrier						
Year (Dec. 31)	United	Braniff	Continental	Delta	National	Eastern	Total
1952	17	7	—	—	—	—	24
1953	40	23	7	20	8	—	98
1954	55	23	6	20	12	—	116
1955	55	25	6	20	12	—	118
1956	55	30	9	25	18	—	137
1957	55	30	9	28	18	20	160
1958	54	30	9	28	18	20	159
1959	43	31	—	28	15	20	137
1960	30	31	—	26	6	20	113
1961	25	29	—	24	6	20	104
1962	21	19	—	21	5	20	86
1963	17	19	—	21	—	20	77
1964	13	17	—	19	—	20	69
1965	13	15	—	19	—	20	67

[a] All of the Eastern aircraft are CV-440s. Six of National's aircraft are CV-440s from 1956 through 1961; the five remaining in 1962 were CV-440s. The five aircraft purchased by Braniff in 1956 were CV-440s. The distribution of CV340s and CV-440s in Braniff's fleet after 1960 is inconsistently reported in the sources used.

Table E-30

Convair 880 Aircraft in Fleets of U.S. Domestic Trunk Airlines, 1932–1965.

	Carrier			
Year (Dec. 31)	TWA	Delta	Northwest	Total
1960	1	9	4	14
1961	20	12	6	38
1962	20	16	8	44
1963	26	16	3	45
1964	27	16	4	47
1965	26	16	4	46

Table E-31

Convair 990 Aircraft in Fleets of U.S. Domestic Trunk Airlines, 1932–1965.

	Carrier
Year (Dec. 31)	American
1962	15
1963	19
1964	19
1965	18

Table E-32

Martin 202 Aircraft in Fleets of U.S.
Domestic Trunk Airlines, 1932–1965.

Year	Carrier		
(Dec. 31)	Northwest	TWA[a]	Total
1947	9	—	9
1948	24	—	24
1949	24	—	24
1950	21	12	33
1951	—	12	12
1952	—	12	12
1953	—	12	12
1954	—	12	12
1955	—	11	11
1956	—	11	11
1957	—	11	11
1958	—	10	10

[a] 202A aircraft.

Table E-33

Martin 404 Aircraft in Fleets of U.S.
Domestic Trunk Airlines, 1932–1965.

Year	Carrier		
(Dec. 31)	Eastern	TWA	Total
1951	9	9	18
1952	56	40	96
1953	60	40	100
1954	60	40	100
1955	60	39	99
1956	59	38	97
1957	58	37[a]	95
1958	58	37	95
1959	56	29	85
1960	52	20	72
1961	36	—	36
1962	16	—	16

[a] Twenty-seven 404s are attributed to
TWA in Statistical Study of U.S. Civil Air-
craft (as of Jan. 1, 1958), p. 5. See note c,
Table D-22, p. 186.

Table E-34

Stinson Single Engined Aircraft in Fleets of U.S. Domestic Trunk Airlines, 1932–1965.

Year (Dec. 31)	Carrier							
	American	United	Bowen [a]	Luding-ton [b]	Trans-American [c]	Wyo-ming [d]	Long & Harmon [e]	Total [f]
1932	16	1	1	1	8	5	—	32
1933	8	—	—	—	—	4	5	17
1934	—	—	—	—	—	6	5	11
1935	—	—	—	—	—	6	—	6
1936	—	—	—	—	—	1	—	1

[a] Merged with Braniff, 1935.
[b] Merged with Eastern, 1936.
[c] Corporate existence terminated after control assumed by Aviation Corporation, 1932.
[d] Inland from 1938.
[e] Merged with Braniff, 1935.
[f] Omits Stinson single engined aircraft—presumably "Reliants"—operated by Continental, Mid-Continent and Northwest in 1943, 1944, and 1945.

Table E-35

Stinson Trimotor Aircraft in Fleets of U.S. Domestic Trunk Airlines, 1932–1965.

Year (Dec. 31)	Carrier					
	American	Ludington [a]	Pennsylvania [b]	Trans-American [c]	Eastern	National Airways [d]
1932	10	9	3	4	—	—
1933	10	—	—	—	8	5
1934	17	—	—	—	5	5
1935	11	—	—	—	—	5
1936	15	—	5	—	—	3
1937	3	—	—	—	—	3
1938	—	—	—	—	—	2
1939	—	—	—	—	—	2
1940	—	—	—	—	—	2

	Central [e]	Delta	Chicago & Southern	Colombia [f]	National	Total
1932	—	—	—	—	—	26
1933	—	—	—	—	—	23
1934	5	5	—	—	—	37
1935	5	7	6	5	3	42
1936	—	1	—	—	3	27
1937	—	—	—	—	3	9
1938	—	—	—	—	2	4
1939	—	—	—	—	—	2
1940	—	—	—	—	—	2

[a] Merged with Eastern, 1933.
[b] Pennsylvania Central after 1936; Capital after 1948.
[c] Corporate existence terminated after control assumed by Aviation Corporation, 1932.
[d] Northeast after 1941.
[e] Merged with Pennsylvania, 1936.
[f] Operated Detroit, St. Louis, Cincinnati route, 1935 only.

Table E-36

Fokker Single Engined Aircraft in Fleets of
U.S. Domestic Trunk Airlines, 1932–1965.

	Carrier			
Year		National		
(Dec. 31)	TWA	Parks [a]	Western	Total
1932	6	5	8	19
1933	2	4	8	14
1934	—	4	—	4
1935	—	1	—	1

[a] Merged with Western, 1937.

Table E-37

Fokker F-10 Aircraft in Fleets of U.S. Domestic Trunk Airlines, 1932–1965.

	Carrier					
Year				Trans-		
(Dec. 31)	American	Eastern	TWA	American [a]	Western	Total
1932	14	3	4	2	5	28
1933	7	—	4	—	5	16
1934	—	—	2	—	—	2

[a] Corporate existence terminated after control assumed by Aviation Corporation, 1932.

Table E-38

Fokker F-32 Aircraft in Fleets of U.S.
Domestic Trunk Airlines, 1932–1965.

	Carrier		
Year			
(Dec. 31)	American	TWA	Total
1932	7	2	9

Table E-39
Condor "CO" Transports in Fleets of U.S.
Domestic Trunk Airlines, 1932–1965.

	Carrier
Year	
(Dec. 31)	Eastern
1932	5
1933	5
1934	4

Table E-40

T-32 Condor II Aircraft in Fleets of U.S Domestic Trunk Airlines, 1932–1965.

| Year (Dec. 31) | Carrier | | |
	American	Eastern	Total
1933	9	8	17
1934	15	8	23
1935	10	7	17
1936	3	5	8

Table E-41

Curtiss-Robertson "Kingbird" Aircraft in Fleets of U.S. Domestic Trunk Airlines, 1932–1965.

| Year (Dec. 31) | Carrier |
	Eastern
1932	9
1933	9
1934	5
1935	5

Table E-42

"Travel Air" Aircraft in Fleets of U.S. Domestic Trunk Airlines, 1932–1965.

| Year (Dec. 31) | Carrier | | | | |
	American	Northwest	Trans-American [a]	Long-Harmon [b]	Total
1932	8	3	1	—	12
1933	—	2	—	1	3
1934	—	—	—	1	1

[a] Corporate existence terminated after control assumed by Aviation Corporation, 1932.
[b] Merged with Braniff, 1935.

Table E-43

Hamilton "Silver Streak" Aircraft in Fleets of U.S. Domestic Trunk Airlines, 1932–1965.

| Year (Dec. 31) | Carrier |
	Northwest
1932	9
1933	9
1934	8
1935	1

Table E-44

Fairchild 100 Aircraft in Fleets of U.S. Domestic Trunk Airlines, 1932–1965.

	Carrier
Year	
(Dec. 31)	*American*
1932	20
1933	10

Table E-45

Fairchild 71 Aircraft in Fleets of U.S. Domestic Trunk Airlines, 1932–1965.

	Carrier		
Year			
(Dec. 31)	*American*	*Pennsylvanian*	*Total*
1932	17	3	20

Table E-46

Bellanca "Pacemaker" Aircraft in Fleets of U.S. Domestic Trunk Airlines, 1932–1965.

	Carrier		
(Dec. 31)	*Rapid Air Transport* [a]	*Pacific Seaboard* [b]	*Total*
1932	2	—	2
1933	2	5	7
1934	—	6	6

[a] Operated Kansas City–Omaha route, 1932, 1933.
[b] Chicago and Southern after 1934.

Table E-47

Metal Aircraft "Flamingo" Aircraft in Fleets of U.S. Domestic Trunk Airlines, 1932–1965.

	Carrier
Year	*United States*
(Dec. 31)	*Airways* [a]
1932	9
1933	9

[a] Operated Kansas City–Denver route in 1932, 1933.

Table E-48

Ford Trimotor Aircraft in Fleets of U.S. Domestic Trunk Airlines, 1932–1965.

Year (Dec. 31)	Carrier					
	American	Eastern	TWA	United	Northwest	Trans-American [a]
1932	16	5	19	19	3	1
1933	15	—	16	2	3	—
1934	14	—	15	5	3	—
1935	4	—	10	1	1	—
1936	—	—	4	—	—	—

	Carrier					
	Hanford [b]	National Parks [c]	Pennsyl-vanian	National	Braniff	Total
1932	—	—	—	—	—	63
1933	2	1	5	—	—	44
1934	2	—	5	3	—	47
1935	3	—	5	—	2	26
1936	2	—	—	—	2	8

[a] Corporate existence terminated after control assumed by Aviation Corporation, 1932.
[b] Mid-Continent from 1938.
[c] Merged with Western, 1937.

Table E-49

Ryan "Brougham" Aircraft in Fleets of
U.S. Domestic Trunk Airlines, 1932–1965.

	Carrier
(Dec. 31)	*Rapid Air Transport* [a]
1932	1
1933	1

[a] Operated Kansas City–
Omaha route, 1932, 1933.

Table E-50

Northrop "Alpha" Aircraft in Fleets of
U.S. Domestic Trunk Airlines, 1932–1965.

Year	Carrier
(Dec. 31)	*TWA*
1932	6
1933	6
1934	6

Table E-51

Beechcraft 18 Aircraft in Fleets of U.S.
Domestic Trunk Airlines, 1932–1965.

Year	Carrier		
(Dec. 31)	*TWA*	*Inland*	*Total*
1937	1	—	1
1938	—	—	—
1939	—	—	—
1940	—	—	—
1941	—	—	—
1942	—	—	—
1943	—	2	2
1944	—	1	1

Table E-52

Vultee V-1-A Aircraft in Fleets of U.S.
Domestic Trunk Airlines, 1932–1965.

		Carrier		
Year (Dec. 31)	American	Bowen [a]	Braniff	Total
1934	8	2	—	10
1935	8	—	2	10
1936	10	—	—	10

[a] Merged with Braniff, 1935.

Table E-53

Viscount 745 Aircraft in Fleets of U.S.
Domestic Trunk Airlines, 1932–1965.

		Carrier		
Year (Dec. 31)	Capital [a]	North-east	United	Total
1955	8	—	—	8
1956	54	—	—	54
1957	59	—	—	59
1958	59	7	—	66
1959	57	10	—	67
1960	51	10	—	61
1961	—	9	47	56
1962	—	9	46	55
1963	—	—	46	46
1964	—	—	45	45
1965	—	—	44	44

[a] Merged with United, 1961.

Table E-54

Viscount 812 Aircraft in Fleets of U.S.
Domestic Trunk Airlines, 1932–1965.

	Carrier
Year (Dec. 31)	Continental
1958	14
1959	15
1960	13
1961	13
1962	12
1963	11
1964	11
1965	11

Table E-55

Sud Caravelle 210 Aircraft in Fleets of U.S.
Domestic Trunk Airlines, 1932–1965.

Year (Dec. 31)	Carrier United
1961	17
1962	20
1963	20
1964	20
1965	20

Table E-56

Bac-111 Aircraft in Fleets of U.S. Domestic
Trunk Airlines, 1932–1965.

Year (Dec. 31)	Carrier Braniff
1965	12

About the Author

Almarin Phillips is Professor of Economics and Law and Chairman of the Department of Economics at the University of Pennsylvania. He has served as a consultant to the RAND Corporation since 1964, working primarily in questions relating to the economics of technological change. He has been associated in consultative or research capacities with a number of government agencies, nonprofit institutions, and private companies. In addition to his duties at Pennsylvania, he is currently the Co-Director of Financial Studies of the President's Commission on Financial Structure and Regulation and a Senior Fellow of the Brookings Institution.

Dr. Phillips' field of study is Industrial Organization, with special emphasis on government regulation of business and the economics of technological change. He is the author of *Market Structure, Organization and Performance* (Harvard University Press, 1962), the co-author of *Problems in Basic Operation Research Methods for Management* (John Wiley and Sons, 1961) and has published numerous other articles in professional journals and books.

Index

Selected List of Rand Books

1.   Becker, Abraham S. *Soviet National Income 1958–1964*. University of California Press, Berkeley & Los Angeles, California, 1969.

2.   Downs, Anthony. *Inside Bureaucracy*. Little, Brown and Company, Boston, Massachusetts, 1967.

3.   Fisher, Gene H. *Cost Considerations in Systems Analysis*. American Elsevier Publishing Company, New York, 1970.

4.   Fishman, George S. *Spectral Methods in Econometrics*. Harvard University Press, Cambridge, Massachusetts, 1969.

5.   Gurtov, Melvin. *Southeast Asia Tomorrow: Problems and Prospects for U.S. Policy*. Johns Hopkins Press, Baltimore, Maryland, 1970.

6.   Harman, Alvin J. *The International Computer Industry: Innovation and Comparative Advantage*. Harvard University Press, Cambridge, Massachusetts, 1970.

7.   Jorgenson, D. W., J. J. McCall and R. Radner. *Optimal Replacement Policy*. North-Holland Publishing, Amsterdam and Rand McNally & Company, Chicago, Illinois, 1967.

8.   Leites, Nathan and Charles Wolf. *Rebellion and Authority*. Markham Publishing Company, Chicago, Illinois, 1970.

9.   Marschak, Thomas A., Thomas K. Glennan, Jr., and Robert Summers. *Strategy for R & D*. Springer-Verlag, New York, 1967.

10.   McKean, Roland N. *Efficiency in Government through Systems Analysis: With Emphasis on Water Resource Development*. John Wiley & Sons, Inc., New York, 1958.

11.   Meyer, John R., Martin Wohl, and John F. Kain. *The Urban Transportation Problem*. Harvard University Press, Cambridge, Massachusetts, 1965.

12.   Nelson, Richard R., Merton J. Peck, Edward D. Kalachek. *Technology, Economic Growth and Public Policy*. The Brookings Institution, Washington, D.C., 1967.

13.   Pascal, Anthony. *Thinking about Cities: New Perspectives on Urban Problems*. Dickenson Publishing Company, Belmont, California, 1970.

14.   Quade, Edward S. Quade and Wayne I. Boucher. *Systems Analysis and Policy Planning: Applications in Defense*. American Elsevier Publishing Company, New York, 1968.

15.   The RAND Corporation. *A Million Random Digits with 100,000 Normal Deviates*. The Free Press, Glencoe, Illinois, 1955.